Practical Welding

Macmillan Texts for Industrial, Vocational and Technical Education

Practical Welding

Stuart W. Gibson
MSc, DME, Cert Ed, C&G (FTC), Sen M Weld I, MAWS, MAWTE,
Registered Welding Engineer,
Former Lecturer in Charge of Welding, Hopwood Hall College
and Postgraduate Researcher in Welding, Manchester University

Project Advisor: *Bernard K. Amoako-Awuah*
Course Officer, Welding and Fabrication Department,
Kumasi Technical Institute, Kumasi, Ghana

Macmillan Education
Between Towns Road, Oxford OX4 3PP
A division of Macmillan Publishers Limited
Companies and representatives throughout the world

ISBN 0 333 60957 3

First published 1994

www.macmillan-africa.com

Cover illustration courtesy of Tony Stone/T. Vine

Printed and bound in Malaysia

2008 2007 2006 2005
13 12 11 10 9 8 7

To Anne and Wendy

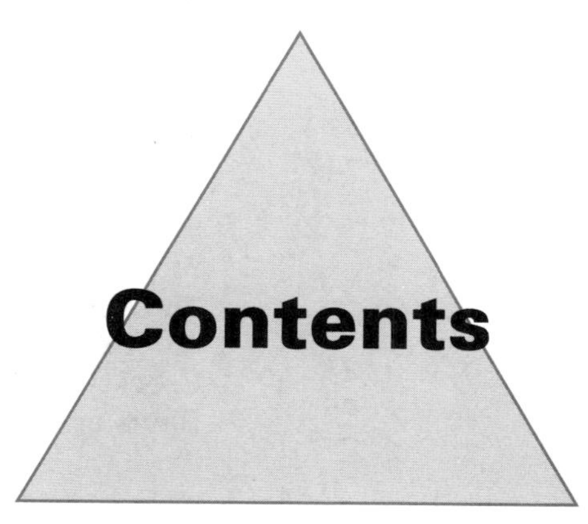

Contents

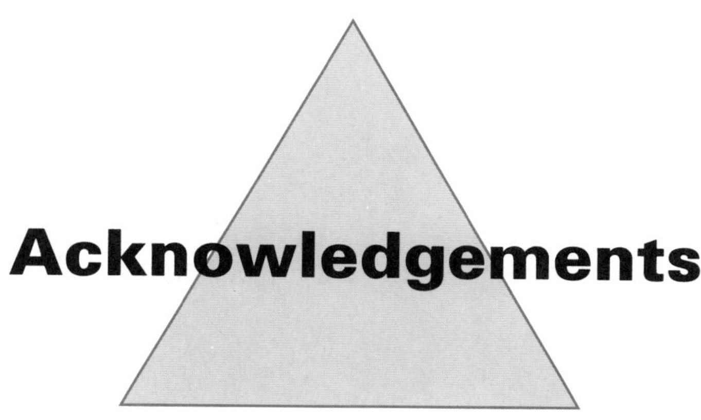

Acknowledgements

The author would particularly like to thank the following companies and organisations:

The International Institute of Welding; TWI, Cambridge; Hopwood Hall College; UTP (UK) and UTC Engineering, Nigeria and Ghana; Leica, UK and Africa; The British Oxygen Company Ltd; BSI, Milton Keynes; Co-Weld UK Ltd; British Federal Ltd; Murex Welding Products Ltd; The ESAB Group; Signs and Labels Ltd; Frosts Auto Restoration Techniques Ltd, UK; Lincoln Electric.

With special thanks to:
Mr Edward Nock, UTP Ltd and Dr R.B.G. Yeo, Lincoln Arc Welding Foundation.

Extracts from British Standards are reproduced with the permission of BSI. Complete copies can be obtained by post from BSI Sales, Linford Wood, Milton Keynes, MK14 6LE, UK.

Every effort has been made to ensure that the information contained in this book is accurate at the time of going to press. However, the author and publisher do not assume responsibility or liability for any applications produced from the information. In welding, the application can vary considerably from job to job and it is the responsibility of the user to carry out work to statutory requirements.

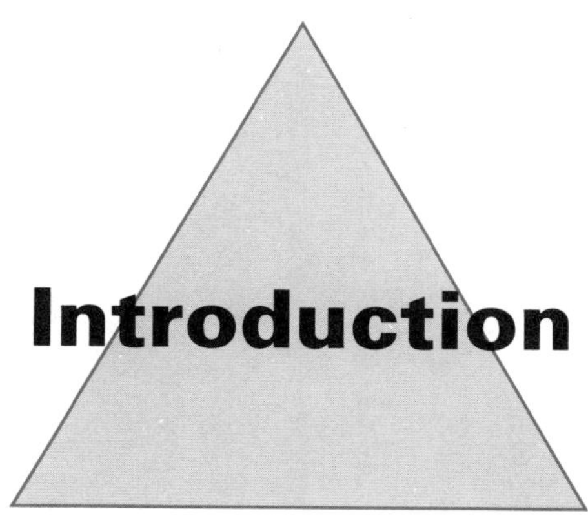

Introduction

This textbook has been written to help students learning welding through courses at technical institutes, senior technical schools or brigades. As the name of the book implies, it will also be of use as a reference for practical welders and will not be out of place in either the welding school or the welding workshop. The main processes covered include gas welding, manual metal arc, TAGS and MAGS. Other processes are included in the key words and definitions section at the end of the book.

Most of the text relates directly to the practical aspects of welding. Information on such topics as first aid, basic metallurgy and engineering drawing has also been included, together with some 'test your knowledge' exercises at the ends of the chapters.

These items are included because welders have to think with their heads as well as using their hands. Knowing why you have to do certain procedures as well as just knowing that you have to do them can make the difference between a welder and a good welder!

So, whether you have just started welding today, or have been welding for many years, may I wish you every success with your future in this interesting and worthwhile career.

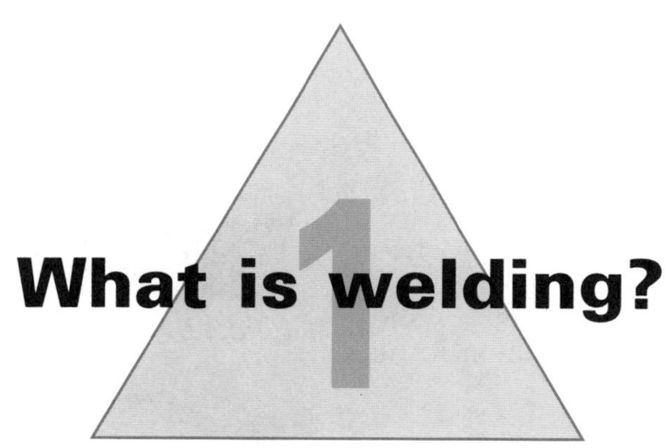

1 What is welding?

Introduction

Welding is a process of joining materials together into one piece.

Various materials can be welded together, including plastics, but in this book we shall be looking at the joining of metals, and mainly the metal known as mild or low-carbon steel. This is the material that is most commonly used in the construction industry.

Forge welding – the process of heating metals and hammering them together to form a join – was practised thousands of years ago, particularly by the Egyptians. In modern industry, many different materials need to be welded together, and so a number of welding processes are in use, some of them very specialised. However, when you are starting welding, the main welding processes that you need to know about are:

1. **Oxyacetylene welding**, also known as gas welding.
   This process uses the chemical energy of a blowpipe flame to melt the edges of the metal parts to be joined together.
2. **Manual metal arc welding** (MMA)
3. **Tungsten arc gas-shielded welding** (TAGS)
4. **Metal arc gas-shielded welding** (MAGS)
   These three processes all use an electric arc (electrical energy) to melt the edges of the metal parts to be joined together.
5. **Resistance welding**
   This process uses the resistance heating effect of an electric current to melt the metals to be joined.

Figure 1.1 In the Middle Ages, many knights' helmets were forge welded. The helmet belonging to Edward, the Black Prince (1330–1376) , was made from three pieces welded in such a way that the joints could not be seen.

Figure 1.2 Between about 1400 and 1600, fine bronzes were being made in the kingdom of Benin, an advanced civilisation in the region of West Africa that is now Nigeria. Benin bronzes are thought to be some of the finest art produced in Africa.

Each of these five processes has its own chapter in this book.

Some welders specialise in one or more of these processes, but most welders are skilled in all five. This may seem a lot to learn, but as you progress you will soon see that you can transfer the skills you have learnt in one process to another, and many points (such as safety) are common to all five.

What items are welded?

The list of items that are welded is almost endless. It includes ships, jet engines, rockets, the Space Shuttle, lorries, cars, trains, bridges, metal furniture, metal containers and replacement hip joints. For interest, try making your own list and see how many items you get. Figures 1.3–1.9 show some typical examples. The smallest welded components are probably those used in electronic circuits. The largest include ships and metal-framed buildings.

Figure 1.3 Welded road tanker.

Figure 1.4 Most road and rail bridges are of welded construction.

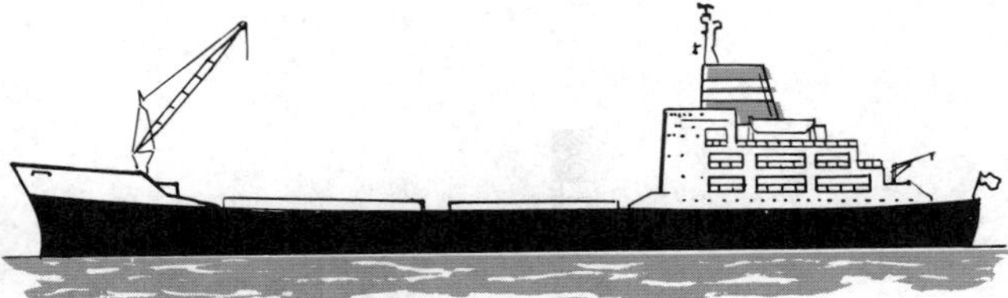

Figure 1.5 Welded tanker ship.

Figure 1.6 Railway lines and locomotives are welded.

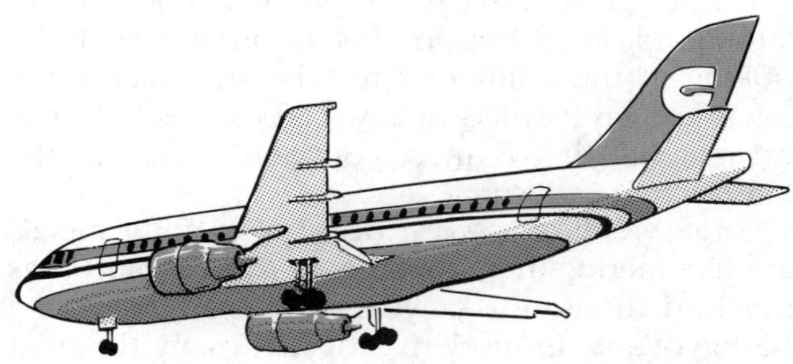

Figure 1.7 Aircraft contain many welds.

Figure 1.8 Modern cars and road vehicles are of welded construction.

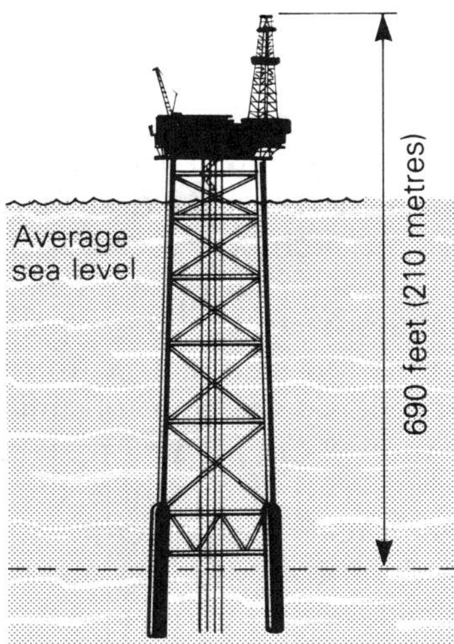

Figure 1.9 What we tend to forget about welded oil-rig platforms is just how much of the structure lies below the surface of the sea.

Welding processes

Modern welding processes have to produce high-quality welded joints that will withstand severe weather and loading conditions. Sophisticated methods known as **non-destructive testing** are used to test welds. They include X-ray, gamma-ray and ultrasonic techniques. With the first two methods, engineers can 'see' inside the weld in much the same way that a doctor can see inside a patient when using an X-ray machine in hospital. Ultrasonic inspection passes high-frequency sound into the weld and the surrounding metal, and the way the sound bounces back shows whether the weld is acceptable.

> Processes that melt the metals to form a weld are known as **fusion welding processes**.

Sometimes the edges of parts can be fused together by raising their temperature to melting point and allowing the molten metal to run into one weld. The upturned edge weld shown in Figure 1.10 is an example of this. The edges of thin plate are melted together by carefully passing either an oxyacetylene flame or an electric arc along the joint at the correct speed. With this method, no extra metal is required. In most welds, however, extra metal has to be added to the joint while it is still molten. This extra metal is known as **filler metal**.

Figure 1.10 An upturned edge weld.

Because of the intense heat involved in welding, the surfaces of the metals being joined can react with the surrounding atmosphere to form impurities. If these impurities are not controlled in some way they can prevent the metal from flowing properly, so that the metals do not weld together. Impurities can also form inclusions inside the weld, weakening the finished joint. Various methods are used to control these impurities and prevent atmospheric contamination of the weld.

In oxyacetylene welding of mild steel, the flame acts as protection for the weld. This is explained in detail later in this book. In oxyacetylene welding of other materials, such as aluminium or stainless steel, a powdered chemical **flux** is used for protection. A flux is also used when brazing (see below). The flux is usually added to the rod of filler metal by dipping its heated end into the powdered flux. This action is repeated when more flux is required. In manual metal arc welding, the rods are precoated with flux and are called **electrodes**.

In TAGS and MAGS welding, a **gas shield** is used. These gas shields are covered in detail in Chapters 7 and 8.

> Welding processes that do not melt the metals to form a weld are known as **solid-state welding** processes.

One such process is **friction welding**, in which one component is rubbed against the other (which is usually rotated) until the surfaces become flat. When seizing begins to occur, pressure is applied and movement stopped. A similar type of welding can take place in a car engine if it runs without oil and seizes up!

Welding is not always the best way of joining components. Sometimes the welder or welding engineer has to decide on other methods.

Many racing cars and competition motorcycles use **brazing** or **bronze welding** in their construction, as well as fusion welding. These techniques can allow some flexibility or 'give' at the joints, which is sometimes required when a racing car

Figure 1.11 Brazing is used in the construction of competition motorcycles.

corners very quickly or a motorcycle leaps over a bump.

Brazing and bronze welding use a brass filler rod that melts at a lower temperature than the metals being joined, which have only to be heated to red heat for the brass to run into the joint. In fusion welding, the metals being joined would have to be melted, as well as the filler material.

A powdered flux is required for brazing and bronze-welding. It helps to clean the work surfaces and allows the brass to run freely.

CHECK YOUR UNDERSTANDING

- Welding is a process of joining materials together into one piece.
- The five most common welding processes are: oxyacetylene welding, manual metal arc welding (MMA), tungsten arc gas-shielded welding (TAGS), metal arc gas-shielded welding (MAGS) and resistance welding.
- Welding is used to make many items, both large and small, that we use in our everyday lives.
- Sophisticated methods such as X-ray, gamma-ray and ultrasonic techniques can be used for the non-destructive testing and examination of welds.
- Various methods are used to prevent atmospheric contamination of the weld during welding. In the oxyacetylene welding of mild steel, the flame acts as protection. Manual metal arc welding employs a chemical flux, while the TAGS and MAGS processes use a gas shield.
- Brazing and bronze welding are other joining processes, which employ filler materials with a melting point lower than that of the metals being joined. They are called non-fusion processes as the metals being joined are not melted.

REVISION EXERCISES AND QUESTIONS

1. What does the word 'weld' mean?
2. Make your own list of 20 items that use welding in their manufacture.
3. Name one very large type of structure that uses welding in its construction.
4. Name one very small item that is welded.
5. Give the full names of the five most commonly used welding processes.
6. Name two non-destructive methods sometimes used in weld examination.
7. In manual metal arc welding, what method is employed to help prevent atmospheric contamination of the weld?
8. Name two non-fusion joining processes.

(Further practice questions can be found on page 202.)

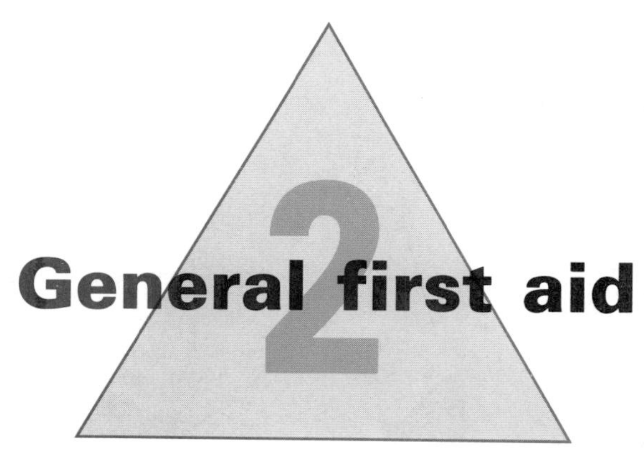

2 General first aid

Introduction

▲ For any injuries other than very minor ones, you should call for expert medical attention, but first aid can help and comfort the patient until the doctor or ambulance arrives. First aid can save lives and there are many organisations worldwide that run short courses to train qualified first-aiders.

A short first-aid course will help to ensure that you are properly trained and able to help if an accident occurs. This chapter lists some of the basic points of first aid that anyone working in the welding and fabrication industries should be aware of. The methods described have been used many times to comfort, ease pain and save lives.

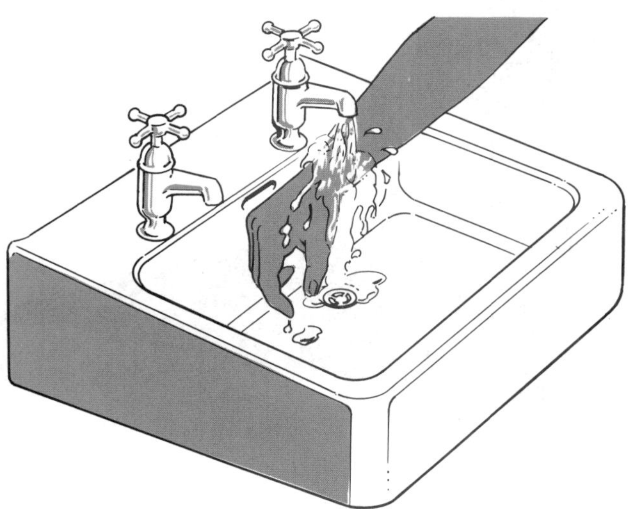

Figure 2.1 Immerse a small burn or scald in cold water or under cold running water for at least 10 minutes.

Burns and scalds

Burns cause damage to body tissue by heat, chemicals or radiation. Burns caused by steam or hot liquids are called **scalds**. With welding processes, burns are the most common injury and are usually not serious. Welders' gloves and other protective equipment give protection most of the time, but minor burns can be caused by sparks and spatter or by accidentally touching hot metal.

If possible, immerse the burn or scald in cold water or under cold running water for at least 10 minutes, until the pain reduces (Figure 2.1). Then cover the burn with dry gauze or clean fabric and a bandage. Do not remove clothing or apply ointments. Do not break blisters. If the burn is more than 3 cm in diameter, seek medical advice.

Arc burn: similar to severe sunburn

If skin is exposed to the rays from an electric arc, it can become tender and swollen, and may possibly blister. The affected skin will also feel hot. This is why you should ensure that all skin is covered with suitable protective clothing when electric arc welding, in addition to the protection provided from sparks and hot metal.

Treatment

Cool the skin gently by sponging it with cold water. If the skin is not broken, apply sunburn cream. Do not break blisters. If there is extensive blistering, seek qualified medical aid.

Arc eye or welder's flash

The front of the eye, called the cornea, can be injured if it is exposed to the ultraviolet light

Figure 2.2 Bathe eyes with clean, cold water.

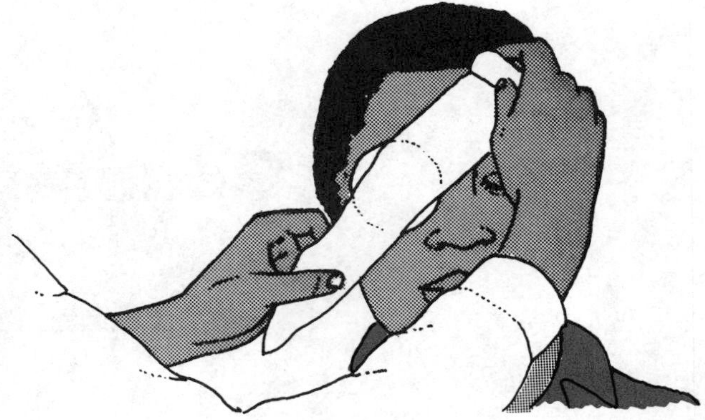

Figure 2.3 Apply clean pads.

produced by the electric welding arc. This can sometimes happen when you walk past welding operations that are not screened off properly, or if your welding helmet is not positioned correctly or has a cracked filter lens. The symptoms usually appear up to 6 hours after exposure to the welding arc. They consist of intense pain in the affected eye(s) and a feeling as if they are full of sand. Eyes affected will be sensitive to light, will be red in colour, and may water in severe cases.

Treatment

Bathe the eye(s) with cold water and then apply pads of clean, non-fluffy material (Figures 2.2 and 2.3). Arc eye can last for up to 48 hours. In severe cases, seek medical attention; special welder's eye drops are available from a doctor or hospital which will help to ease the pain. Wearing dark glasses can help to ease discomfort in the later stages of arc eye.

Electrical injuries

If an electric current passes through the body it can cause severe and sometimes fatal injuries. It can affect the heart muscles, causing the heart to stop beating and the breathing to stop.

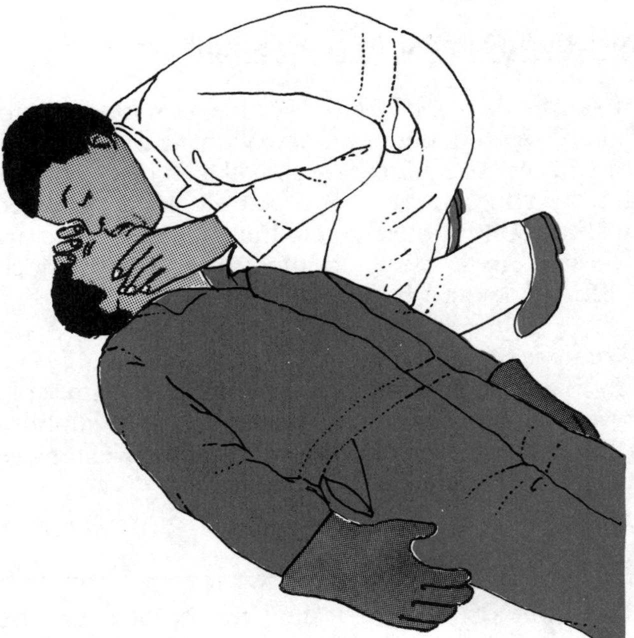

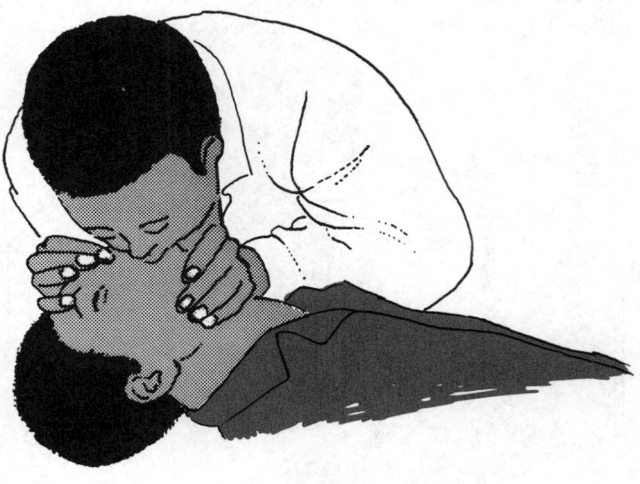

Figure 2.4 Mouth-to-mouth ventilation.

> ▲ Never touch the casualty with bare hands until you are sure that the current has been turned off or the casualty is no longer in contact with the electrical source.

With high-voltage electricity, such as electrical transmission lines, do not approach the accident area until the police or authority in charge say that it is safe to do so. High-voltage electricity can 'arc' over considerable distances and insulating materials will not provide any protection if this happens.

Treatment

If the injured person's breathing and heart have stopped, start resuscitation by using mouth-to-mouth ventilation and applying external chest compression (Figures 2.4 and 2.5). If the injured person is breathing normally but is unconscious, place them in the recovery position on their side, unless you suspect a fracture of the spine (see the section below on treatment of fractures).

Tend any obvious injuries and treat the casualty for shock while you are waiting for medical assistance to arrive. Tell medical authorities how long the casualty was in contact with the electrical source.

Mouth-to-mouth ventilation

Remove any obvious obstructions from the casualty's face and loosen their collar. Open the airway by placing one hand under the casualty's neck, the other hand on the forehead, and tilt their head backwards.

Transfer your hand from the neck and push the casualty's chin upwards. This will lift their tongue forwards, clearing the airway. Remove any debris that might be in the mouth or throat.

Open your mouth wide and take in a deep breath. Pinch the casualty's nostrils together with your fingers. Sealing your lips around the mouth, blow into the casualty's lungs until you can see the chest rise. Then remove your mouth well away from the casualty's and breathe out any excess air. Watch the chest fall, then take a fresh breath and repeat the procedure. Check the casualty's pulse to ensure that the heart is beating. Figure 2.6 shows the position of the pulse on the carotid artery.

If the heart is not beating you must carry out external chest compression straight away.

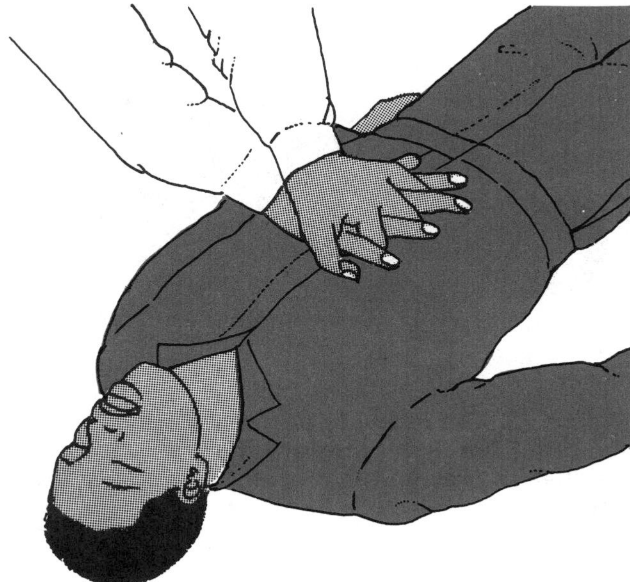

Figure 2.5 External chest compression.

External chest compression

Lay the casualty on their back and kneel alongside. Place the heel of one hand in the centre of the lower region of the breastbone, keeping your fingers off the ribs. Cover this hand with your other hand and lock fingers together (see Figure 2.5).

Keeping your arms straight, move forwards until your arms are vertical. Press down on the lower part of the breastbone about 4 to 5 cm ($1\frac{1}{2}$ to 2 inches) for an average adult. Then move backwards, releasing the pressure. Perform 15 compressions at the rate of about 80 per minute. (To judge the approximate timing count one and two and

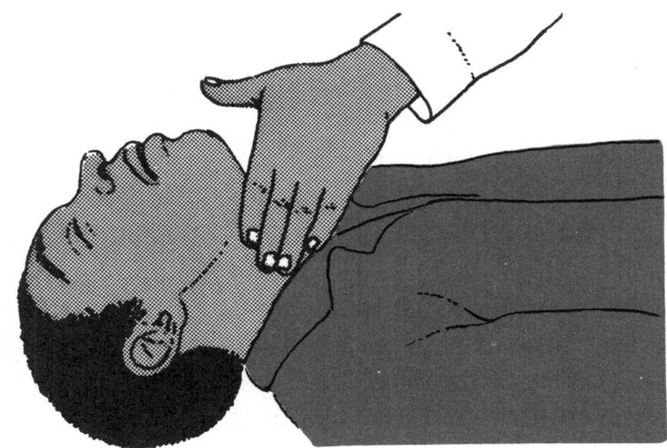

Figure 2.6 Position of the carotid pulse.

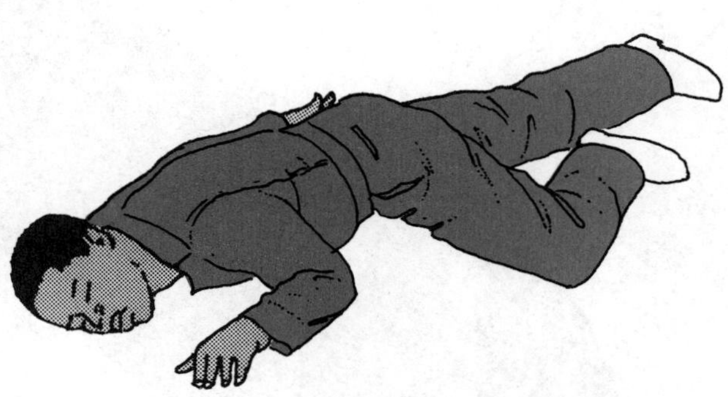

Figure 2.7 The recovery position. Carefully move the arm from under the casualty and place it parallel, to prevent them from rolling on to their back.

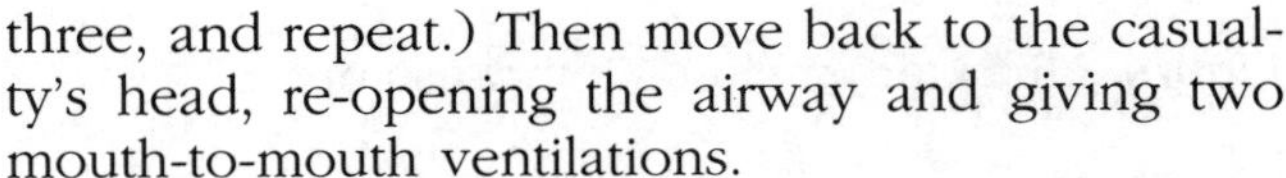

three, and repeat.) Then move back to the casualty's head, re-opening the airway and giving two mouth-to-mouth ventilations.

Continue giving 15 compressions followed by two ventilations, checking for heartbeat after one minute. Continue, checking the heartbeat every three minutes. As soon as the heartbeat returns, stop compression immediately and continue mouth-to-mouth ventilation until natural breathing returns. Place the casualty in the recovery position (Figure 2.7). When resuscitation is successful, the carotid pulse will return.

Shock

If a person has been injured they often become quite weak because they are in a state of shock. You should immediately reassure and comfort the casualty, loosen any tight clothing and keep the casualty warm with extra clothing or a blanket. If the casualty is thirsty, moisten their lips with water but do not give them anything to drink.

Bleeding and wounds

Get the casualty to sit or lie down and elevate the bleeding limb if no fracture is suspected. Apply a clean pad and bandage. If blood seeps through, apply a further pad and apply pressure. Continue applying pressure with the second pad until bleeding stops or medical help arrives.

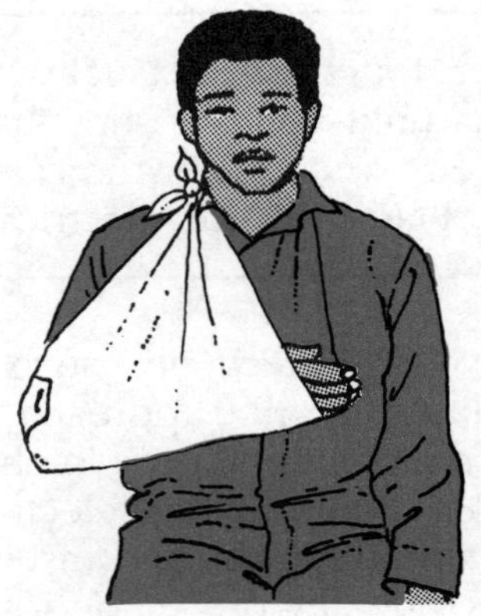

Figure 2.8 One method of supporting an injured arm in a padded sling.

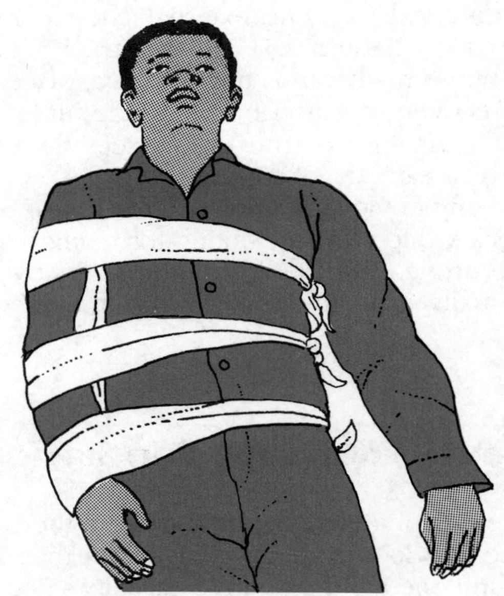

Figure 2.9 Securing an injured arm if the elbow cannot be moved.

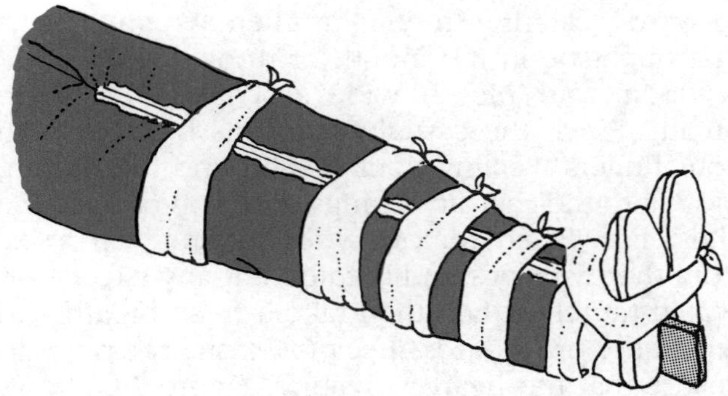

Figure 2.10 Supporting a fractured leg if a splint is available. Pad the splint, and bandage avoiding the site of fracture.

Treatment of a fracture

The main first-aid treatment is to prevent movement in the area of the fracture until qualified medical attention arrives. If you must move a casualty, then support the part with padding or by hand. For a short journey to hospital, you may be able to immobilise the injured part by securing it to a sound part of the body using padding and bandages. Bandages must be firm, but not so tight that they affect the blood circulation. For a long journey over rough ground, you may need extra bandages and splints. You can use virtually any suitable strong stick or piece of metal as a splint – even rolled-up newspaper. Keep checking to ensure that the bandages are not too tight. See Figures 2.8–2.10.

> ▲ Remember: if you suspect a fracture of the neck or spine, do not move the patient unless it is absolutely necessary because their life is in danger from some other cause. It is always best to comfort the patient and carefully tend to obvious injuries, restricting movement until qualified medical help arrives. Moving a patient with a fracture of the spine can cause permanent injury – even paralysis – if done incorrectly.

CHECK YOUR UNDERSTANDING

- For any injuries other than very minor ones, always seek expert medical attention.
- For burns of less than 3 cm diameter, immerse the area under cold water or cold running water for at least 10 minutes.
- If skin is exposed to the rays of an electric arc, the area can become tender and swollen. This condition is known as 'arc burn'. It should be treated by gently sponging with cold water. If the skin is not broken, you can apply sunburn cream.
- The condition called 'arc eye' or welder's flash is fairly common. Eyes can be affected either by direct or by reflected exposure to the ultraviolet light produced by the electric welding arc. The symptoms – pain and a 'sand in the eye' feeling – can last up to 48 hours. Bathe the eyes with cold water and cover with pads of clean, non-fluffy material. Special welder's eye drops are available from a doctor or hospital, which can help to ease the pain.
- If someone has received an electric shock, *never* touch them until you are sure that the current has been turned off.
- If breathing and heart have stopped, carry out mouth-to-mouth ventilation and apply external chest compression.
- If a person has been injured they often become quite weak because they are in a state of shock. Reassure and comfort them, loosen any tight clothing, but keep the casualty warm with extra clothing or a blanket. If the casualty is thirsty, moisten their lips with water but do not give them anything to drink.
- If a casualty is bleeding, get them to sit or lie down, elevate the bleeding limb if possible, and apply a clean pad and bandage.
- If you suspect a fracture, prevent movement in the area of the fracture until qualified medical attention arrives.
- When bandages are applied, keep checking to ensure that they are not too tight.

REVISION EXERCISES AND QUESTIONS

1. Describe the recommended treatment for a minor burn.
2. What is the first thing you should do if someone has received an electric shock?
3. How can you try and start someone breathing again?
4. If a person has been injured, they can sometimes suffer from shock. What is the first-aid treatment for shock?
5. Why must bandages not be tied too tightly?

(Further practice questions can be found on page 202.)

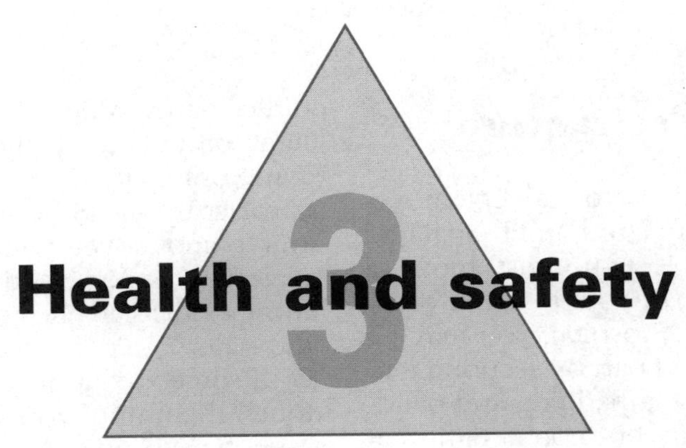

3 Health and safety

Introduction

Safety is everyone's responsibility. We are responsible both for our own safety and for that of other people.

Because of this, we must understand correct working methods and be able to notice if something is not as it should be. It is our duty to report unsafe equipment and to warn others about unsafe working practices.

This chapter covers safety points that are in most cases common to all welding processes and welding workshops. The names of regulations may vary from one country to another, but the content is concerned with safety in welding and therefore applies to any areas or workplaces where welding takes place.

The Health and Safety at Work etc. Act 1974

This Act is very important. It covers the legal duties of employers, employees and self-employed persons. Health and safety are everyone's responsibility. One of the important aims of the Act is to encourage employers and employees to work together to make a safer workplace.

Figure 3.1 Some common hazard signs.

General duties of employers

The following points are summarised from the Act.

1. It is the duty of every employer to ensure the safety, health and welfare of all employees at the workplace. This includes the maintenance of plant and the working environment, and also the provision of safe entrances to and exits from the workplace.
2. Safety and the absence of risks to health must be ensured during all handling, storage and transportation operations.
3. Instruction, training and supervision must be provided so far as is reasonably practicable.
4. A written statement of the general policy with respect to health and safety of employees at work must be drawn up.
5. Provision is also included in the Act for the election of employees as safety representatives.

General duties of employees

As an employee it is your duty to take reasonable care of your own health and safety. You must not take risks or endanger others by your actions. You must also cooperate with the employer on health and safety matters.

Control of Substances Hazardous to Health Regulations 1988 (COSHH)

Under these regulations, all substances used in the workplace must be assessed. The assessment should include:

1. listing substances used in the workplace;
2. stating the possible harmful effects of these substances;
3. noting where the substances are used, handled and stored;
4. assessing who might be exposed to them and the length of exposure involved;
5. looking at ways of preventing or controlling such exposure.

In welding, there are various special hazards: the fumes and radiation from manual metal arc welding operations, for example. If substances have been assessed as being hazardous, then anyone who might come into contact with them must be told about the assessment. Figure 3.1 shows some common hazard signs.

The COSHH control measures to limit or prevent exposure are as follows.

1. Replace the substance with a safer alternative.
2. Introduce technical or engineering methods of controlling exposure.
3. Reduce exposure by following the safe systems of work.

If these methods do not give adequate control, then, in addition, suitable protective clothing should be provided.

Welding safety precautions

Fusion welding and cutting processes involve intense heat, either from an electric arc or a gas flame. In this section we look at ways of protecting the body from this heat and minimising discomfort so that high-quality welding can be undertaken. The information in this section is based on the Health and Safety at Work etc. Act and the control measures listed by COSHH.

In the arc welding processes, rays are given off that are high in infrared and ultraviolet emissions. If you look at an arc without proper eye protection, you can get what is called **arc eye**. This is a painful condition causing irritation of the eyes, which can last for up to 48 hours in severe cases. Anyone with this condition should seek medical advice, as eye drops that will ease the pain are available.

The welder's eyes and face must therefore be protected from these rays, and also from the intense heat and light rays coming from the arc. The shield should cover the sides of the face and have a special filter lens (like very strong sunglasses) that is made to British Standard specification BS 679.

A list of recommended filters is given in Table 3.1. The EW number increases as the filter becomes more powerful (the letters 'EW' stand for 'electric welding'). Where two or more shade numbers are recommended for a particular process and current range, the higher shade numbers should be used for welding in dark surroundings and the lower shade numbers for welding in bright daylight.

Types of welding shield

The arc welder can choose which type of shield to use for particular applications. The **handshield** (Figure 3.2) is probably less tiring and in some cases easier to use than the helmet or **headshield** (Figure 3.3), but gives less protection to the head.

When welding overhead (a skill that requires some practice), a leather cap is also worn. For work inside aluminium or stainless steel fabrications, protection to the back of the head and neck may also be required to protect these areas from reflected rays.

The filter glass of the shield is protected by a plain cover glass, which should be kept clean and replaced when spatter damage (damage by small particles of molten metal given off from the welding operation) makes it difficult to see through.

Some shields allow the filter to be lifted while still leaving the clear glass in position. This allows the welder to see to chip burnt flux (which is called slag) off the weld, while still protecting the eyes from flying chippings.

Figure 3.4 shows one of the latest types of solar-powered welding mask. It has a light-reactive lens that automatically adjusts to the correct shade of filter according to the intensity of the arc. The adjustment time is 2 milliseconds (2 thousandths of a second). The lens instantly clears when welding stops, to allow protection with good visibility for slag removal or repositioning of work.

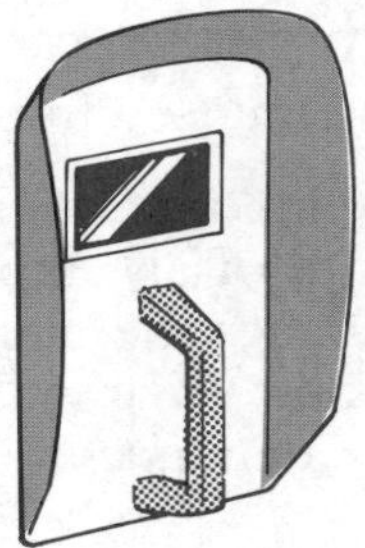

Figure 3.2 Welding handshield.

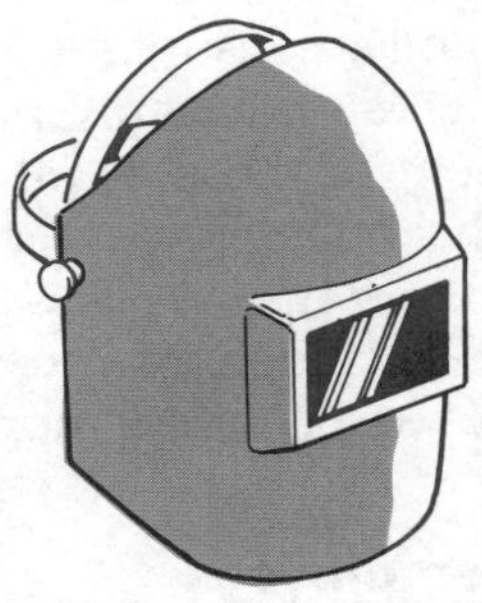

Figure 3.3 Welding helmet or headshield.

Table 3.1 Protection of Eyes Regulations 1984: Schedule No. 1, Process No. 24

Welding process	Approximate welding current required (in amps)	Filter(s)
Metal arc welding (coated electrodes)	Up to 100	8/EW
Continuous covered-electrode welding		9/EW
Carbon dioxide shielded continuous covered-electrode welding	100–300	10/EW 11/EW
	Over 300	12/EW 13/EW 14/EW
Automatic carbon dioxide shielded metal arc welding (bare wire)	Over 500	15/EW 16/EW
Inert gas tungsten arc welding	Up to 15	8/EW
	15–75	9/EW
	75–100	10/EW
	100–200	11/EW
	200–250	11/EW
	250–300	13/EW 14/EW

Figure 3.4 Solar-powered welding mask. (Courtesy of Frost Auto Restoration Techniques Ltd, UK)

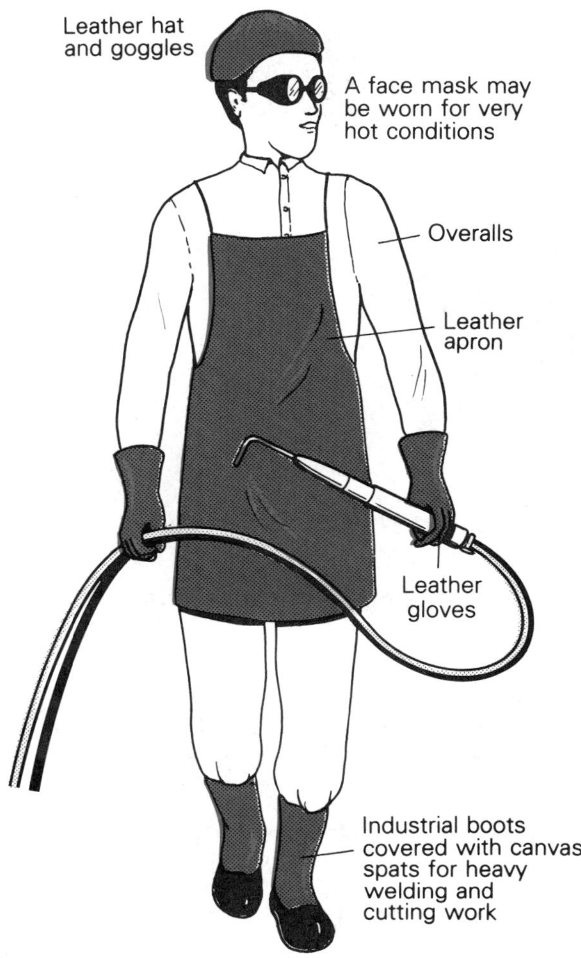

Figure 3.5 **Protective equipment for gas welding and cutting.**

Protection against burns from sparks, hot metal arcs and flames

For general welding, a leather apron is usually worn over the top of overalls. For heavy-duty welding, spats can be worn over the top of industrial boots to protect the feet from particles of hot metal and sparks. Leather gloves provide protection during normal operations and can be supplemented with leather sleeves for heavier work. Heavy-duty gauntlets are also made. See Figure 3.5.

> ▲ Remember: leather gloves are not made for picking up hot metal. They are designed to protect the hands from heat, sparks and spatter when welding. Always use tongs for picking up small pieces of hot metal.

Figure 3.6 **Gas welding goggles.**

For gas welding, it is not usually necessary to wear a helmet like the ones used for electric arc welding. Goggles manufactured in accordance with BS 679 are satisfactory for protecting the eyes from sparks, heat and light radiated from the work (Figure 3.6). Gas welding goggles are made in different styles, and various types are available for wearing over spectacles if required.

Goggles are provided with a filter glass to BS 679, and a protective cover glass. The cover glasses should be cleaned as required, and should be replaced when they are so damaged that they obscure vision.

Precautions to avoid electric shocks

> ▲ Damp and wet conditions greatly increase the severity of an electric shock, if a live conductor is touched.

Take care, therefore, when changing electrodes, by wearing gloves so that your bare hands do not come into contact with welding terminals. Wearing of thick-soled industrial boots and standing on dry boards are further precautions against electric shock in damp conditions.

All metal casings on electrical equipment should be connected to earth so that electricity is safely discharged if there is a malfunction and a live conductor accidentally touches the case. Good earth connections are essential. If they are poor, the

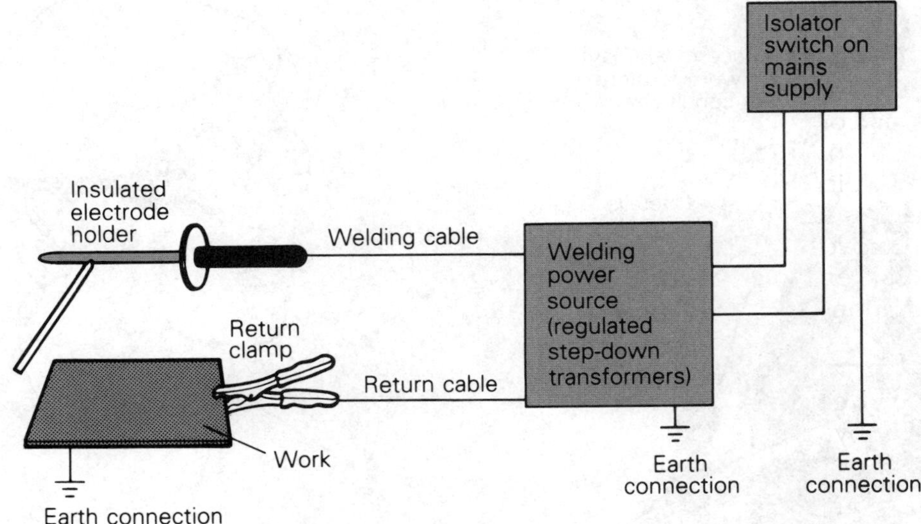

Figure 3.7 Block diagram of an alternating-current welding circuit showing earth connections.

resistance to the path of electricity will be high. The electric current might then follow the easier path to earth through the human body when the live metal part is touched, causing electrocution.

In a large fabrication shop, several people may be working on a fabrication at one time. There may be people welding, drilling holes, marking and so on, and there may be several pieces of electrical equipment in use. It is therefore vital that the work is earthed. Most companies bury a large cast-iron or copper plate about $1\frac{1}{2}$ metres square and 2 metres deep to act as the earth. Cables are carried through steel conduit within the factory, and this conduit is connected to the earthing plate or plates, so that should any part become live it will immediately discharge to earth.

For welding transformers, an extra earthing wire connects the metal parts of the equipment to the main earthing system. This extra earth is sometimes included in the supply cable (Figure 3.7).

All electrical equipment should be regularly checked and maintained by qualified personnel, and any damaged equipment should be clearly labelled as such and taken out of service until repairs can be undertaken.

> ▲ All emergency switches for electrical equipment should be clearly marked and located in positions that are easily accessible.

Precautions to avoid the risk of fire and explosion

These risks are greatest with gas welding and cutting. If you intend to carry out these operations, you should try to obtain and read the following publications from the Health and Safety Executive: Booklet 32, *Repairs of Drums and Small Tanks: Explosion and Fire Risk*, and Booklet 50, *Welding and Flame-cutting using Compressed Gases*.

Because you may have difficulty in obtaining these, the main safety precautions are summarised in this section, and details of safe working and mechanical protection devices appear in Chapter 4 on gas welding.

> ▲ Both the gases most commonly used for gas welding must be treated with care and respect.

Acetylene, for example, forms a potentially explosive mixture with air within the range of 2–82 per cent of acetylene. Such a range could be achieved merely from leakage or escape. This is why all gas welding equipment must be well maintained.

Oxygen is non-flammable but will support and increase combustion in flammable materials. The atmosphere surrounding the work must not be allowed to become enriched with oxygen (from a leaking hose or pipe for example); the slightest spark under these conditions can cause a 'flash' fire in which everything flammable in the area is burnt in a matter of seconds.

Oxygen can ignite oil, so it is very important that the workshop and working clothes are clean.

All the fusion welding processes produce sparks and hot metal, so it is vital that any materials likely to catch fire are moved well away from welding operations, and fire extinguishers should be sited at convenient locations.

> ▲ Remember: entire factories have been destroyed by fires arising from unattended hot metal or sparks from welding and cutting processes.

All emergency exits should be clear of obstruction on both sides. They should be clearly marked with exit signs and well maintained for ease of operation.

Using and storing cylinders of compressed gas

Here is a checklist of the main safety precautions to be taken when using and storing cylinders of compressed gas (see also Figure 3.8).

1. Keep full and empty cylinders apart from each other in clearly marked storage areas. The storage room should be fireproof and have flameproof electrical fittings. It should be well ventilated.
2. Never smoke, wear oily or greasy clothing or allow exposed flames in the storage room.
3. In storage and in use, cylinders should always be protected from snow and ice and also from the direct rays of the sun.
4. Acetylene cylinders should always be kept in an upright position.
5. Oxygen and combustible gases such as acetylene and propane should not be stored together.
6. Keep cylinders away from heat, grease and oil. Heat will increase the pressure of the gas and can weaken the cylinder wall, while oil and grease can ignite spontaneously in the presence of pure oxygen.
7. Use a cylinder trolley to transport cylinders, to avoid damage from dropping or bumping cylinders violently together. Always handle cylinders with care.
8. In use, always protect cylinders from the sparks and flames of welding and cutting operations and ensure that they are clear of electrical apparatus if there is a danger of stray arcing.
9. Never test for leaks with a naked flame; always use soapy water.
10. Always shut off the gas supply when the cylinders are not in use, even for a short time, and particularly when transporting cylinders. Don't overtighten the valve when shutting off the cylinder; just tighten it enough to prevent any leakage.
11. Never use fittings made of copper or copper alloy with more than 70 per cent copper; copper can form an explosive compound when in contact with acetylene.
12. Blow out the cylinder outlet by quickly opening and closing the cylinder valve to clear out any dirt or dust, before fitting the regulator. Do not use oil or grease on valves or gas welding equipment. Check equipment before and after use, and have it serviced at regular intervals.
13. Always ensure that cylinders are secure and will not fall over, either in use or in storage.
14. If a cylinder spindle valve should become frozen, thaw it out slowly with warm water. *Never* use a flame.
15. If an acetylene cylinder becomes heated for any reason, take it outside immediately and immerse it in water or spray it with water. Open the valve and keep it as cool as possible until the cylinder is empty. Then inform the cylinder suppliers.

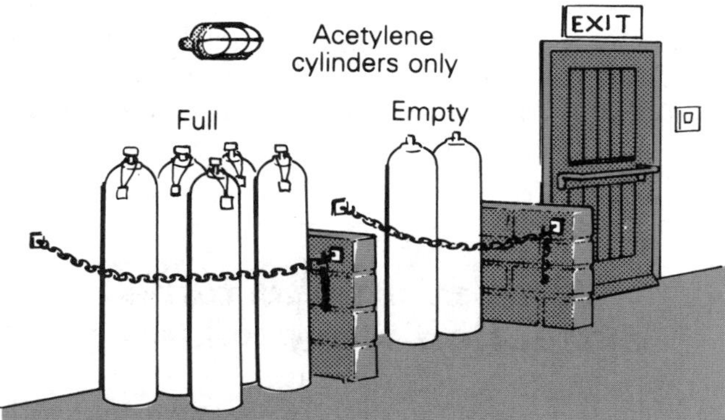

Figure 3.8 **The storeroom should be well ventilated, fireproof and fitted with flameproof electrical fittings. Keep full and empty cylinders apart from each other in clearly marked storage areas.**

Table 3.2 Know your fire extinguisher colour code

Fire extinguisher type	Colour code	Suitable for use with	Comment
Water	Red	Wood, paper, textiles, etc.	Unsafe on all electrical equipment at all voltages
Dry powder	Blue	Flammable liquids, high voltages	Safe on high voltages
Foam	Yellow	Flammable liquids	Unsafe on all electrical equipment at all voltages
Carbon dioxide (CO_2)	Black	Flammable liquids, high voltages	Safe on high voltages
Vaporising liquids	Green	Flammable liquids, high voltages	Safe on high voltages

Welding and cutting vessels that have held combustibles

You should *never* perform welding or cutting on a vessel that has contained an inflammable liquid unless the proper precautions are taken. Proper facilities for ensuring safety are essential.

If a vessel has to be welded or flame cut and its previous contents are unknown, then a chemical analysis is required. Always treat it as if it had contained an inflammable substance, *however long it may have been empty*.

To prevent explosions in this type of work, there are two main approaches:

1. removing the inflammable material;
2. making the material non-explosive and non-inflammable.

The inflammable material can be removed either by steaming or by boiling. For steaming, remove the filler cap and drainage plugs from the vessel. Any tools used in this process must be of a non-sparking type, such as special tools made of bronze. Then empty the vessel and position it so that condensed steam can easily drain away. Low-pressure steam is used as shown in Figure 3.9, and steaming should be continued until the whole tank is hot to the touch. Two or three hours of steaming are usually necessary.

For boiling, the vessel should be fully opened and emptied, again using non-sparking tools. It should then be immersed in boiling water. Sometimes an alkaline degreasing agent can be used, but this should be of a type that will not corrode the vessel. Continue the boiling for at least half an hour and longer if necessary.

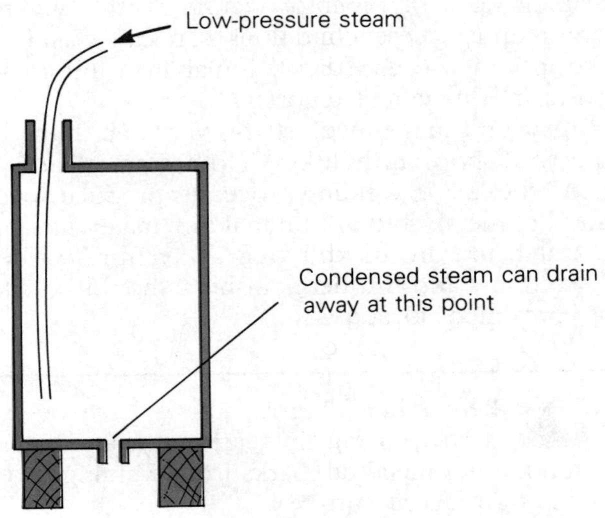

Figure 3.9 Arrangement for steaming a vessel.

After steaming or boiling, the vessel should be chemically tested, a certificate should be issued to say that all the contents have been removed satisfactorily and the vessel marked ready for welding or cutting.

The material can be made non-explosive and non-inflammable after steaming or boiling by replacing all the air in the vessel with an inert gas or carbon dioxide. When this method is used, a simple non-return valve can be employed to prevent excessive loss of gas and to avoid excessive pressure build-up.

In most countries, a certificate has to be issued by a responsible person, usually a chemist, stating that, after analysis, the vessel is clean of all previous contents and is safe to weld. For large vessels, which a welder may have to work inside, the welder may not even enter the vessel until such a certificate has been issued. Suitable methods of fume extraction and ventilation must then be installed as discussed below.

Ventilation and fume extraction when welding

This section looks at some of the main methods and considerations involved in the control of fumes in a general workshop where welding is taking place on mild steel.

Because all fumes are potentially hazardous, and some can be fatal, they are covered by the

COSHH regulations and those of the Joint European Directive. This means that the potential hazards involved in welding different materials must be assessed, and the COSHH control measures must be put into force.

When welding mild steel, the fumes are not usually harmful if the correct precautions are observed.

Particular care and specific control measures have to be taken when using electrode coatings containing **fluorides**. This includes low-hydrogen electrodes and the welding of monel, nickel and stainless steels or any metal with a high chromium content.

Welding and cutting of materials that have been painted, brass and galvanised or cadmium-plated metals, should be carried out in a well-ventilated area with fume extraction at the point of work. The COSHH assessment in such cases may also advise the use of a respirator as well.

If a welder is exposed to a source of fumes, seek medical assistance immediately.

Vapours from degreasing operations

▲ These are particularly dangerous in welding operations, because many such vapours decompose by the action of the ultraviolet radiation given off from the arc to form phosgene or other poisonous gases.

Degreasing operations using **trichloroethylene** or similar solvents should therefore not be carried out anywhere near welding operations, to prevent the vapours from being drawn into the area near the arc. Any work that has been degreased using solvents should be completely dry and free from solvent residue before welding starts.

Gases produced by the action of the arc and heat

Gases are formed when fluxes burn and decompose, and by the effects of ultraviolet and infrared radiation on air. The ultraviolet light from an arc can cause the oxygen in air to change its molecular form and become **ozone**. Ozone is very chemically active; if inhaled, it can produce severe irritation and a loss of lung capacity. Ozone is the only gas in a welding atmosphere that can be filtered out, as it changes back to oxygen on contact with solids.

Nitrogen oxides can be formed by the action of heat and ultraviolet radiation. These oxides can irritate the lungs and, in high concentrations, can cause cyanosis (a blue coloration caused by lack of oxygen in the blood). This condition can be fatal. Another toxic gas found in welding is carbon monoxide, which is poisonous in high concentrations.

Most other gases met with in welding have a low toxicity, but remember that any gas can replace air in the environment. The shielding gases used in TAGS and MAGS welding will displace air; in a confined space there is a risk of asphyxiation if air is not replenished at the same rate that the diluted atmosphere is extracted.

Argon and **carbon dioxide**, which are both widely used shielding gases, are heavier than air and can settle at floor level. If they are not extracted, they can build up into a stagnant blanket of asphyxiating gases (Figure 3.10). An extractor duct at floor level and a fan-blower replenishing fresh air into the confined area will avoid this situation. Any extracted fumes, which will usually contain nitrogen oxides, should be discharged in such a way that they do not contaminate other work areas.

Methods of fume extraction

Basically, there are three main methods of controlling and reducing welding fume levels.

1. The atmosphere in the welder's helmet can be constantly replenished with **fresh air**. Special welding helmets can be obtained for this purpose, and these probably provide the best answer in protecting the welder in normal situations. Full breathing apparatus may also be worn by the welder underneath the helmet, when working in particularly hazardous situations. Both of these methods, while protecting the welder, will do nothing to prevent fume build-up in the workshop.
2. **Small extractor ducts** that can be placed near the welding operation can be very effective, as they extract the fumes at source (Figures 3.11, 3.12). They need to be moved frequently to keep them close to the welding operation if they are to work at maximum efficiency. The correct use of these small extractors will greatly reduce the level of fumes in the surrounding atmosphere.

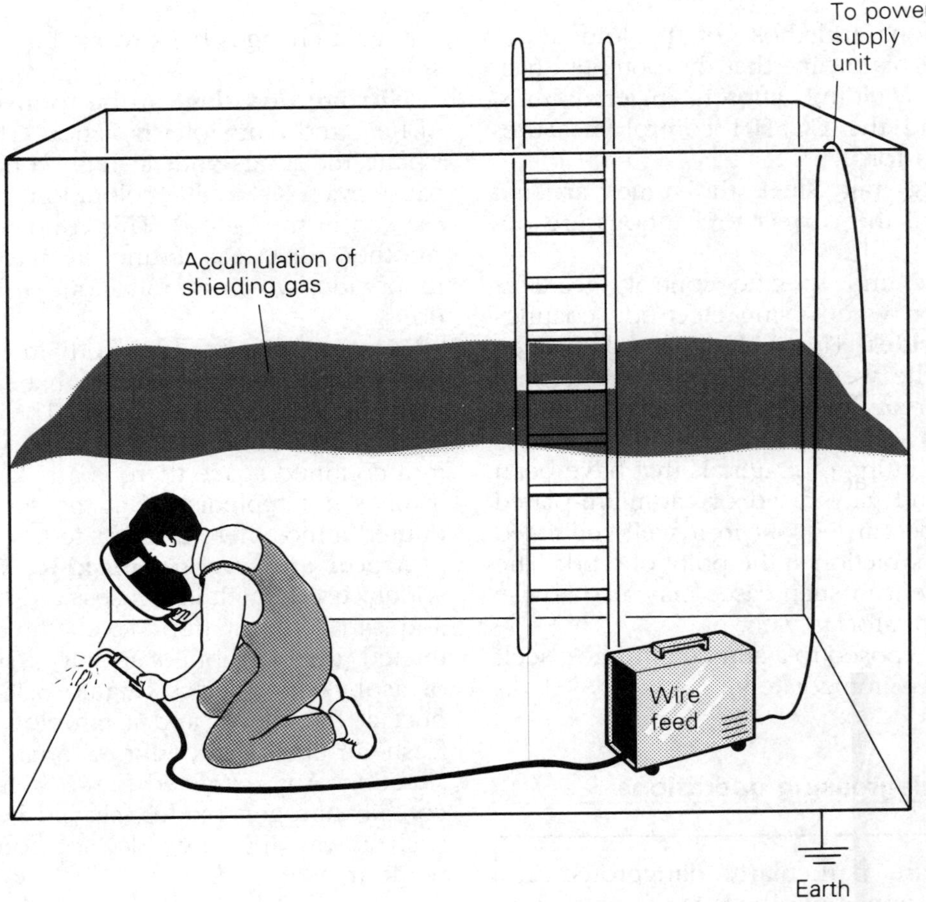

Figure 3.10 Sketch showing build-up of asphyxiating gas due to inadequate ventilation and air replenishment. This is a very dangerous situation.

3. **Roof extractor hoods** will help to keep the overall fumes in a workshop down to an acceptable level (Figure 3.13). However, if the fumes go directly outside together with large quantities of air, this can cause problems when heating a workshop in the winter months. Systems that recirculate the extracted air through filters can be installed; such systems, although more expensive to install, will soon pay for themselves with savings in heating costs.

How fume levels are measured

The fumes produced by welding and cutting operations can be carried into the zone around the welder's head by convection currents of hot air rising from the work, or even by badly sited extraction equipment. The chemical composition of the fumes will determine to what extent the substances constitute a health hazard.

The maximum level for each chemical compound to which a welder can be exposed is specified as the **occupational exposure limit** or OEL. Every year, the Health and Safety Executive in the UK publishes a list giving the OELs for the substances commonly found in industrial atmospheres. These limits form a basis from which the acceptability of a working atmosphere can be determined.

It is usual to take measurements of the atmosphere in two main areas: the **breathing zone**, which represents the breathing atmosphere of the welder and will probably have the highest level of fume concentration as it is close to the welding operation; and the **background atmosphere**. An analysis of the background levels is important when deciding if it is safe for other people to work in the surrounding area while welding is taking place.

Fume content is measured by drawing a known volume of air through a filter. The fumes are then analysed chemically. The total amount is calculated

Figure 3.11 Local extraction of welding fumes.

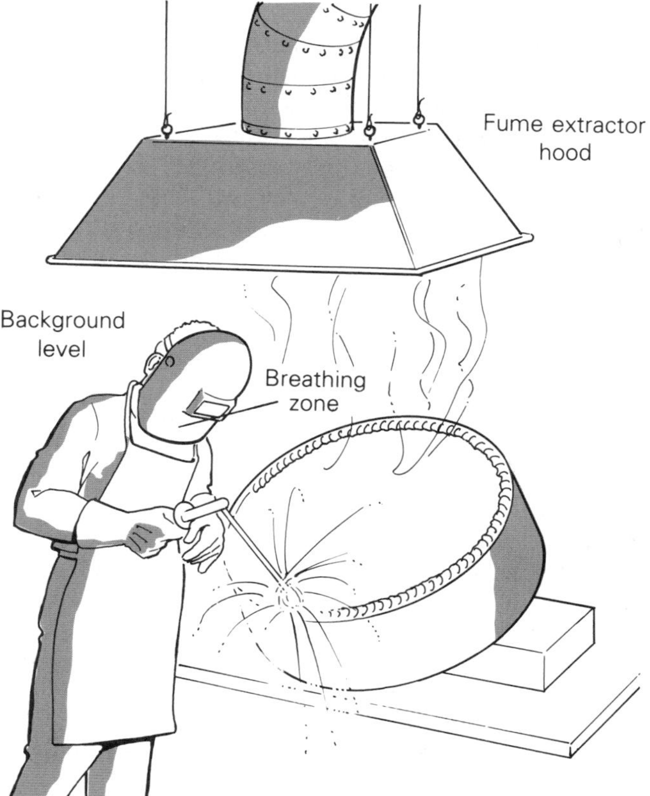

Figure 3.13 Overhead extraction of fumes.

Figure 3.12 Example of local fume extraction when manual metal arc welding. (Courtesy of TWI, UK)

in milligrams of fumes per cubic metre of air, and the relative amounts of individual compounds are compared with the relevant OELs.

When welding outdoors, there is normally enough natural air movement to disperse the welding fumes. In a normal factory, even though there may be some air movement in the workshop, fumes can collect near the ceiling if there is not adequate extraction.

Good fume extraction is essential when welding in a confined space, such as inside a tank, as the fume level can quickly exceed the recommended limits.

CHECK YOUR UNDERSTANDING

- Health and safety are the responsibility of all employers, employees and self-employed persons.
- Hazardous substances, areas and processes should be labelled with the appropriate hazard sign.
- The three control measures to limit or prevent exposure to hazards are: (1) substitute the

substance with a safer alternative; (2) introduce technical or engineering methods of controlling exposure; (3) reduce exposure by following the safe systems of work. If these methods do not give adequate control, then, in addition, suitable protective clothing should be provided.

- To prevent arc eye, a welding shield or mask fitted with the correct shade of filter must be worn, and screens must be placed around the welding area to protect other people.
- All electrical equipment should be correctly earthed and the on/off switch should be easily accessible and clearly labelled.
- All emergency exits should be clear of obstructions on both sides. They should be clearly marked with exit signs and well maintained for ease of operation.
- All personnel should be familiar with the fire extinguisher colour code and the main safety precautions to be taken when using and storing cylinders of compressed gas.
- Adequate ventilation and fume extraction are required when welding.
- The vapours from degreasing operations can decompose by the action of ultraviolet radiation given off from an electric arc and will form phosgene or other poisonous gases.
- Copper or an alloy of copper should *never* be used on an acetylene supply as it will form a contact explosive.

REVISION EXERCISES AND QUESTIONS

1. Who is responsible for safety?
2. Why should screens be placed around an electric arc welding operation?
3. Explain why it is very important that electrical equipment is correctly earthed.
4. What type of fire extinguishers do you have in your company or college welding workshop?
5. Why should welding never be carried out near degreasing operations?
6. Explain why copper or an alloy of copper should never be used on an acetylene supply system.

(Further practice questions can be found on page 202.)

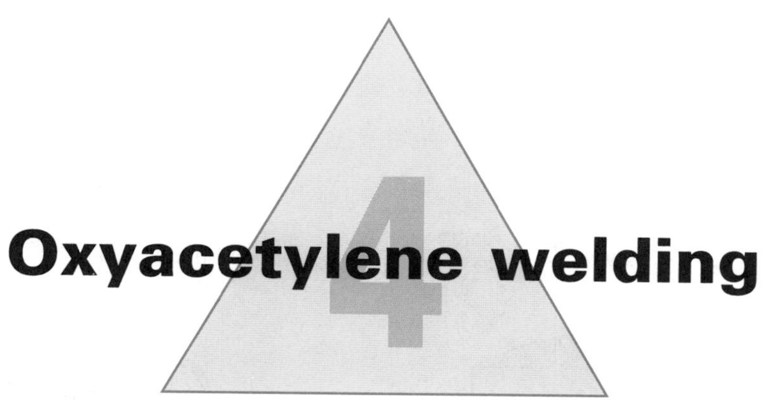

Oxyacetylene welding

Introduction

Oxyacetylene welding is known as **gas welding**. There are two systems used for gas welding: the **high-pressure system** and the **low-pressure system**.

Why oxyacetylene? Oxygen and acetylene are used because they provide a flame with the highest temperature: approximately 3250°C at a point just in front of the flame's inner cone.

The high-pressure system uses acetylene supplied in cylinders. The low-pressure system uses acetylene produced on the premises in an acetylene generator. As the name 'low-pressure' implies, this acetylene is at a lower pressure than cylinder acetylene. The equipment involves special safety precautions and a blowpipe that has an injector system to allow the low-pressure acetylene to be sucked through by the higher-pressure oxygen.

This chapter concentrates on the high-pressure system, which is the most widely used and therefore the one that you are most likely to learn welding on. However, the next section contains a brief description of the low-pressure system, for information.

The low-pressure system

In the low-pressure system, acetylene gas is produced by a special **acetylene generator**. The gas is piped through a special hydraulic back-pressure valve to the low-pressure **welding** or **cutting torch**, into which oxygen is fed from high-pressure cylinders. In most countries, you need a special licence to install and operate an acetylene generator, and the generator must be certified to comply with the regulations of the country concerned. Make sure that you have read the manufacturers' instructions in detail.

The generator produces acetylene by the chemical reaction of calcium carbide and water. Again, in most countries, you need to obtain a special licence from the authorities in order to store calcium carbide.

There are two main types of generator: **water to carbide** and **carbide to water** (Figure 4.1). Stationary acetylene-generating plant should be installed either in the open air or in a well-ventilated building, well away from the main workshops. The generators and fittings should be regularly serviced.

The generator house must be properly ventilated to prevent the risk of an explosive or toxic atmosphere being formed. It should be well lit, but electric lights should be located outside the building so that their light passes in through sealed glass windows. Switches and other electrical fittings are not allowed inside the building because of the danger of sparks, which could cause an explosion. Smoking, flames, welding plant and inflammable materials are not allowed in the generator house or near an open-air generator.

Many of these precautions also apply to portable plant. Portable plant should only be used, cleaned or recharged in the open air or in a well-ventilated workshop, well away from inflammable material and welding and cutting operations.

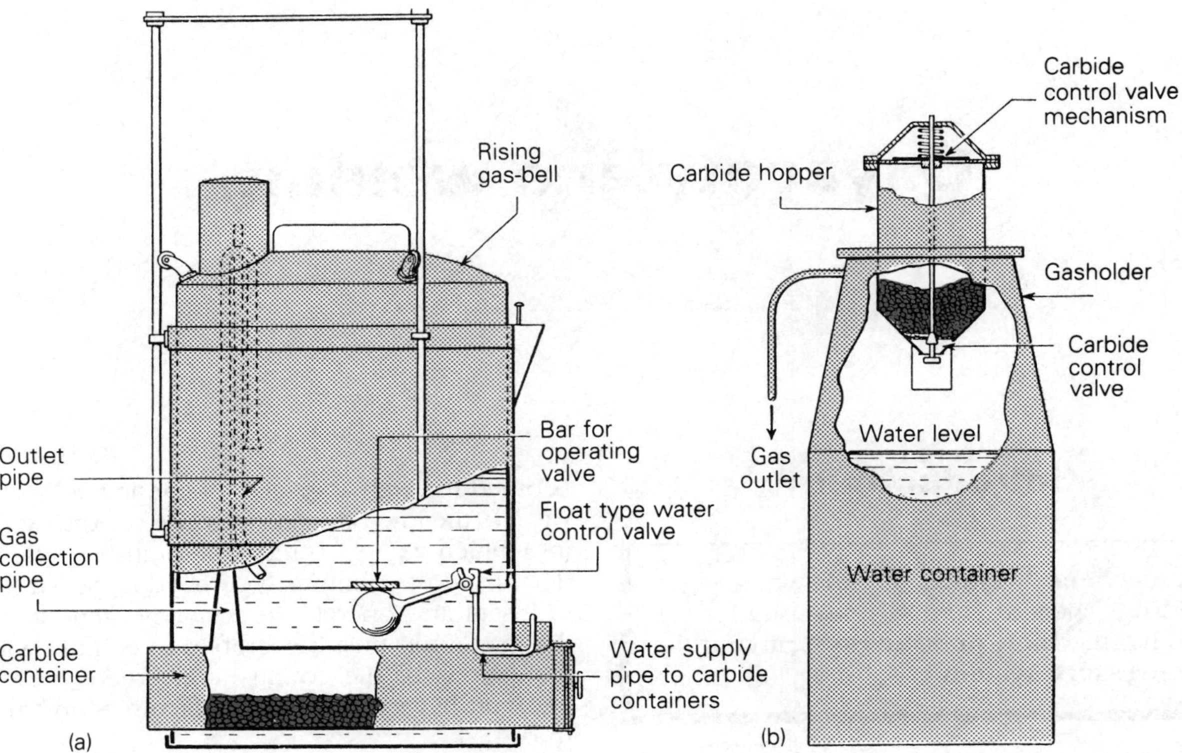

Figure 4.1 Acetylene generators: (a) water to carbide; (b) carbide to water. (Courtesy of TWI, UK)

Hydraulic back-pressure valve

A properly designed back-pressure valve must be fitted to the supply line between the generator and each blowpipe, to prevent a back-fire or reverse flow of gas reaching the generator. The valves should be regularly inspected, and the water level should be checked every day. Figure 4.2 shows a section through a typical hydraulic back-pressure valve. Only blowpipes of the injector type, designed for low-pressure operation, should be used. Use of a high-pressure blowpipe on this type of system can cause an explosion.

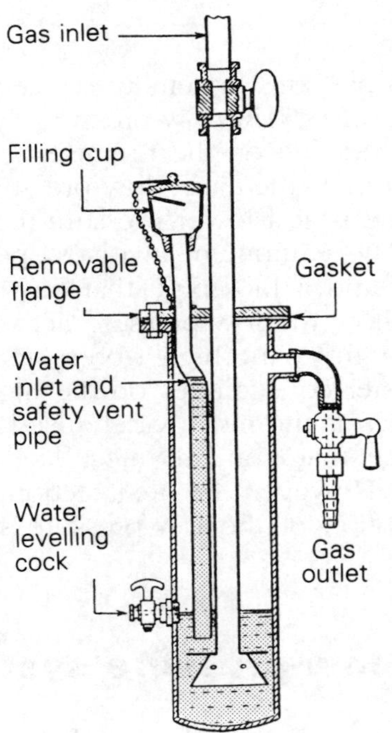

Figure 4.2 Hydraulic back-pressure valve.

The high-pressure system

A typical high-pressure welding outfit is shown in Figure 4.3.

Acetylene

For the high-pressure welding system, acetylene gas is stored in steel cylinders that are colour-coded in maroon.

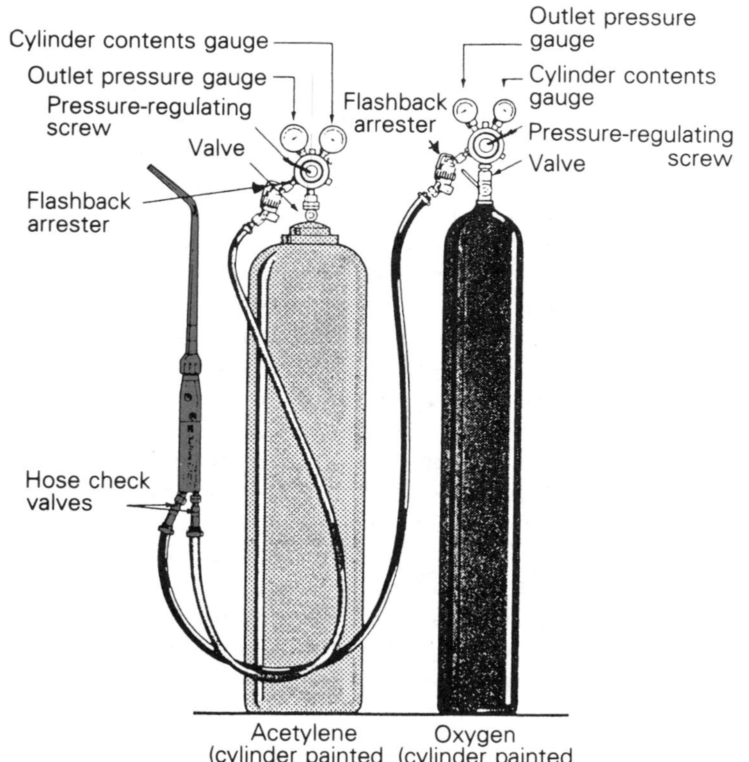

Figure 4.3 Typical high-pressure welding outfit.

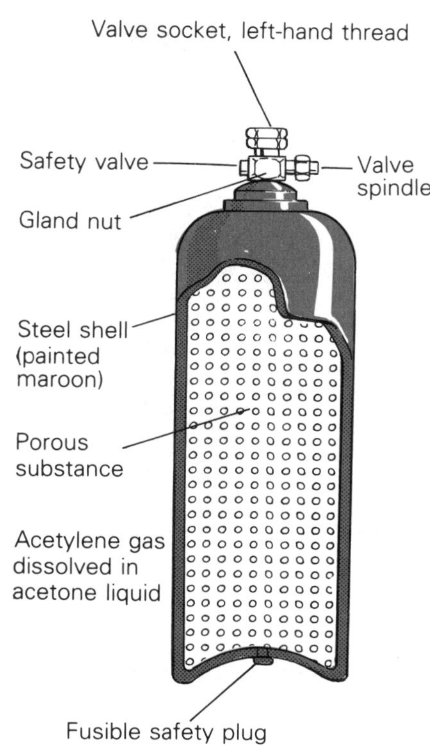

Figure 4.4 Cut-away view of acetylene cylinder.

Acetylene is unstable when under pressure. For storage in cylinders it is therefore dissolved in a chemical called acetone. For this reason it is called **dissolved acetylene**.

A porous material such as charcoal, synthetic asbestos or kapok is also placed inside the cylinder to divide the available space for the dissolved acetylene into a large number of small cells. This can prevent the acetylene from decomposing suddenly through the whole cylinder if accidental local heating occurs. It can therefore help to prevent an explosion (Figure 4.4).

At room temperature and normal atmospheric pressure, acetone liquid will dissolve about 25 times its own volume of acetylene. If the pressure is increased to 15 bar (200 lbf/in^2), it can dissolve about 375 times its own volume.

A full acetylene cylinder is pressurised to 15 bar (200 lbf/in^2) and will contain between 5.7 m^3 and 8.6 m^3 of acetylene gas, depending on the size of the cylinder. (1 cubic metre (m^3) = 1000 dm^3; 1 litre (l) = 1 dm^3.)

All connecting nuts and fitments on the acetylene supply have a left-hand thread. They also have notches on them to indicate this.

Manifold systems

In larger workshops, when a single cylinder is not sufficient, several cylinders can be coupled together in a manifold system. The cylinders in a **manifold** system are connected to the main pipe by 'pigtail' pipes (Figure 4.5). The main pipe then takes the gas to the line regulators and welding stations. Manifold systems must always be installed by professional suppliers.

▲ Pipes for acetylene must not be made out of copper, as this would cause an explosive compound known as copper acetylide to be formed. Steel pipes are normally used for the acetylene supply.

Figure 4.5 The use of 'pigtail' pipes to connect cylinders in a manifold system.

How to determine the amount of acetylene in a cylinder

Because the acetylene is in the dissolved condition, the amount in a cylinder cannot be determined accurately from the reading on the pressure gauge. The most accurate way to determine the quantity of gas in a cylinder is to weigh it and subtract this weight from the weight of a full cylinder. (The weight of a full cylinder is usually given on the label.) The volume of gas can then be calculated, taking 1 litre of acetylene gas to weigh 1.1 g.

Acetylene should not be drawn from a cylinder at a rate of more than one-fifth of the cylinder's capacity per hour. If this rate is exceeded, high amounts of acetone can be found in the gas.

Oxygen

Oxygen is non-flammable but will support and increase the combustion of flammable material. It is very important that an atmosphere does not become enriched with oxygen (from a leaking hose or pipe for example); the slightest spark under these conditions can cause a 'flash' fire in which everything flammable in the area is burnt in a matter of seconds.

Oxygen can ignite oil, so it is very important that the workshop and working clothes are clean.

Various substances, such as cloth, paper, oil and grease, will all burn explosively in an atmosphere that has been enriched with oxygen.

Do not store oxygen in the same area as flammable materials such as other gases, paint, solvents and oil. Store cylinders in a well-ventilated area; do not use any oil or grease on gas equipment. Check for leaks using soapy water or a 1 per cent solution of Teepol in water. (Teepol is a product manufactured by Shell.)

Oxygen for welding is supplied in solid drawn steel cylinders, which are painted black and are charged up to a pressure of 200 bar (2900 lbf/in^2) (Figure 4.6). The valve at the top of the oxygen cylinder has a right-handed screw thread for connection of the oxygen regulator.

The volume of oxygen contained in a cylinder is approximately proportional to the pressure. For every 10 litres of oxygen consumed, the pressure will fall by about 2 bar. This means that we can use a pressure gauge to show how much oxygen remains in the cylinder.

If large quantities of oxygen are required, several cylinders can be coupled together in a manifold system to give the required volume or flow rate.

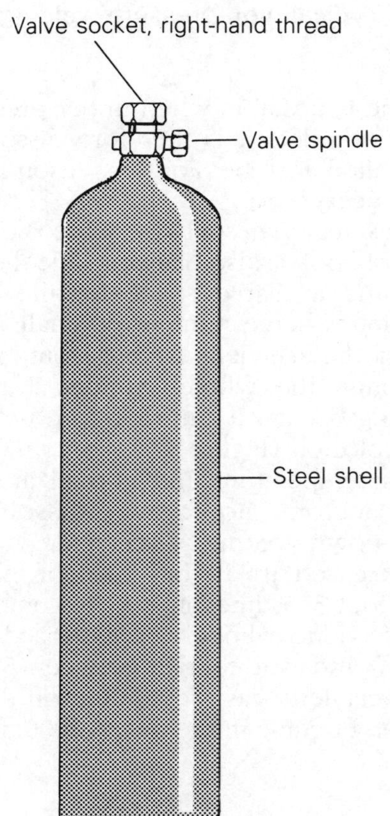

Figure 4.6 Oxygen cylinder: colour-coded black.

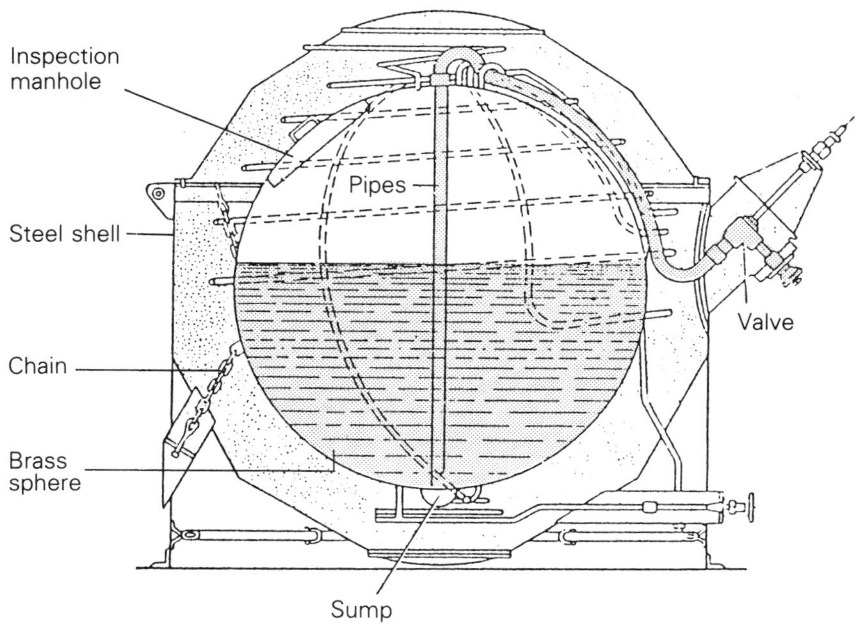

Figure 4.7 One type of storage tank for liquefied oxygen. (After D. Glizmanenko and G. Tevseyev)

Liquid oxygen tanks

If consumption is very high, oxygen can be supplied and stored in liquid form. This requires a special installation and particular codes of practice.

One type of tank for storing liquid oxygen is shown in Figure 4.7. It consists of a thin-walled brass sphere suspended on chains, inside a steel shell. The top of the sphere has an inspection manhole, which can be sealed. Outside the sphere there is a sump. The space between the shell and sphere is filled with thermal insulating material. (This could be magnesium carbonate, mypore or aerogel.)

The tank is filled and emptied through a pipe with a valve, which takes a detachable metal flexible hose. Liquid oxygen enters the hose from another reservoir under pressure. Storage tanks are fitted with pressure gauges.

Losses of liquid oxygen in storage tanks due to evaporation range between 0.4 and 0.7 per cent per hour of the oxygen held in the tank. The percentage loss increases as the tank is emptied.

Liquid oxygen can also be stored in vacuum-insulated vessels. The air from the space between the walls of such a vessel is evacuated to a residual pressure of 10^{-5}–10^{-6} mmHg. Still another variety of storage includes vessels with vacuum-powder insulation. This consists of powdered magnesia, aerogel or silica gel filling the space between the walls, which have been evacuated to a residual pressure of 10^{-1}–10^{-2} mmHg.

Vacuum-insulated and vacuum-powder-insulated tanks weigh less than those with conventional insulation, and losses of oxygen due to evaporation in them are between 0.1 and 0.15 per cent per hour of the oxygen held.

Gas pressure regulators

Pressure regulators for welding have a high-pressure gauge, which indicates the pressure of gas in

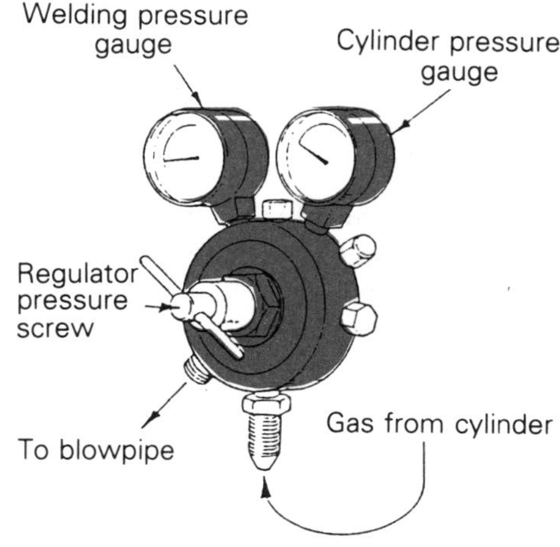

Figure 4.8 Pressure regulator.

the cylinder, and a low-pressure gauge, which indicates the required welding pressure set by the regulator valve (Figure 4.8). In a **single-stage regulator**, the high pressure from the cylinder is reduced in a single stage to the required welding pressure. A **two-stage regulator** is more accurate, and the gas pressure is less likely to fluctuate. In this type of regulator, the high pressure is reduced in two stages down to the welding pressure to be delivered to the blowpipe.

The colour band on an oxygen regulator is blue; on an acetylene regulator it is maroon or red.

The cylinder and hose connections on the oxygen regulator have right-hand threads; they are left-handed on the acetylene regulator. The acetylene connection nuts have chamfers or grooves cut in them to indicate that they are left-hand threaded.

The outlet gauge on the oxygen regulator reads up to 4.8 bar (70 lbf/in^2). The outlet gauge on the acetylene regulator reads up to 1 bar (14.5 lbf/in^2).

The high-pressure or inlet gauge on the oxygen regulator reads up to 100 bar (1450 lbf/in^2). The inlet gauge on the acetylene regulator reads up to 8 bar (115 lbf/in^2).

Gas welding hoses

High-pressure gas welding hoses are made with a neoprene lining and cover, and consist of three layers of rubberised canvas. This makes them light, and resistant to abrasion. They are colour-coded blue for oxygen and red for fuel gas.

Hose lengths are from 5 to 20 metres, with bore diameters of 4.5 mm for a maximum working pressure of 7 bar (100 lbf/in^2) and 8 mm for a maximum working pressure of 12 bar (175 lbf/in^2). Bore diameters of 10 mm are available for a maximum working pressure of 15 bar (217 lbf/in^2). British Standards BS 924J and BS796J cover hoses for welding and cutting.

Hose connectors

Connectors of the nipple and nut types are available for each type of hose with 6.4 mm ($\frac{1}{4}$ in BSP) and 10 mm ($\frac{3}{8}$ in BSP) nuts. These brass fittings are used to connect the welding or cutting hose to the regulator or flashback arrester. 'O'-clips are used to secure them to the hose (Figure 4.9). Again, to save any confusion, all nuts for the fuel gas line are grooved and have left-hand threads, while the nuts for use on the oxygen line are smooth and have right-hand threads (Figure 4.10).

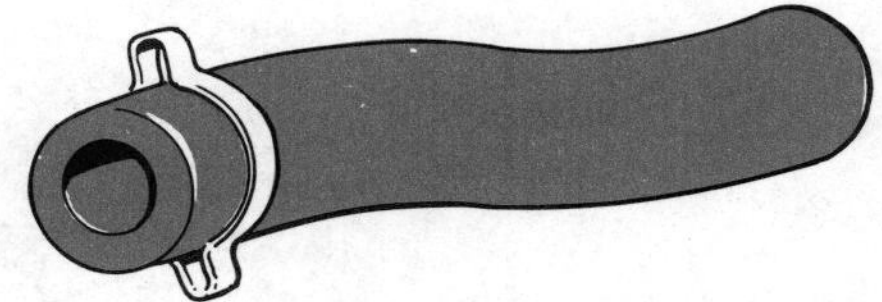

Figure 4.9 High-pressure hose is secured to connectors by 'O' clips, which are closed by long-nosed pliers.

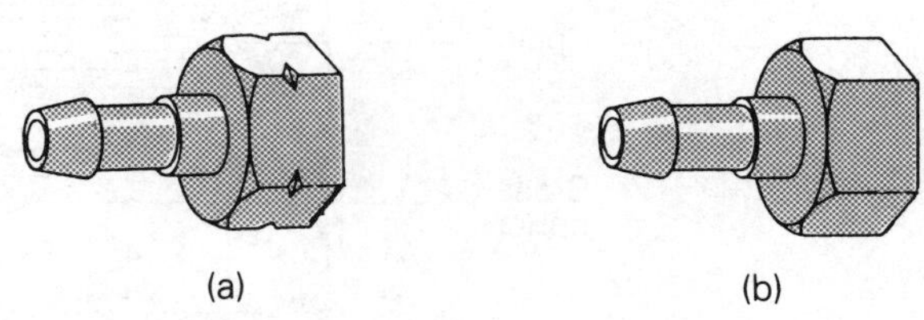

Figure 4.10 (a) Grooved nut connector with left-hand thread for combustible gas; (b) plain nut connector with right-hand thread for non-combustible gas.

Hose check valves or hose protectors

Hose check valves are an automatic safety device incorporating a spring-loaded non-return valve (Figure 4.11). They prevent the feedback of gases from regions of higher or lower pressures, and hence prevent oxygen and fuel gas from mixing in the hoses. This reduces the risk of a flashback from a partially or totally blocked nozzle or a leaking blowpipe valve.

Hose check valves should be connected between the blowpipe and each hose. The connection at the blowpipe is by a left-hand-threaded nut for acetylene and a right-hand-threaded nut for the

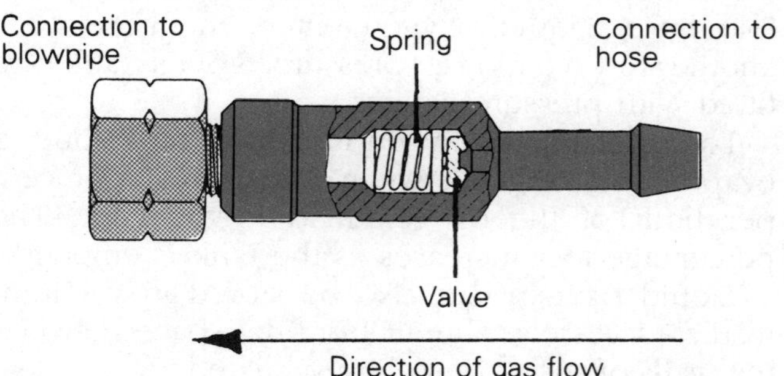

Figure 4.11 Hose check valve/protector. It contains a spring-loaded valve, which will seal off the line if a backflow occurs.

oxygen supply. They are fastened to the hoses by 'O'-clips.

Although the check valves will prevent a backfire from damaging the hoses, and can reduce the risk of a flashback, they will not actually stop a flashback. For full protection against the dangers of a flashback, arresters must be fitted.

Flame traps (flashback arresters)

In gas welding and cutting equipment, flame traps protect the operators and equipment against the hazard of mixed-gas explosions. The explosion or flashback can occur when backfeeding of gases takes place. A mixture of gases is then present in either the oxygen or fuel gas hose. Flame traps are designed to arrest the most severe forms of flashback under all operating conditions. They should carry full Health and Safety Inspectorate approval for operation within the recommended working pressures specified for each model. Approved flame traps should be installed in both the oxygen and the fuel gas lines, immediately downstream of the pressure regulator (Figure 4.12).

Figure 4.12 Flame traps. (Courtesy of Murex Welding Products Ltd)

High-pressure and low-pressure blowpipes for welding and cutting

The high-pressure blowpipe

The high-pressure blowpipe is simply a mixing chamber, with regulating valves to vary the pressure of the gases as required. Figure 4.13 shows a simple cross-sectional view of a high-pressure blowpipe. The oxygen and acetylene enter the blowpipe through separate connections and then mix in the gas mixer, arriving at the nozzle in approximately equal volumes.

A selection of **nozzles** is supplied with the blowpipe. These have openings of varying sizes (see Table 4.1 later in this chapter), and each is stamped with a number, usually indicating the consumption of gas in cubic feet or litres per hour depending on the make.

These nozzles will cover a range of welding requirements from thin sheet to heavy-duty welding.

A high-pressure blowpipe *must not* be used on a low-pressure system.

The low-pressure blowpipe

The low-pressure blowpipe contains an **injector system**. High-pressure oxygen travels through the injector and draws the low-pressure acetylene into the mixing chamber, giving it sufficient velocity to

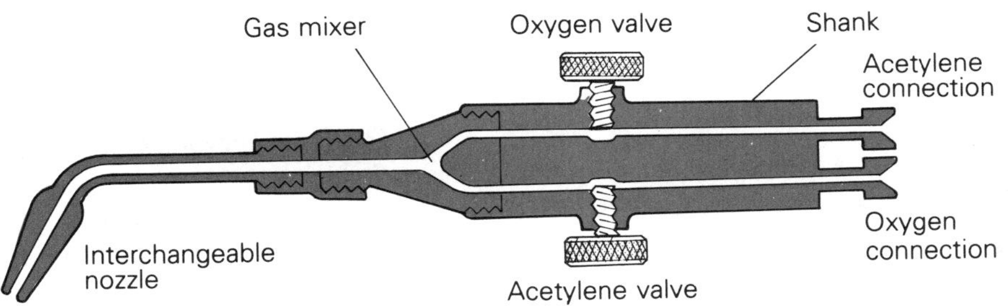

Figure 4.13 Principle of the high-pressure blowpipe.

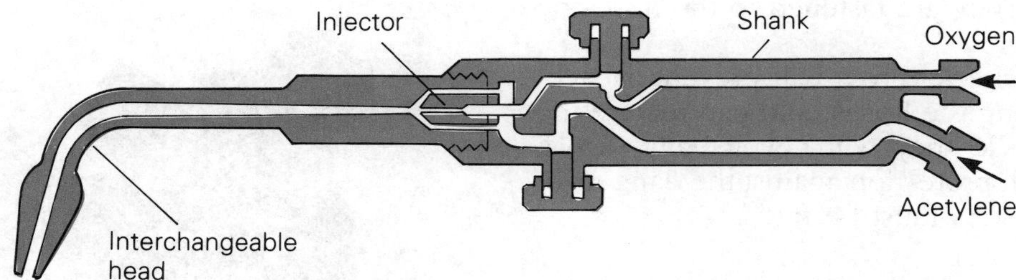

Figure 4.14 Principle of the low-pressure blowpipe.

maintain a steady flame (Figure 4.14). The injector will also help to prevent backfiring.

It is usual for the whole head to be interchangeable with this type of blowpipe, as the head contains both the nozzle and the injector, and the injector size will vary for each nozzle size.

The low-pressure welding blowpipe is more expensive than the high-pressure type. It can be used on the high-pressure system, but its use has fallen over the last few years compared with the high-pressure blowpipe and high-pressure system.

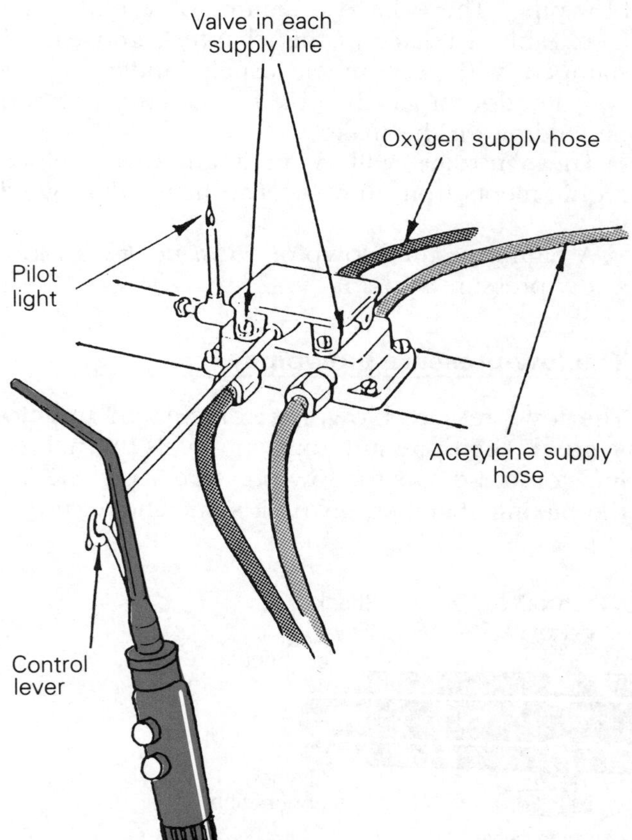

Figure 4.15 The gas economiser.

The gas economiser

The gas economiser is a very useful item of equipment designed for use with pipeline distribution of oxygen and acetylene to welding points. It contains two valves, which are normally held open by a spring but will be closed by the weight of a blowpipe hung on the control lever arm (Figure 4.15).

Oxygen and acetylene supplies are coupled to the inlet side of the fitting, and the gas hoses to the blowpipe are coupled to the outlet side. When the blowpipe is lifted off the arm, the gases can be ignited at the pilot light, and the flame can be adjusted to the correct setting in the normal way. Between welding operations, the blowpipe is hung on the arm, shutting off the gases. When the blowpipe is needed again, the flame can be lit from the pilot and welding can be started without loss of time or gas needed to adjust the flame.

Without the use of economisers, a lot of gas can be wasted while the flame is being adjusted, and while the blowpipe is laid aside with the flame burning when a job is being changed or adjusted. Installing gas economisers can reduce gas consumption by as much as 20 per cent.

If a blowpipe is not going to be used for some time, then it should be shut down completely. The economiser is designed for use when there are only short intervals of time between welding operations.

Backfires and flashbacks

When you begin your welding training, you will be told about two occurrences that you should be wary of.

The first is the **backfire**, when the flame snaps back inside the blowpipe or nozzle. Usually, the flame quickly extinguishes itself. This condition is not uncommon, and it is not serious. It is generally caused by insufficient pressure, dirt in the nozzle or some other blockage. You will learn more about the various causes when you begin your practical welding. However, whenever you get a backfire you should always turn off the gases at the cylinder valve – acetylene first, then oxygen – and investigate the cause. Sometimes the nozzle simply requires cleaning with nozzle reamers; these are small reamers specially made for the purpose.

More serious than the backfire is the **flashback**. This is a backfire that has gone back to the hoses. If this condition is not attended to correctly, it can become extremely dangerous and may even lead to an explosion. A flashback starts as a backfire, so this is why you must turn off the gas at the cylinder valves as soon as a backfire occurs, to stop it from developing into a flashback.

There are various safety devices on the equipment, such as one-way valves where the hoses connect to the blowpipe, and flashback arresters where the hoses connect to the regulators. Regulators are also valves, and the equipment is fitted with a main cylinder valve.

▲ With these devices, oxyacetylene welding is made much safer, but the biggest safety factor of all is the operator turning off the cylinder valves quickly when there is any doubt.

Using gas welding equipment

▲ When assembling equipment, never use oil or grease as these substances can ignite causing an explosion. Soapy water can ease a thread and will also indicate if there is a leak.

Any connections that do not assemble easily need to be replaced, but remember that acetylene fitments have left-hand threads and oxygen fitments have right-hand threads.

Before opening the cylinder valves check:

1. hoses for burns or cuts that may leak;
2. all connections for tightness;
3. that the regulator pressure valve is off (loose);
4. that both blowpipe valves are closed.

The cylinder valves should be opened just half a turn using the valve spindle key.

When shutting down equipment:

1. check that the cylinder valves are shut off;
2. check that the hoses have been emptied of oxygen and acetylene, by opening the blowpipe valves until the welding pressure gauge indicates zero and then closing both blowpipe valves;
3. turn off the regulator valve (loosen the pressure-adjusting screw).

Lighting the blowpipe

To light the blowpipe, set the regulators to the recommended pressures. Do this under the supervision of a skilled welder, until you have got the procedure perfected. When the regulators are set correctly, turn on the acetylene valve on the blowpipe, and light the acetylene at the nozzle with a spark lighter. Do not use a match.

At first the flame will be yellow and smoky. The soot and smoke being given off are **carbon**, as combustion is incomplete because of the shortage of oxygen in the flame. Use the acetylene valve on the blowpipe to increase or decrease the yellow flame until the black smoke reduces and then finally disappears. The acetylene supply is now right for the particular size of nozzle you are using.

Now turn on the oxygen at the blowpipe valve. As you increase the pressure of the oxygen, the flames gradually take on the appearance of the **neutral flame**, with a small blue inner cone and a larger outer envelope. If there is a feathery white plume around the inner cone, this is the **carburising flame**, which indicates that a little more oxygen is required to obtain the neutral flame.

If the inner cone is small and tapered, this indicates that there is too much oxygen. This flame is called the **oxidising flame**; the oxygen needs to be reduced slightly at the blowpipe valve in order to obtain the neutral flame.

The three different types of gas welding flame and their uses are shown in Figure 4.16.

When using the neutral flame for welding mild steel, the part of the flame just in front of the inner cone is used (Figure 4.17).

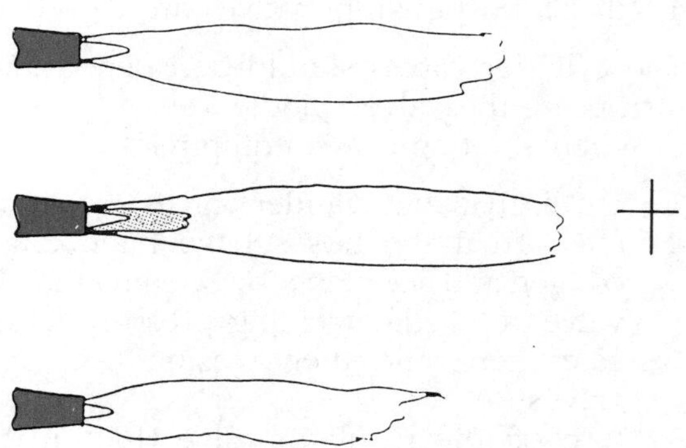

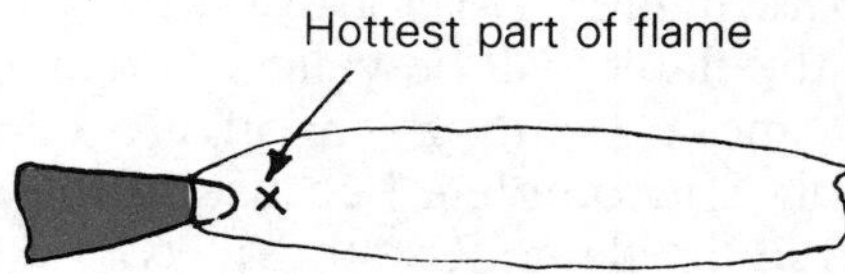

Figure 4.16 The three types of welding flame. (a) Neutral flame. This burns equal quantities of oxygen and acetylene. (b) Carburising flame. This has an excess of acetylene, which gives a carbon-rich zone round the inner cone. It is used for hardsurfacing. (c) Oxidising flame. This has an excess of oxygen, which gives an oxygen-rich zone just beyond the cone. It is used for brazing and bronze welding.

Figure 4.17 The hottest part of a neutral flame.

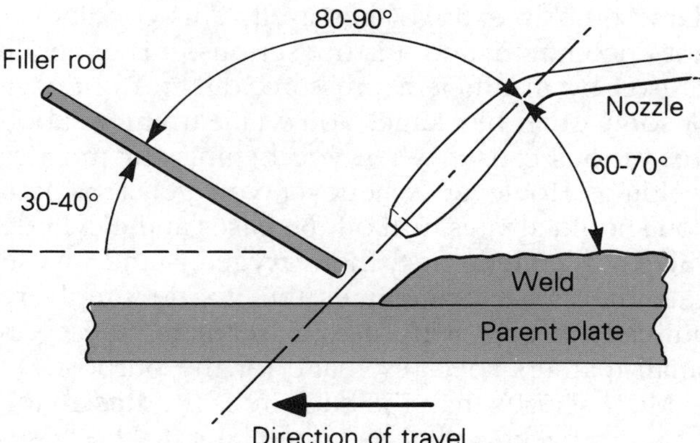

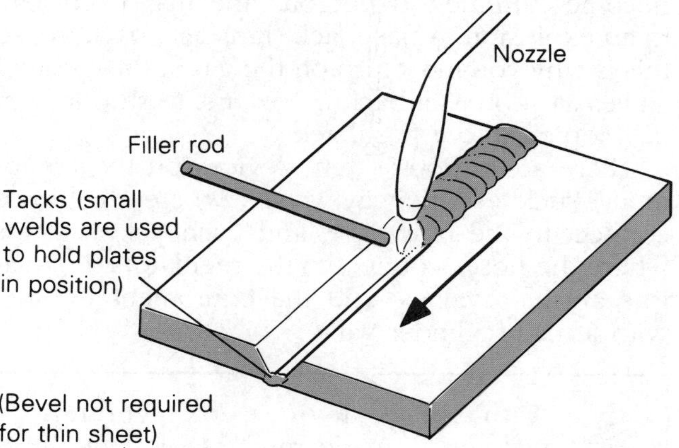

Figure 4.18 The leftward technique of gas welding.

The leftward technique of gas welding

When you have mastered the technique of lighting the blowpipe and adjusting the neutral flame correctly, you will be ready to practise the leftward technique of gas welding. This will usually involve some practice, under supervision, on scrap pieces of material.

The first stage is to deposit a straight bead of weld on a single piece of material and then, when you have perfected this, to practise joining two pieces. The ultimate aim is to achieve a standard of weld quality that will enable you to produce the required testpieces, if you want to become a qualified welder.

The leftward method of gas welding is used for welding steel plate up to 5 mm in thickness. It can also be used for welding non-ferrous metals.

When the blowpipe is held in the right hand, the weld travels from right to left, with the filler rod in front of the nozzle (Figure 4.18). The inner cone of the flame, which should be in the neutral condition for welding mild steel, is held close to the metal but not touching it.

For the best welding conditions, the blowpipe and filler rod should be held at approximately the angles shown in Figure 4.18. The nozzle is given either circular or slight side-to-side movements in order to obtain good and even fusion at the sides of the weld.

To commence welding by this technique, play the flame on the start of the joint until a molten pool is formed. Welding then proceeds by filler rod being fed or dipped into the molten pool. The rod is melted by this dipping action and not by the flame itself.

Do not hold the filler rod continuously in the molten pool, as this could prevent the heat of the flame and thus the molten pool from reaching the lower parts of the weld joint, resulting in possible lack of fusion.

The correct technique is to dip the rod in and

Table 4.1 Typical nozzle sizes and gas pressures for oxyacetylene welding

Mild steel thickness			Nozzle size	Operating pressures				Consumption of gas			
				Acetylene		Oxygen		Acetylene		Oxygen	
(mm)	(in)	(SWG)		(bar)	(lbf/in²)	(bar)	(lbf/in²)	(l/h)	(ft³/h)	(l/h)	(ft³/h)
0.9	–	20	1	0.14	2	0.14	2	85	3	85	3
1.2	–	18	2	0.14	2	0.14	2	110	4	110	4
2	–	14	3	0.21	3	0.21	3	170	6	170	6
2.6	–	12	5	0.21	3	0.21	3	200	7	200	7
3.2	1/8	10	7	0.21	3	0.21	3	250	9	250	9
4	5/32	8	10	0.21	3	0.21	3	280	10	280	10
5	3/16	6	13	0.28	4	0.28	4	400	14	400	14

SWG stands for 'standard wire gauge'

out of the pool at regular intervals as the weld proceeds. The frequency of this action will be determined by the size of the weld being deposited, and the correct action improves with practice.

Figure 4.19 shows examples of BS 4872 testpieces.

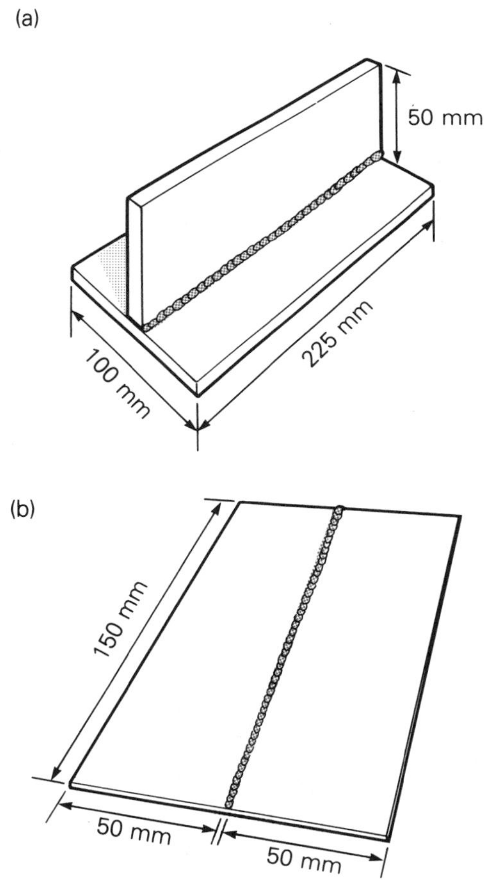

Figure 4.19 BS 4872 testpieces: (a) 'T' fillet weld in the horizontal position on steel 3 mm thick; (b) square-edge butt weld in the flat position on steel 1.5 mm thick.

These testpieces are used as end tests on some basic welding courses.

> Filler rods and wires for gas welding are contained in British Standard 1453. Group A covers steel. General-purpose low-carbon mild steel filler rods are in category A1 of this standard.

Nozzle sizes and gas pressures

As the thickness of the work increases, the flame will be required to supply more heat. This is made possible by increasing the nozzle size and the regulator gas pressures (in accordance with manufacturers' instructions).

If you try to weld thick metal with a small nozzle by increasing the gas pressure, there comes a point where the flame leaves the end of the nozzle. This indicates that the pressure is too high, resulting in a very noisy flame. It is much better to work with a 'soft' flame, which is obtained by using the correct nozzle size and pressure settings.

At the other extreme, if you try to weld with a nozzle that is too large for the work, by reducing the supply of gas at the blowpipe valves instead of changing to a smaller nozzle, then small explosions will occur at the nozzle. This is because the gas tends to build up round the nozzle in small bubbles. These small explosions indicate that the gas pressure is too low.

Table 4.1 lists typical nozzle sizes and gas pressures for oxyacetylene welding. Always consult the manufacturer's information, as this information can vary slightly with different makes of blowpipe.

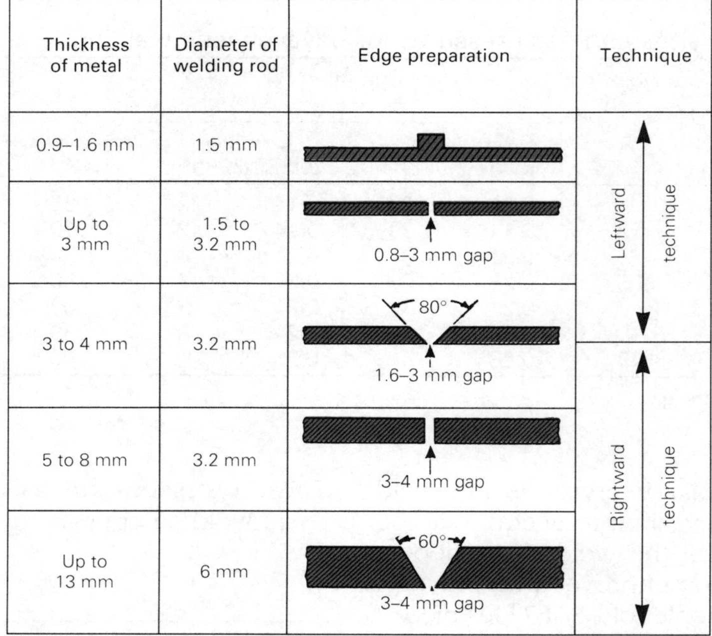

Thickness of metal	Diameter of welding rod	Edge preparation	Technique
0.9–1.6 mm	1.5 mm		Leftward technique
Up to 3 mm	1.5 to 3.2 mm	0.8–3 mm gap	
3 to 4 mm	3.2 mm	80°; 1.6–3 mm gap	
5 to 8 mm	3.2 mm	3–4 mm gap	Rightward technique
Up to 13 mm	6 mm	60°; 3–4 mm gap	

Figure 4.20 **Edge preparations for different thicknesses of plate. Above 13 mm thickness, plate can be bevelled and welded from both sides.**

The rightward technique of gas welding

As the plates get thicker, different edge preparations are employed. These different edge preparations are shown in Figure 4.20. Notice that as the plate gets more than 4 mm thick, it is recommended that another technique, the rightward technique, is used.

These days it is more usual to use one of the arc welding processes on materials above 4 mm thickness, but the rightward method is handy to know. Some welding courses include it, and a brief description is given here.

The rightward technique is shown in Figure 4.21. Some of the advantages of this method on thicker plate are as follows.

1. It is faster and uses less filler rod, so it is less expensive.
2. There is less expansion and therefore less contraction.
3. The flame remains over the deposited metal, giving an annealing action.
4. A better view of the molten pool is obtained, allowing for greater control of the welding operation.

Gas welding can be used for **positional welding** (welding in the vertical and overhead positions). These notes cover the flat position only, as you will need to perfect this technique thoroughly before you can learn positional welding.

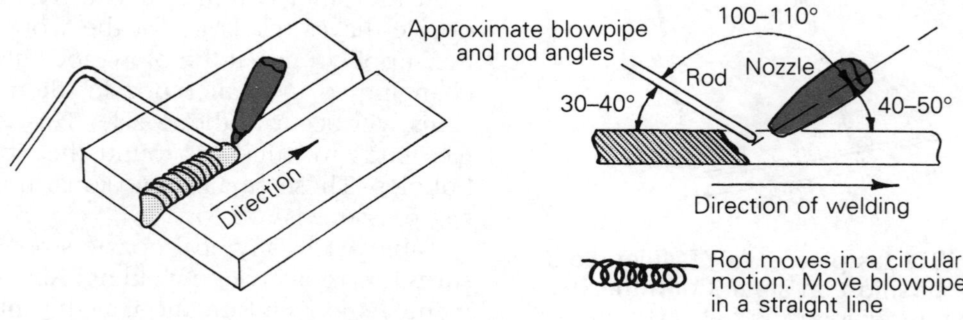

Figure 4.21 The rightward technique of gas welding.

CHECK YOUR UNDERSTANDING

- Oxyacetylene welding is also known as gas welding.
- There are two systems used for gas welding: the high-pressure system, using cylinders of acetylene, and the low-pressure system, using acetylene produced in a special acetylene generator. The high-pressure system is the most widely used.
- Acetylene is burnt in oxygen because it provides a flame with the highest temperature: approximately 3250°C at a point just in front of the flame's inner cone. This is sufficient to melt most metals in order to weld them.
- All connecting nuts and fitments on the acetylene supply have a left-hand thread. They also have notches on them to indicate this.
- Oil or grease must *never* be used on gas welding equipment as these substances can ignite, causing an explosion. Soapy water can ease a thread and will also indicate if there is a leak.
- There are various safety devices on gas welding equipment, such as hose check valves and flashback arresters. However, the biggest safety factor of all is the operator turning off the cylinder valves quickly when there is any doubt.
- There are three different types of gas welding flame: the neutral flame, the carburising flame and the oxidising flame.
- The leftward method of gas welding is used for welding steel plates up to 5 mm in thickness. The rightward method is used for welding materials above this thickness.

REVISION EXERCISES AND QUESTIONS

1. What type of thread is used on the acetylene supply?
2. What is the approximate temperature of a neutral oxyacetylene flame at a point just in front of the inner cone?
3. Oil must never be used to lubricate gas welding equipment. What can be used?
4. Sketch the three different types of gas welding flame and name them.
5. What is the biggest safety factor to remember when gas welding?
6. Which gas welding method would you use for welding steel plate 6 mm thick?

(Further practice questions can be found on page 202.)

Electricity and magnetism

Introduction

Before we deal with the various electrical methods of welding, it is important to ensure that all students have a good grasp of the basics of electricity and magnetism. That is what this chapter aims to provide.

Students who are confident that they are familiar with the material in this chapter can safely move on to Chapter 6.

Conductors, insulators and resistors

Conductors

> Materials that can carry an electric current with a minimum of resistance are said to be good electrical conductors.

Thermal conductivity – the ability to transfer heat by conduction through the material – is closely related to electrical conductivity. Copper, for example, is a better conductor of electricity than iron,

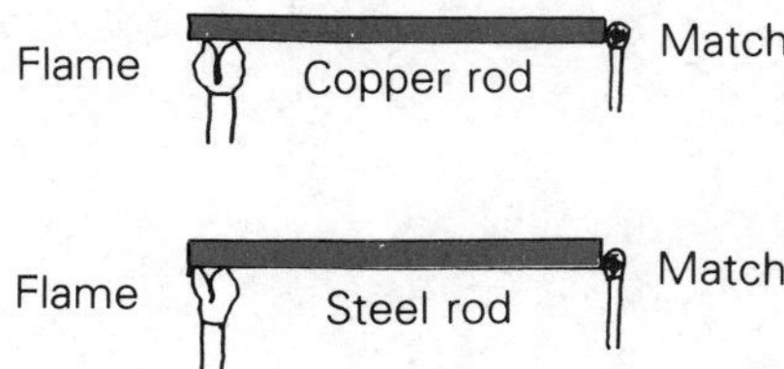

Figure 5.1 **The copper rod ignites the match first. This shows that copper is a better conductor than steel.**

although both materials will conduct electricity. You can prove that copper is also a better conductor of heat than iron by holding two rods, one of copper and one of iron or steel, and placing the ends of the rods in a flame. The copper rod will get hotter much faster than the steel one (Figure 5.1).

Here is a list of metals. The thermal and electrical conductivity of the metals decrease from top to bottom of the list.

1. Silver
2. Copper
3. Aluminium
4. Zinc
5. Nickel
6. Iron
7. Steel
8. Tin
9. Lead

Insulators

Insulators prevent the passage of electricity or heat. Not all insulators will do both; rubber and certain plastics are good insulators of electricity but will melt when exposed to higher levels of heat.

Different materials are therefore chosen for heat insulation and electrical insulation. The working temperature must also be considered when selecting electrical insulation materials.

Remember: there is no such thing as a perfect insulator. All materials will allow the passage of electricity if a high enough pressure is applied.

In welding, where the voltages are generally low, glass, porcelain, rubber, mica and various plastics are used as insulators. These insulators can fail if they become damp or wet, as water is a very good conductor of electricity. All electrical equipment must be kept dry, to avoid damage and the risk of electrocution.

Resistance

All substances will resist the flow of an electric current, converting part of the electrical energy into heat, but some substances offer more resistance than others. (This is not strictly true. There are materials called superconductors that have negligible electrical resistance, but as they have to be cooled to temperatures of –250°C and below, you are not likely to meet them in welding practice!) The amount by which a conductor resists the flow of a particular current depends on its physical dimensions, the nature of the material from which it is made, its temperature and occasionally the extent to which it is illuminated, because of a property called photoconductivity.

The filament in an electric light bulb and the element in an electric fire glow because of the heating effect caused by their resistance to the flow of electricity.

Good conductors such as copper and aluminium offer only small resistance but, when they are formed into wire or cable, their resistance will increase as their length increases, and decrease as their cross-sectional area increases.

This is an important fact to remember when electric welding, because we need to keep voltage drop in the cable down to a minimum. Lengths of cable should therefore not be too great, as there are obvious limits to increasing the cross-sectional area of cable.

Electrical circuits

In the simple circuit shown in Figure 5.2, there is a fixed electromotive force (e.m.f.), which is the electrical 'pressure' available at the terminals of the generator when no current is flowing. In welding, this is known as the **open-circuit voltage**.

The standard symbols for voltage, current and resistance are:

Voltage = V
Current = I
Resistance = R

To measure these quantities for welding purposes we would use the **ampere** (symbol capital A) for the unit of current, the **volt** (capital V) for the unit of e.m.f. or potential difference (voltage drop across a circuit) and the **ohm** (Ω, a Greek capital omega) for the unit of resistance.

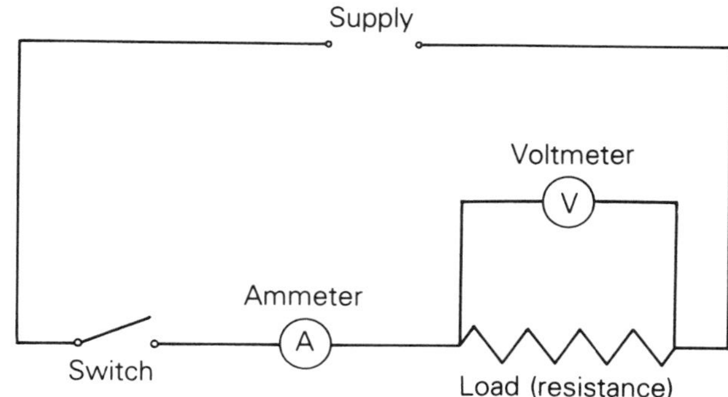

Figure 5.2 A simple electric circuit.

Ohm's law

Ohm's law states that for any circuit, the current is proportional to the e.m.f. and inversely proportional to the resistance. This gives the useful formula:

$$I = \frac{V}{R}$$

This can also be written as

$$\frac{V}{I} = R \text{ and } V = I \times R$$

One way of remembering these formulae is to write down the letters in a triangle (Figure 5.3). Then covering up the unit required gives its value in terms of the other two units. For example, when we cover V, it shows $I \times R$. If we cover R it shows

$$\frac{V}{I}$$

To find the resistance of a wire in ohms, when a pressure of 30 volts is applied with a current of 5 amps flowing:

$$R = \frac{V}{I} = \frac{30}{5} = 6 \text{ ohms resistance}$$

To find the voltage drop due to a resistance of

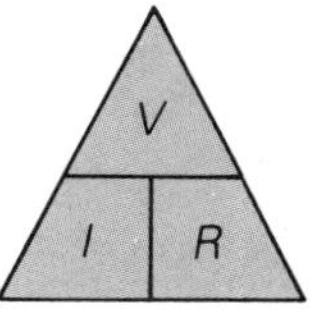

Figure 5.3 The Ohm's law triangle.

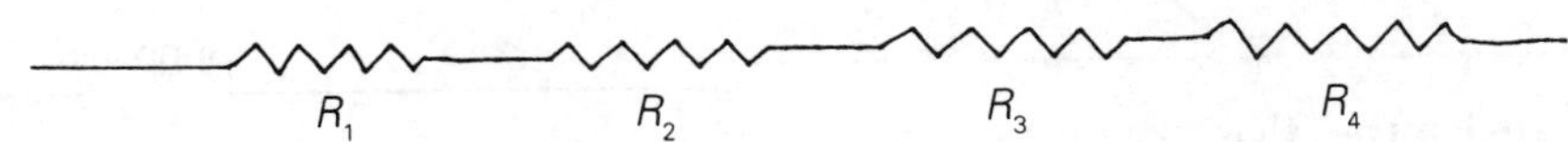

Figure 5.4 Resistances connected in series.

0.2 ohms when a current of 160 amps is flowing through it:

$$V = I \times R = 160 \times 0.2 = 32 \text{ volts drop}$$

The watt

The amount of power in a circuit is measured in **watts**. Power is the rate of doing work and the watt is based on the amount of work done per second in a circuit where the difference of pressure is 1 volt and a current of 1 ampere is flowing. This is defined as 1 watt. 1000 watts = 1 kilowatt (kW).

> Power in watts = volts × amps

The joule

The joule (J) is the unit of work, energy and quantity of heat. A joule is the amount of work done when a force of 1 newton (N) moves a distance of 1 metre (m). 1 watt (W) = 1 joule per second (J/s). The newton is defined as the force that will act on a mass of 1 kilogram (kg) to give it an acceleration of 1 metre per second per second (1 m/s^2).

As an example, to find the output of a welding generator in kilowatts and joules per second, if the output is 90 volts, 200 amps:

$$90 \times 200 = 18\,000 \text{ W} = 18 \text{ kW and } 18\,000 \text{ J/s}$$

This calculation gives the output of the generator. The power required to drive a generator will always be greater because of frictional and other losses. For a rough estimate of the power in kW required to drive a welding generator, it is usual to add on half the output. For the generator given here, this would be 18 + 9 = 27 kW.

The unit on which electricity companies base their charge to customers is the **kilowatt hour** (kWh); this is usually classed as one unit of electricity.

Resistances connected in series and parallel

In practical circuits, the various components can be connected together in different ways to produce different results.

No matter how complicated a circuit may be, you will find that it consists of two fundamental methods of connection: series and parallel.

When resistances are connected in **series**, they are connected end to end, as shown in Figure 5.4. This gives only one path for the current. The total resistance R is the sum of the individual resistances:

$$R = R_1 + R_2 + R_3 + R_4$$

Resistances are said to be in **parallel** when they form separate branches of a circuit and when the total current fed to them, I, is divided between them (Figure 5.5). With parallel resistances, the reciprocal of the total resistance is the sum of the reciprocals of the branch resistances:

$$\frac{1}{R} = \frac{1}{R_1} + \frac{1}{R_2} + \frac{1}{R_3} + \frac{1}{R_4}$$

A simple welding circuit

Figure 5.6 shows a simple welding circuit made up of an ammeter A, a variable resistance R, electrode holder, electrode and work. A voltmeter V is connected across the circuit.

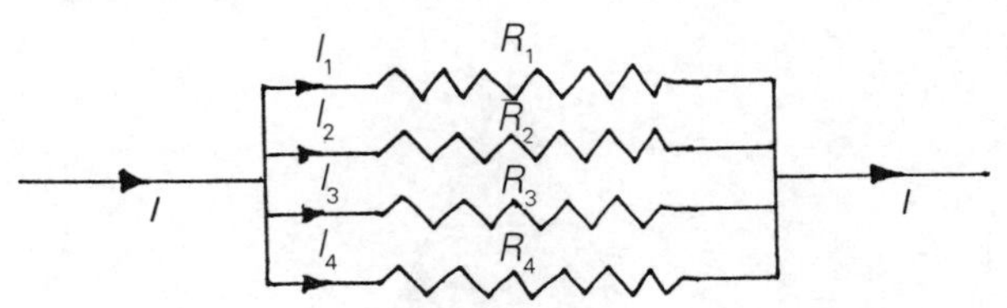

Figure 5.5 Resistances connected in parallel.

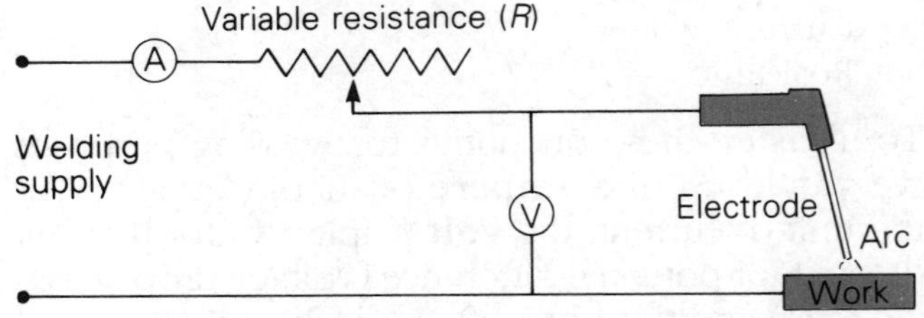

Figure 5.6 A simple welding circuit.

When the electrode is touched to the work, the circuit is completed. The amount of current that flows will depend on the amount of resistance in the circuit.

If the electrode is lifted slightly from the work, say by 4 mm, the current will still flow across the air gap between the end of the electrode and the work, in the form of an electric arc.

The amount of current flowing across the arc can be controlled by varying the amount of resistance R in the circuit. The voltmeter V registers the drop in electrical pressure that occurs as a result of the current being forced across the air gap between the electrode and the work. As the gap between the electrode and the work is increased, so will the voltage drop increase, until the arc finally extinguishes itself when the gap becomes too great.

Magnetism and electricity

There is an ancient story about a Chinese general who, over 3000 years ago, was pursuing his retreating foe when a thick fog descended, completely blotting out all landmarks. Any ordinary Chinese general might well have been forced to stop pursuit, but the ancient story says that this particular general had with him a chariot, in which stood an artificial figure with outstretched arm that always pointed to the south. Directed by this strange figure, the general soon caught up with his enemies and put them to flight.

This story is probably the first hint that the Chinese made use of 'magnetite' or black oxide of iron. It was well known by ancient peoples that a fragment of magnetite, when floating in water on a piece of wood, lined itself up to point one end to the Pole Star. Today we use the modern-day magnetic compass in the same way. The needle points to the earth's magnetic north, which is near to true north.

Commander James Ross discovered the magnetic North Pole. When he arrived there all the compass needles appeared to have lost their power, as there was nowhere for them to point to. The same thing happened to Shackleton in 1909 when his expedition discovered the magnetic South Pole.

Induction

Iron can be magnetised. This process is called **magnetic induction**. When a bar of iron is magnetised, each small particle of the iron effectively becomes a tiny magnet, with north and south poles. This in turn gives the bar of iron a north pole at one end and a south pole at the other. If the bar is suspended on a piece of string, the north pole of the bar will point north.

Around every magnet there are invisible lines of magnetic force, called the **magnetic field**. You can make them visible by placing a sheet of clean paper over the magnet and sprinkling iron filings on to the paper. Tap the paper, and you will see the iron filings line up along the lines of magnetic force (Figure 5.7).

When magnets are placed together, like poles will always repel each other and unlike poles will attract each other (Figures 5.8 and 5.9). These principles, and the invisible but powerful lines of magnetic force given off from a magnet, are used in the production of electricity.

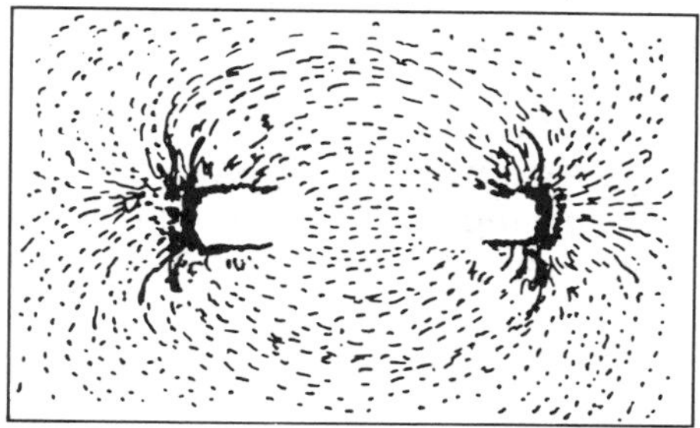

Figure 5.7 A bar's magnetic field can be shown by sprinkling iron filings on to a piece of paper placed over the magnet.

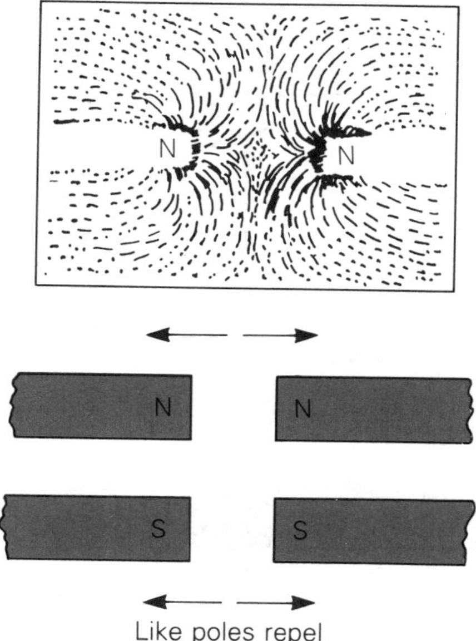

Figure 5.8 Repulsion between like poles.

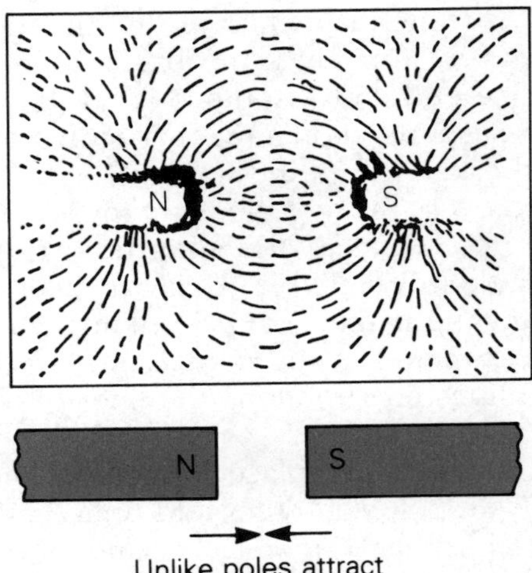

Figure 5.9 **Attraction between unlike poles.**

Magnetic fields around conductors

If you pass a cable through a card held horizontally and then sprinkle iron filings on to the card while the cable is carrying current, you will see that there are lines of magnetic force round the cable. The iron filings indicate them as concentric circles (Figure 5.10).

This effect of a magnetic field around a wire or cable carrying a current is used to magnetise soft iron to make an **electromagnet**. Figure 5.11 shows an iron core with a coil around it to make it into an electromagnet. Figure 5.12 shows the magnetic field set up by a straight conductor. If we were to look at the end of the core around which the electric current is travelling in a clockwise direction (Figure 5.13(a)), the end would be of south polarity (the south pole of the electromagnet). The end around which the current travels anticlockwise (Figure 5.13(b)) would exhibit north polarity (the north pole of the magnet).

In industrial electromagnets, many turns of insulated wire are wrapped around the iron core to make a very strong magnet when the current is switched on. Such magnets can be used in all sorts of ways. An electromagnet attached to a crane can be used to lift awkwardly shaped ferrous metal, such as in a scrap yard. When the metal is over the skip, the magnet is switched off and the metal released.

Because of the magnetic field surrounding a wire or cable when in use, cables such as welding

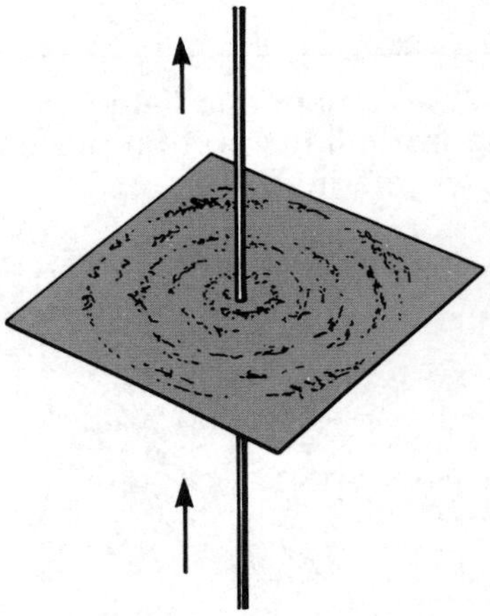

Figure 5.10 **Iron filings showing the magnetic field round a wire that is carrying a current.**

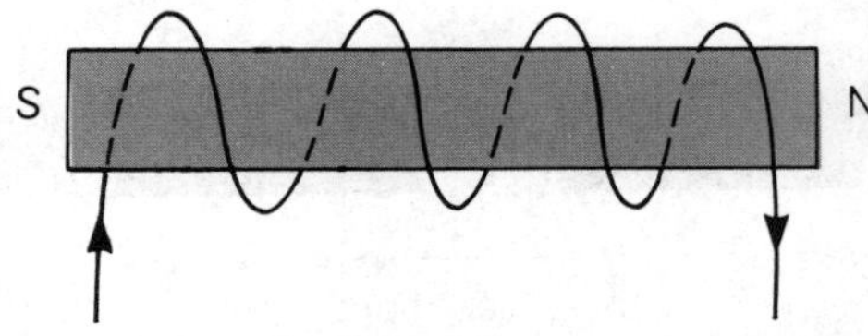

Figure 5.11 **The principle of an electromagnet.**

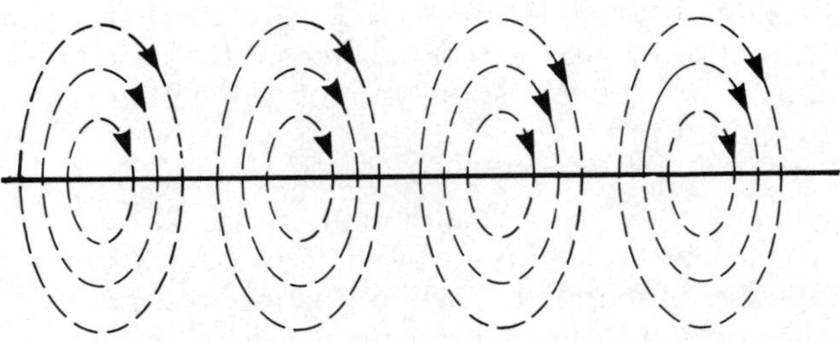

Figure 5.12 **The magnetic field set up by a straight conductor.**

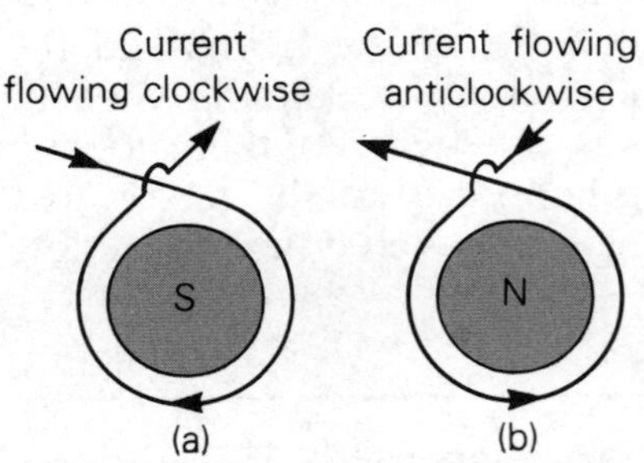

Figure 5.13 **The south and north poles of an electromagnet.**

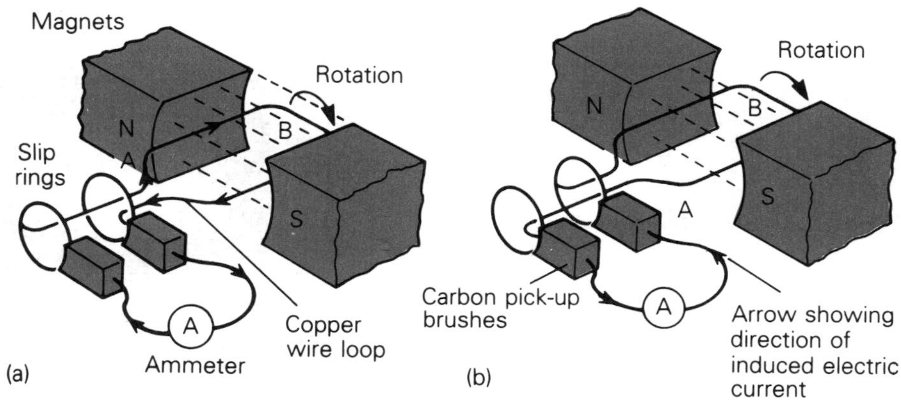

Figure 5.14 The production of alternating current (a.c.).

cables must always be unwound. Never use them with a large amount coiled up; this can cause severe overheating of the cable as a result of electric currents induced by an alternating magnetic field.

In a coiled a.c. cable, the electromotive forces (e.m.f.) set up will overlap and change rapidly as the lines of force alternate direction. The induced e.m.f. opposes the flow through the cable, causing rapid overheating. This is in accordance with **Faraday's law**:

> When an e.m.f. is induced in a circuit by a change in the number of lines of force through the circuit, the magnitude of the e.m.f. is proportional to the rate at which the number of lines changes.

Generating electricity

To produce an electric current, you need three things:

1. a magnetic field;
2. a loop of copper wire;
3. movement of either the field or the loop.

Production of an alternating current

In Figure 5.14 (a), the wire loop is being rotated between two magnets with unlike poles. These magnets are trying to pull together, but they are fastened down so that invisible lines of magnetic force exist between them.

The wire loop is cutting through the lines of force. A current is induced in the wire and picked up from the slip rings by the carbon brushes. The current flow will be in the direction shown by the arrows. When the loop is vertical, no lines of force will be cut, so no current will be produced.

In Figure 5.14 (b), the wire loop has turned half a rotation and the side A–B is now on the right. The loop is again cutting through lines of force and electricity is induced in the loop in the same direction but, because of the position of the slip rings, it is picked up by the carbon brushes for use in the opposite direction: hence alternating current (a.c.) is being produced.

Production of direct current

The production of a.c. and d.c. are similar. The only difference is in the way the electricity is picked up (Figure 5.15). A.c. generators use the two slip rings. D.c. generators use the copper

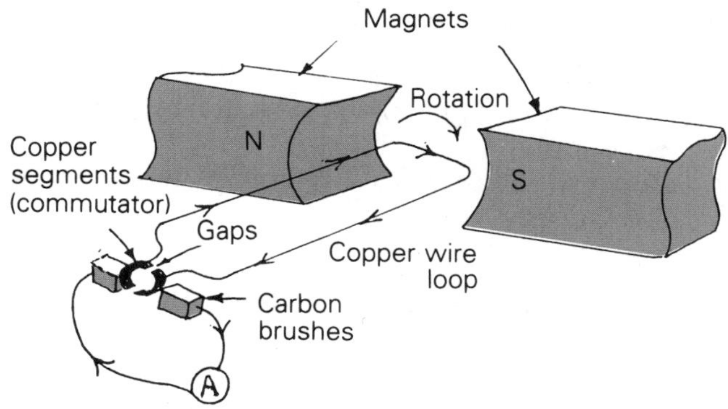

Figure 5.15 The production of direct current (d.c.).

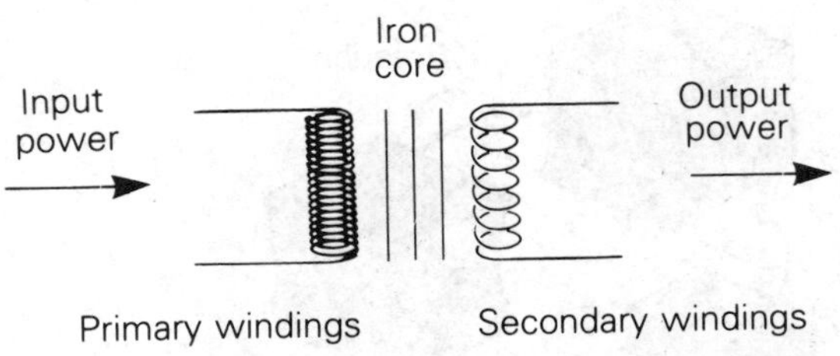

Figure 5.16 How a transformer is usually shown in an electrical circuit.

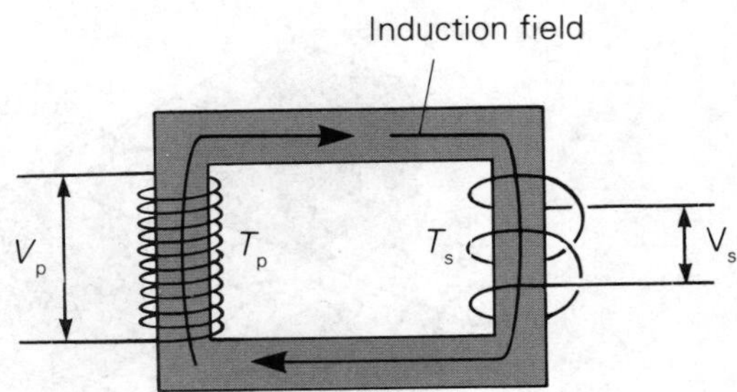

Figure 5.17 Transformation is proportional to the number of turns of wire on both sides of the core.

segments (commutators). If the number of wire loops is increased and if four or more magnets are used, then the electrical power generated will be greater. This fact is used on industrial generators, but basically the design is the same as that shown in Figure 5.15.

Transformers

Transformation is a method by which an a.c. power supply at a particular voltage and current is converted into a supply at a different voltage and current.

The power input to a transformer must equal the power output from a transformer. Consider a power of 8.8 kW (8800 watts) made up of 440 volts at 20 amps. What is the available current from a transformer whose output is at 100 volts?

Input power = $440 \times 20 = 8800$
Output power = $100 \times I$
= 8800
Therefore I = 88 amps

In an electrical circuit diagram a transformer is usually shown as in Figure 5.16. There are basically two types of transformer:

1. **step down** – transforms high-voltage low-amperage supply to low-voltage high-amperage supply;
2. **step up** – transforms low-voltage high-amperage supply to high-voltage low-amperage supply.

Transformation system 1 is used in welding power sources.

A single-phase transformer of the type commonly used in welding consists of a laminated iron core on which are wound two separate insulated coils, the primary and the secondary.

The supply to the transformer can be either 220 volts single phase or 440 volts three phase (see the section on welding power sources later in this chapter). The current varies according to the characteristics of the machine, but is usually less than 60 amperes.

This supply is fed into the primary coil, setting up a magnetic field in the iron laminations. This magnetic field induces an electric current in the secondary coil, and it is this current that supplies the power used for welding.

The two coils are insulated, and are not connected to each other. The type of iron used in the core does not retain its magnetism when the current is switched off. The iron is laminated in thin layers separated by either paper or varnish. This keeps the eddy currents set up in them at a low level. (Eddy currents are stray currents set up in the iron cores of electromagnets and transformers. They cause a considerable waste of energy.) If a solid iron core was used, these currents would be at a high level and severe overheating would result.

> Transformation is proportional to the number of turns of wire on both sides of the core (Figure 5.17).

If T_p = the number of turns on the primary side, and T_s = the number of turns on the secondary side, then

$$\frac{\text{Secondary voltage } (V_s)}{\text{Primary voltage } (V_p)} = \frac{T_s}{T_p}$$

EXERCISE

Consider the transformer shown in Figure 5.18. There are 256 primary turns. How many turns of

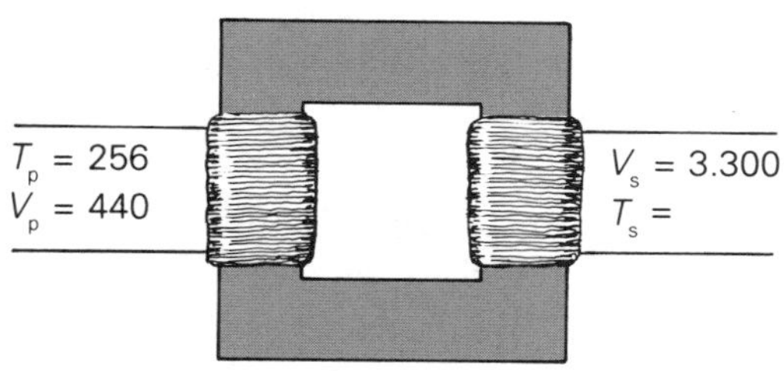

Figure 5.18

conductor are required on the secondary side to produce 3300 volts?

$$\frac{V_s}{V_p} = \frac{T_s}{T_p} \text{ therefore } \frac{3300}{440} = \frac{T_s}{256}$$

$$T_s = \frac{256 \times 3300}{440} = 1920 \text{ turns}$$

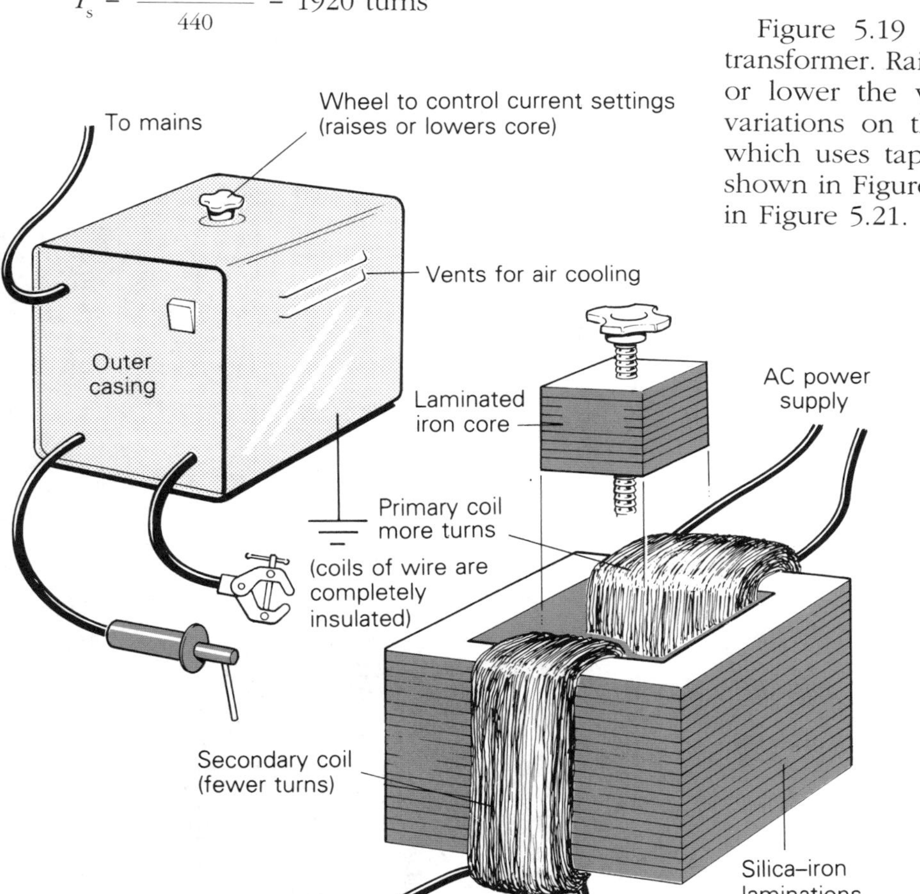

Figure 5.19 A very basic a.c. welding transformer. Raising or lowering the core will raise or lower the welding current.

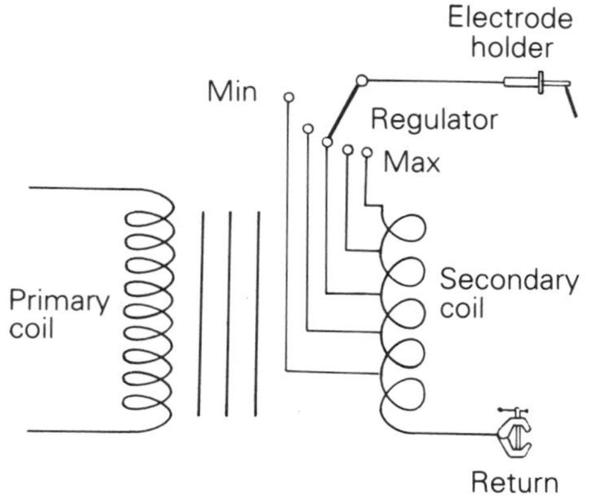

Figure 5.20 **Using tappings from the secondary coil to vary the welding current.**

Figure 5.19 shows a very basic a.c. welding transformer. Raising or lowering the core will raise or lower the welding current. There are many variations on this method. One simple method, which uses tappings from the secondary coil, is shown in Figure 5.20; a further variation is shown in Figure 5.21.

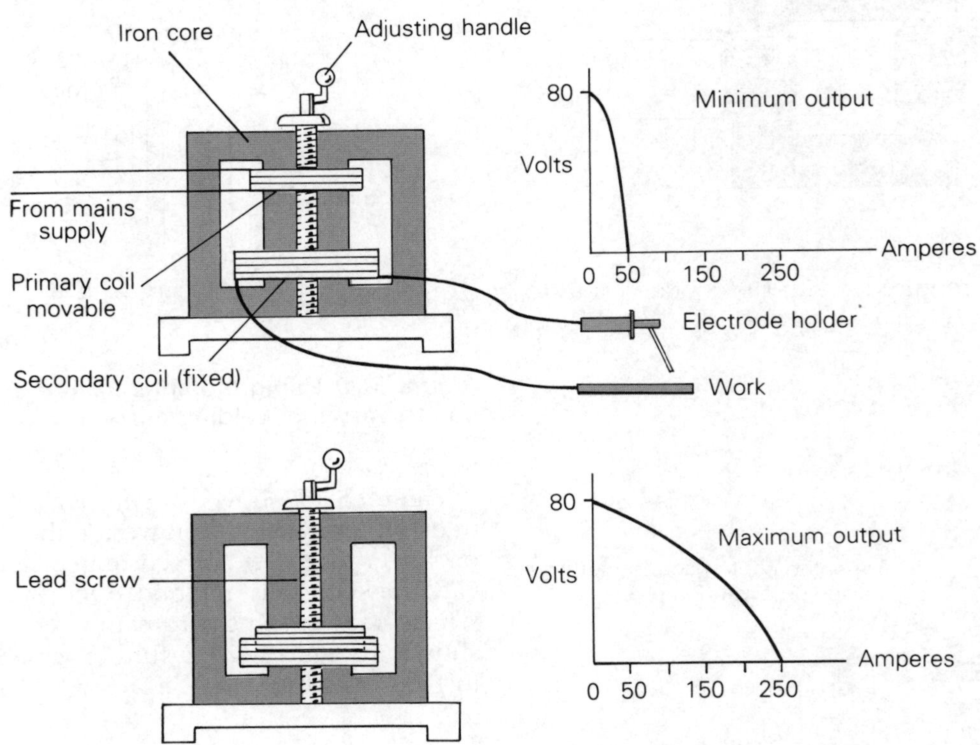

Figure 5.21 How output is varied with a movable-coil a.c. power source.

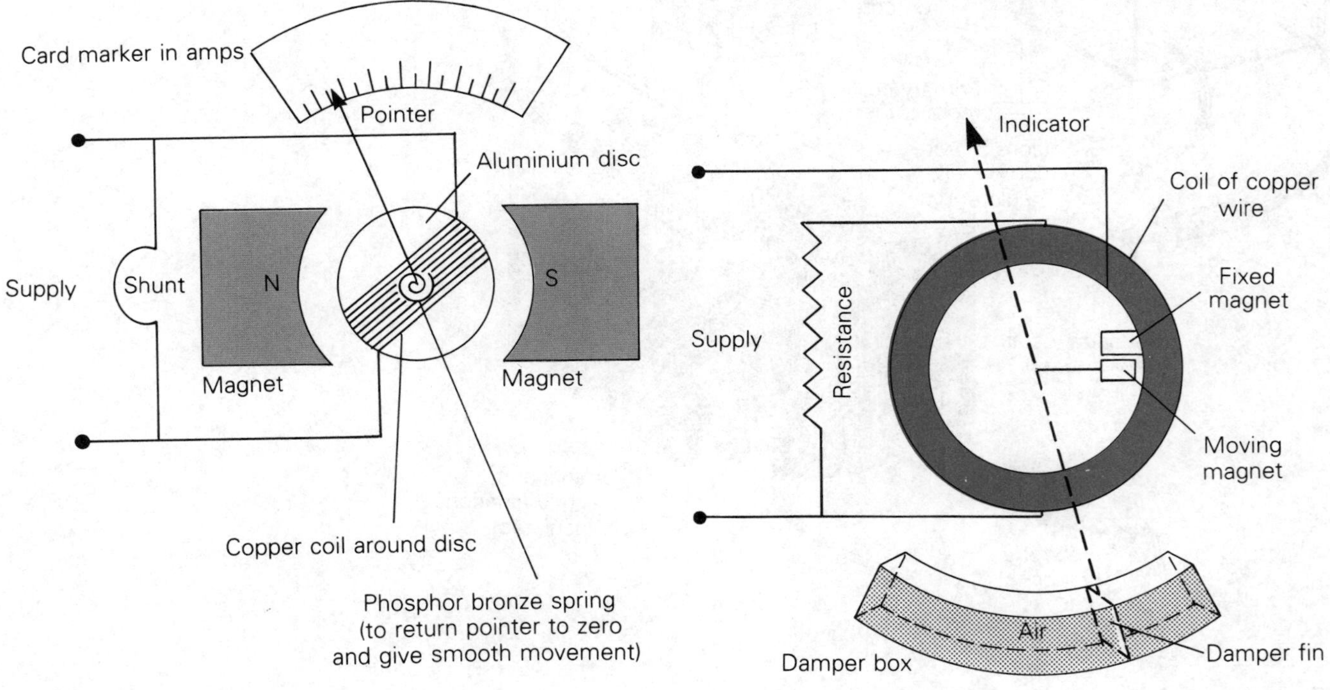

Figure 5.22 The ammeter.

Figure 5.23 The voltmeter.

Measuring electricity

The ammeter

The ammeter is used to measure the amount of current flowing in a circuit. Figure 5.22 shows how it works. A large shunt (very good conductor) takes most of the current, but a small amount is fed through the coil wrapped round the aluminium disc. This current sets up a small magnetic field, which tends to unbalance the magnetic force already in existence between the poles of the permanent magnets, and this unbalancing causes a turning action of the aluminium disc, which in turn moves the pointer.

The voltmeter

Figure 5.23 shows how the voltmeter works. A large resistance (say 200 000 ohms) takes most of the current. This means that the meter requires only a small coil to carry the remaining voltage and current.

The coil induces magnetic fields in the two pieces of iron, making them into magnets. As they are like poles, they repel. The moving magnet turns the indicator needle, giving an indication of the voltage against a marked card placed behind the indicator point. The larger the voltage, the larger the magnetic field and therefore the greater the needle deflection.

The damper box prevents the needle from moving too violently as the magnets repel each other. The fin displaces the air in the box and slows down the movement of the needle. There are several methods of slowing the needle down, including the use of a phosphor-bronze spring.

Welding power sources

From an engineering point of view, there are two main sources of electrical power: batteries and accumulators, which generate electrical energy by

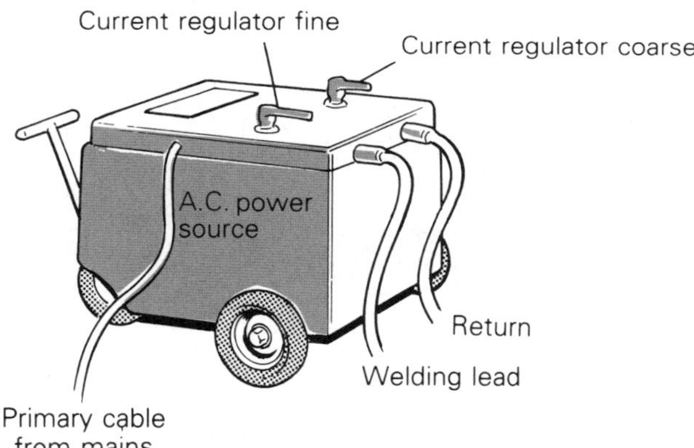

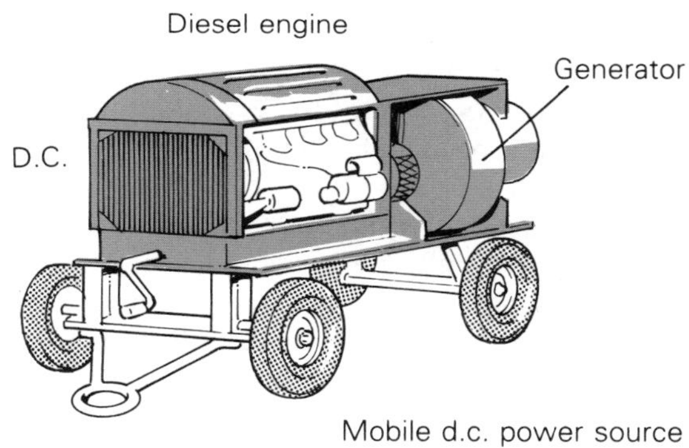

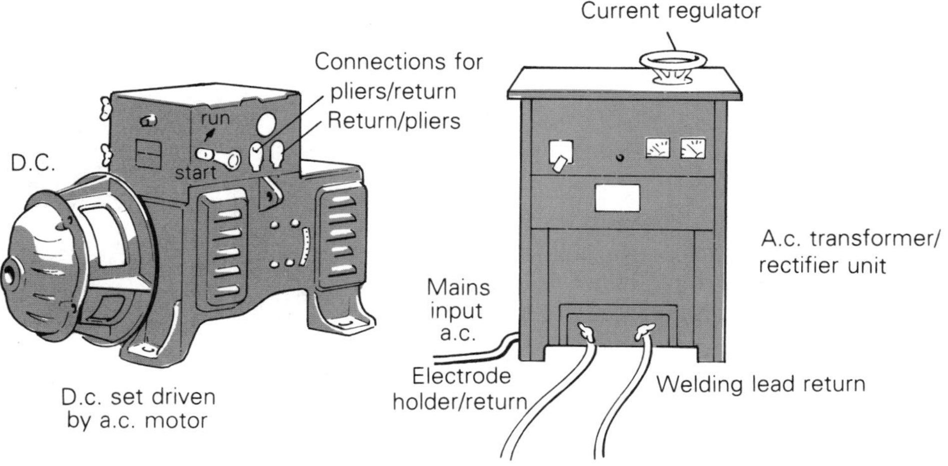

Figure 5.24 Various types of welding power source.

chemical action, and generators, which produce electrical energy by mechanical means.

For welding, generators of a special design are necessary. For welding with an alternating current, a transformer is used in order to change the supply pressure to one suitable for welding.

> Welding power sources are classified into two groups: **alternating current** (a.c.) and **direct current** (d.c.).

Figure 5.24 shows various types of welding power source. Generators may be driven by a motor connected to mains supply, or a petrol or diesel engine.

One big advantage of alternating current is that more than one current at a time can be sent through the same conductor. Three different 50 Hz (cycles per second) currents can be combined in the same conductor. If there is a short space of time between them, they are said to be out of phase.

Figure 5.25 shows the three voltages of the three currents plotted separately. The overall effect can be measured by adding up all three a.c. voltages, or a.c. amperages. If the three waves were placed in phase this would give large voltages and currents.

Three-phase a.c. can be handled with smaller conductors and cables then single-phase a.c. This can give substantial economies when large currents and voltages are to be employed. Common welding set voltages are 240 volts and 480 volts.

One important feature about three-phase a.c. is that by incorporating a device known as a rectifier (sometimes called a choke), the lower half of the wave can be cut out, thus giving a wavy type of direct current.

Rectifiers

A rectifier can be thought of as the electrical equivalent of a one-way valve in a high-pressure gas welding system. It only lets the current flow one way. If the a.c. flowing into the rectifier is single-phase, the output from the rectifier will be very wavy d.c. If, however, three-phase a.c. is put into the rectifier, with all three phases separated (120° out of phase), then the d.c. out of the rectifier will be much smoother (Figure 5.26).

There are several different types of rectifier used in welding sets (Figure 5.27). One of the most common is the **silicon-controlled rectifier** (SCR). Silicon is known as a semiconductor material.

Before solid-state rectifiers such as SCRs were used, vacuum tubes or valves were used to convert a.c. into d.c. 'Solid state' means that the equipment does not use valves.

Selenium is another chemical element that is used in making rectifiers, as it is also a good semiconductor. The selenium rectifier looks like a row of cooling fins on a shaft. Each fin is one diode unit. Diode sections are added in series to increase a rectifier's voltage rating.

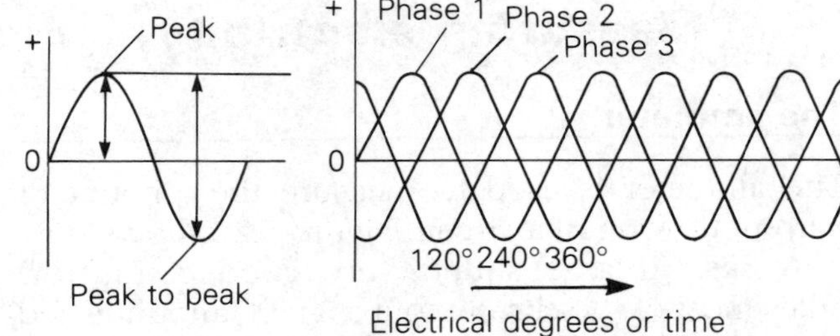

Figure 5.25 **Three-phase a.c. supply.**

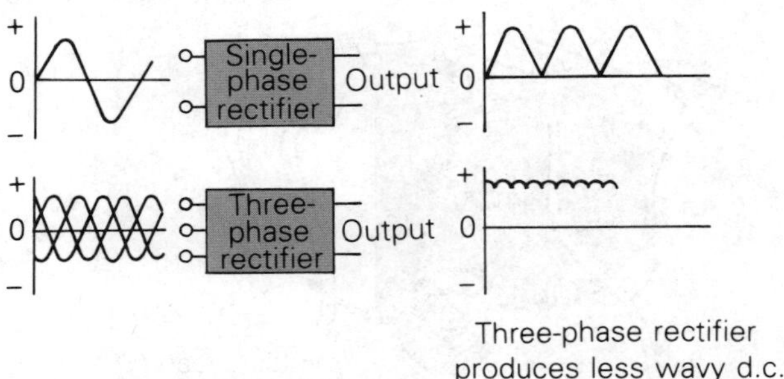

Figure 5.26 **Alternating current can be converted into wavy direct current by using a rectifier.**

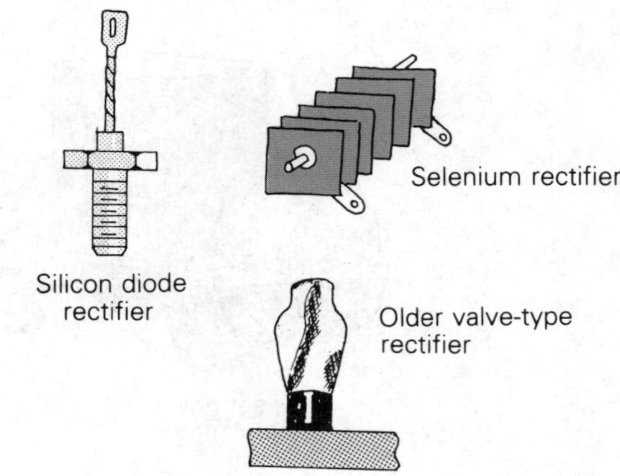

Figure 5.27 **Different types of rectifier.**

Mercury-pool rectifiers, which are like a large glass valve, use vaporised mercury to allow the current to flow in one direction only. These rectifiers are used in certain types of welding equipment where high power is needed. They are often used in resistance welding equipment (see Chapter 9).

The silicon diode looks rather like a big nut and bolt with a piece of braided copper at one end. Silicon rectifiers have a higher voltage rating than those made from selenium.

Comparing a.c. and d.c. welding characteristics

D.c. equipment (generators or rectifiers) produces a strong directional flow of electric current from electrode to workpiece, or vice versa, depending on requirements.

The d.c. system produces an extremely stable arc. It is widely used on pipe welding or positional work under difficult conditions where the length of the arc may vary.

An a.c. current produced by a transformer is less stable because of its alternating cycle. However, modern electrodes are designed to compensate for this by the addition of ionising agents.

With a.c. the open-circuit or striking voltage is usually about 80 volts. This reduces to 25 or 28 volts once the arc is established.

Two-thirds of the arc heat is at the positive end of an arc. This factor can be controlled when using d.c., as either the work or the welding electrode can be connected to the positive terminal. D.c. and a.c. arcs are compared in Figure 5.28.

Striking the arc

The voltage needed to strike an arc is between 65 and 85 volts. In Figure 5.29(a), no welding is being

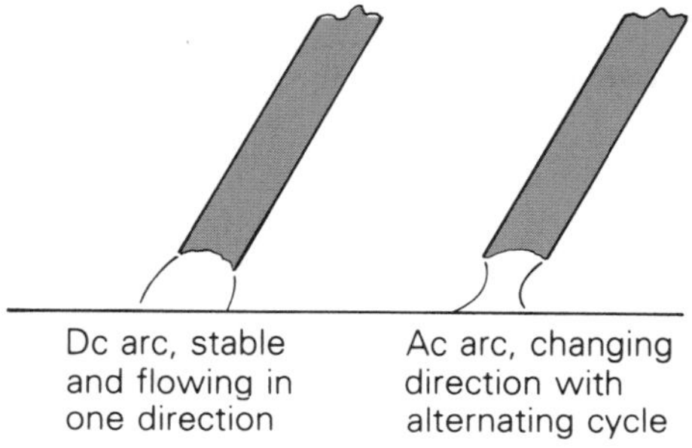

Figure 5.28 Comparing d.c. and a.c. arcs.

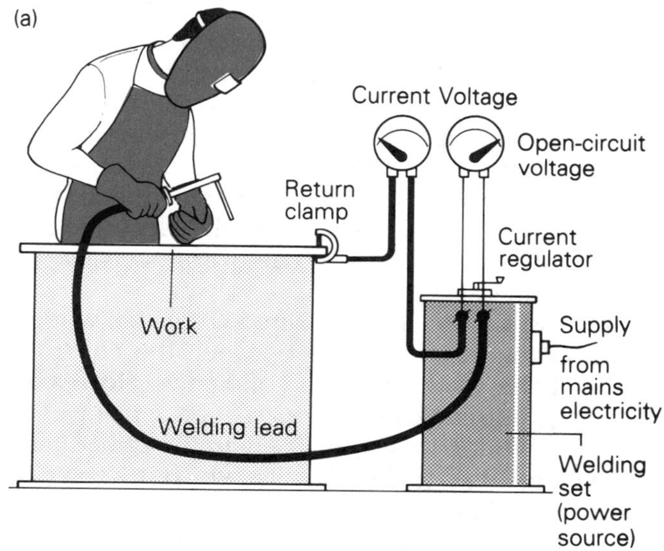

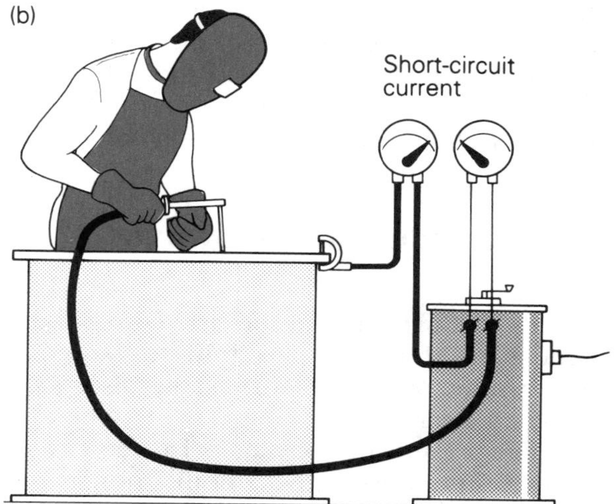

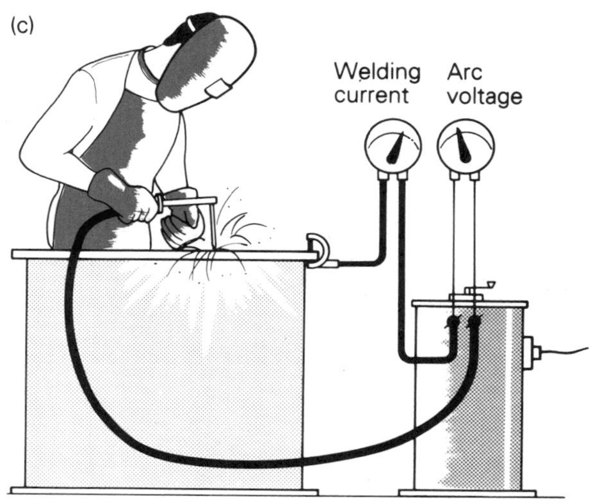

Figure 5.29 The three stages of striking an arc.

done, and so no current is passing through the leads. The ammeter is registering 0. There is, however, an **open-circuit voltage** present; the voltmeter indicates a voltage of 65–85 volts. In (b) the electrode touches the work. At high current, the short-circuit current flows through the leads, the ammeter shows a large increase and the voltage drops to almost zero. The tip of the electrode and the point of contact become warm because of electrical resistance.

In (c), the electrode is lifted from the work a short distance, and the air between the electrode tip and the work is made conductive **(ionised)**. Welding current can then easily pass from electrode to work or vice versa. An arc is formed, and the voltage rises to 20–40 volts, which is known as the **arc voltage**. The current falls to the preset value of the welding machine, giving the conditions for normal welding. The tip of the electrode melts, together with a small area of the work (weld pool). Weld material is transferred from the electrode to the work. A good welding machine must be capable of coping with variations in arc length.

CHECK YOUR UNDERSTANDING

- Materials that can carry an electric current with a minimum of resistance are said to be good electrical conductors. They are usually also good conductors of heat.
- Insulators prevent the passage of electricity or heat. Not all insulators will do both; rubber and certain plastics are good insulators of electricity but will melt when exposed to higher levels of heat.
- The electrical resistance of a conductor is based on the fact that all materials except superconductors will resist the flow of an electric current, converting a proportion of the electrical energy into heat.
- The standard symbols for voltage, current and resistance are:

  voltage = V, current = I, resistance = R.

- Ohm's law states that for any circuit, the current is proportional to the e.m.f. and inversely proportional to the resistance. This gives a useful formula:

$$I = \frac{V}{R}$$

- The amount of power in a circuit is given by the watt (W). Power in watts = volts × amps.
- The joule (J) is the unit of work, energy and quantity of heat.
- Iron can be magnetised; this process is called induction.
- The invisible but powerful lines of magnetic force given off from a magnet are used in the production of electricity.
- The production of a.c. and d.c. are similar; the only difference is in the method of pick-up of the electricity.
- Electric welding power sources provide either alternating or direct current. Some machines can provide both types of current when required, by switching a rectifier unit in or out of circuit.
- The simplest electric welding power source is a transformer unit providing alternating current.
- A d.c. arc is smoother than an a.c. arc, because the d.c. arc will be travelling in one direction only.

REVISION EXERCISES AND QUESTIONS

1. What is a good conductor?
2. What is the name for a material that will prevent the passage of electricity or heat?
3. Give the standard symbols for voltage, current and resistance.
4. Write the Ohm's law formula in symbols.
5. What is the process called by which iron can be magnetised?
6. What type of electric current does a transformer unit supply?
7. Why is a d.c. arc usually smoother than an a.c. arc?

(Further practice questions can be found on page 202.)

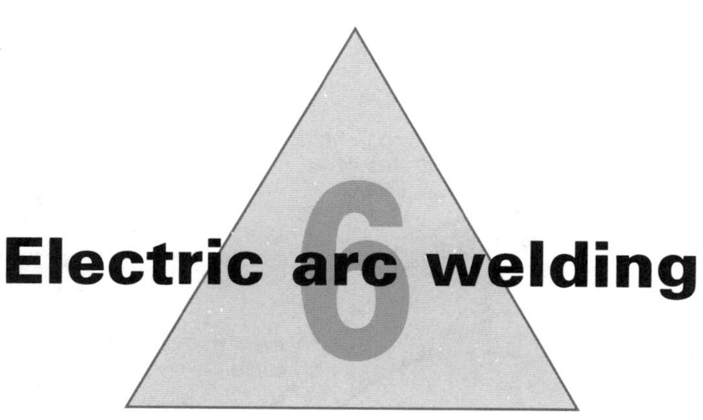

6 Electric arc welding

Introduction

In both gas welding and arc welding, the edges of the parts being joined are melted. If necessary, further metal is added to help form a molten pool between the two parts. The molten pool is then allowed to cool to form the joint. The completed weld is therefore the result of a series of solidified molten pools. We can see this on most welds by looking at the weld ripples: each ripple is the edge of a solidified molten pool.

The main difference between the two methods is in the source of the heat used to obtain the molten pool. In oxyacetylene welding it is the chemical energy of acetylene burning in oxygen; in arc welding it is electrical energy.

Figure 6.1 shows how arc welding was used in the nineteenth century to join the parts of a storage battery, using a carbon electrode. A carbon electrode is classed as non-consumable: that is, it does not melt to form part of the weld.

Modern TAGS welding uses a non-consumable tungsten electrode, so that extra metal has to be added in the form of a filler rod. Manual metal arc welding and MAGS welding use consumable electrodes, which melt to provide extra metal for the weld.

Manual metal arc welding

> In arc welding, electricity is used to form an **electric arc**.

An example of an electric arc is the spark produced by the sparking plug on a car or motorcycle engine. The gap between the electrodes of the plug represents a break in the electrical circuit. Because the gap is small, if the voltage (electrical pressure) is high enough it can force electricity to jump the air gap in the form of a large spark or arc.

An electric arc is therefore really the same as a spark, except that a spark only lasts for a split second, but an arc may continue for some time.

An electric arc is formed when an electric cur-

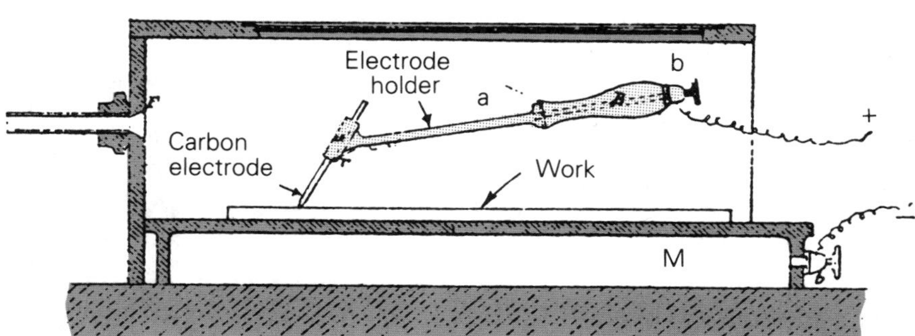

Figure 6.1 De Méritens' carbon arc welding machine, as shown in the French patent of 1881.

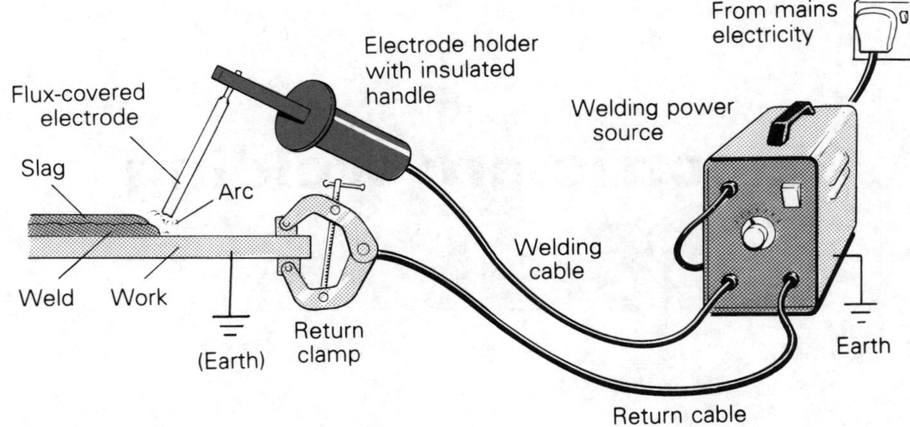

Figure 6.2 Set-up for manual metal arc welding.

rent passes between two electrodes separated by a small air gap. In arc welding, one electrode is the welding rod or wire (called the **electrode**), while the other is the metal being welded. While the arc is operating, heat is released. Either direct current or alternating current can be used to establish an electric arc between the electrode and the workpiece. The voltage at the point of the weld (before an arc is established) is known as the **open-circuit voltage**.

The work is connected to the source of electrical supply (welding set). The electrode holder, held by the operator, is connected to the same source. The electric arc completes the circuit (Figure 6.2).

The arc will not start until the electrode touches the work. This completes the circuit. When the electrode is lifted away slightly, and a gap appears once more, electricity passes across the gap using the lined-up atoms of (ionised) air as a conductor. The arc is stopped, or broken, by moving the electrode further away. Intense heat is developed; temperatures in manual metal arc welding measure up to 6000°C. The heat at the upper end of the arc melts the consumable electrode, while the heat at the lower end of the arc melts the parent metal (the metal being welded) (Figure 6.3).

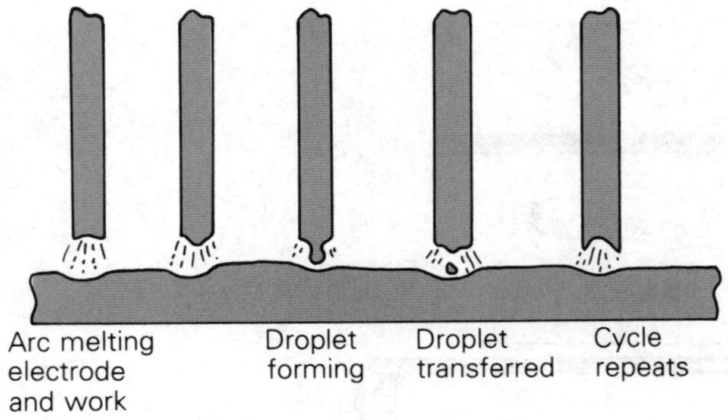

Arc melting electrode and work
Droplet forming
Droplet transferred
Cycle repeats

Figure 6.3 Droplets of molten metal are transferred from the end of the electrode to the molten pool of the shield.

Starting welding and practice welds

> ▲ Before you strike an arc, you must check that the filter in your shield is not cracked.

You can do this by looking at an electric light; it will appear very faint, but should indicate if there are any cracks present.

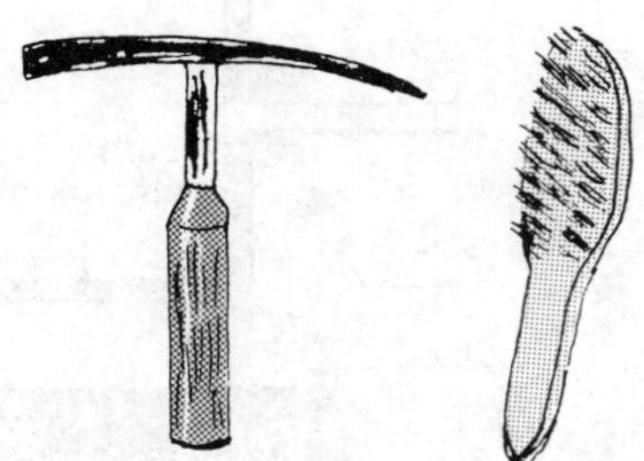

Figure 6.4 Chipping hammer and wire brush.

If you are working in an area already designed for welding, it should have screening to protect other people from the rays of the arc, and the walls should be matt painted to avoid reflections.

As well as your shield, gloves and leather apron, you will need a chipping hammer and wire brush to remove the **slag** (burnt flux) from the completed weld (Figure 6.4). Always wear eye protection during this operation.

Striking and maintaining an arc

There are two ways of establishing or 'striking' an arc. One way is to scratch the electrode across the surface of the plate (like a match) and then lift it slightly to form the arc gap. This method is not very accurate and therefore not recommended. The normal method is to line up the electrode exactly over the spot where you want to strike, position your shield and tap down firmly. Once you tap down and contact is made, you must instantly raise the electrode to the required arc gap. For most smaller sizes of electrode, this arc length should be roughly the same as the diameter of the electrode (Figure 6.5). You must also get used to feeding down the electrode steadily as it burns away.

> One thing that usually happens when you are practising arc striking is that the electrode sticks to the work. If it will not free easily, then turn off the set. It will come unstuck with a sharp tug, or tap from the chipping hammer. As you get more experienced, this will very rarely happen.

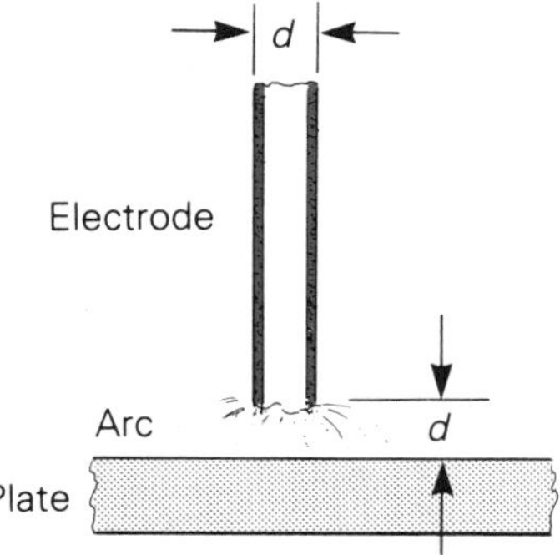

Figure 6.5 Arc length should be roughly the same as the diameter of the electrode.

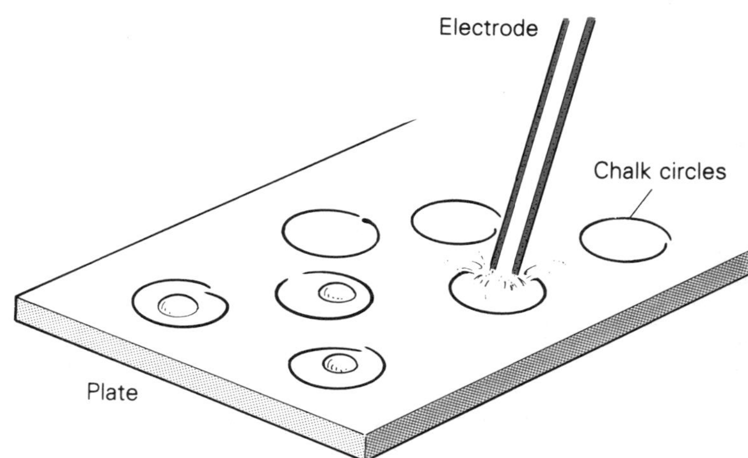

Figure 6.6 Practise striking an arc in the centre of chalk circles.

One of the best methods of practising arc striking is to draw some chalk circles on a piece of scrap and then try and strike in the centre of each circle every time (Figure 6.6).

As you practise with manual metal arc welding, you will notice that the heat is more concentrated than with gas welding, and the welding speeds are much faster.

The coating on the welding electrode is **flux**, which burns to form a gas shield, protecting the molten weld metal from the atmosphere and helping to remove impurities. The flux also helps the metal to transfer and flow, finally setting in a hard slag covering on the surface of the weld, and further protecting it as it cools down (Figure 6.7). The welder later removes this slag using a chipping hammer and wire brush. Clear goggles must be worn for this operation, as slag is usually very hot and flies from the work in needle-like fragments during chipping.

Table 6.1 Typical welding current data for a mild steel electrode

Electrode size (mm)	(SWG)	Typical current (amps)	Length of electrode (mm)
1.6	16	25	250
2.0	14	45	350
2.5	12	65	350
3.5	10	115	450
4.0	8	145	450
5.0	6	215	450
6.0	4	265	450
6.3	($\frac{1}{4}$ in)	285	450
7.0	2	320	450
8.0	($\frac{5}{16}$ in)	360	450

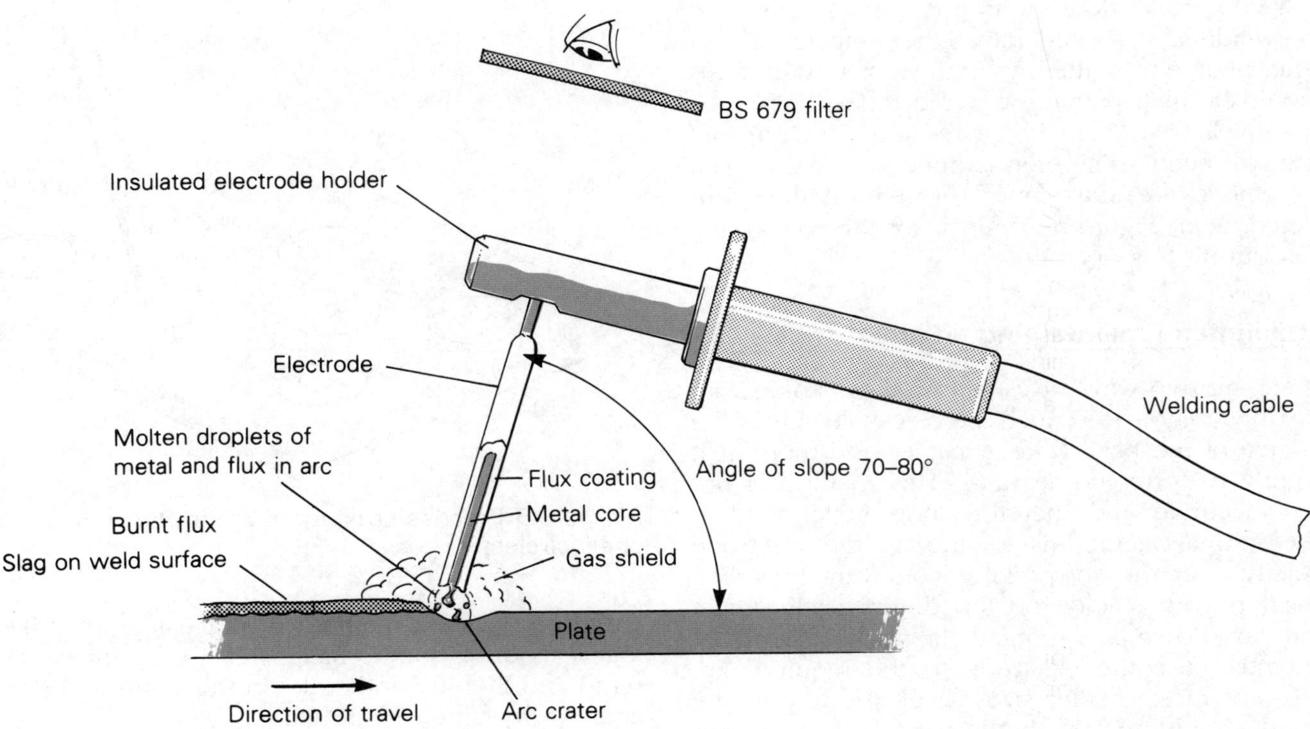

Figure 6.7 The manual metal arc process. The gas shield is formed by burning flux.

Table 6.1 gives typical welding current data for a mild steel electrode. Always consult the manufacturer's data on the packet, as there can be variations between different makes of electrode. Certain special electrodes, including stainless steel, are shorter than the values given in the table, to prevent overheating.

With experience, you will be able to adjust the setting given in Table 6.1 slightly, one way or the other, as the type of work changes. The table is intended just as a guide to get you started.

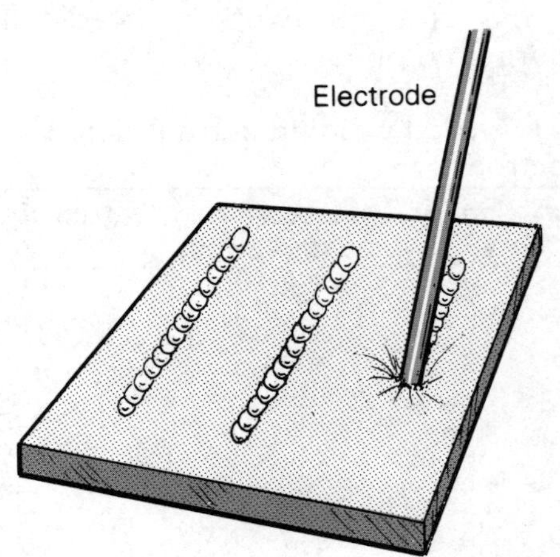

Figure 6.8 Welding straight beads.

Welding straight beads

When you have mastered striking the arc and maintaining it, the next stage is to practise straight runs or beads of weld. Again, try and use some scrap plate (make sure it is thick enough, so that you won't burn it through). Draw some straight chalk lines on the plate and try welding along the lines to give a good, straight, even bead (Figure 6.8).

This is good practice in getting your rate of electrode feed right, so that the arc is kept at the correct length and the speed of travel gives the desired width of bead. The electrode should be held at 90° with a slope angle of 70–80° in the direction of travel. Chip and wire-brush every completed bead, and then give each one a visual examination.

Restarting a weld

Because electrodes will often run out in the middle of a weld, or before the weld is completed, you

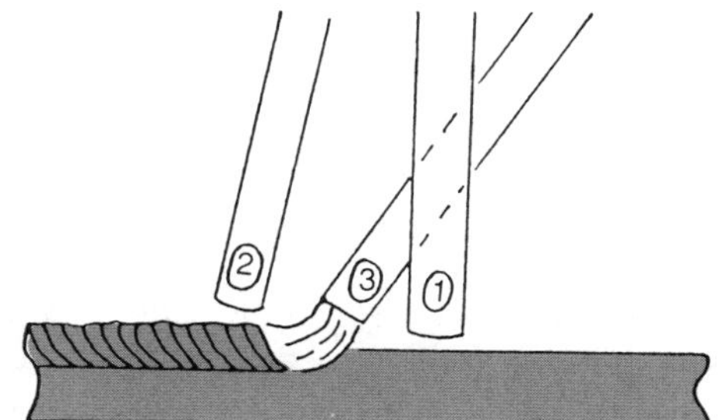

Figure 6.9 Restarting a weld.

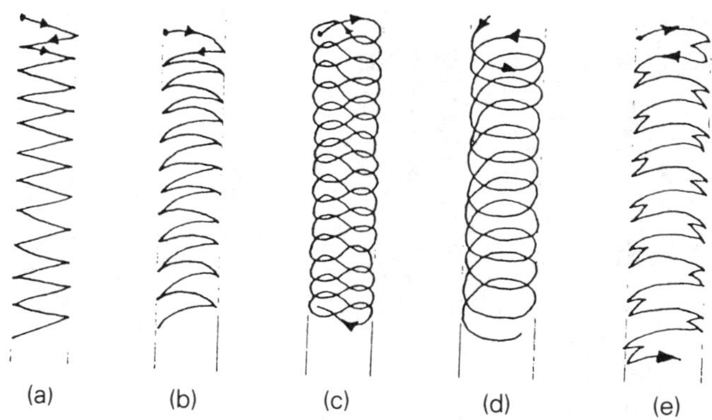

Figure 6.10 Five different types of welding pattern.

need to learn the correct way of restarting a weld.

The recommended method is as follows (Figure 6.9).

1. Chip and clean out the slag from the weld crater and back for at least 12 mm. Wire-brush the whole area.
2. Restrike the arc about 6 mm in front of the crater, then move the arc back into the crater and continue welding. By striking the arc just ahead of the crater, any stray marks will be removed as the weld continues.

Defects can readily occur where a weld starts and finishes, so it is important to maintain the correct procedure. At the end of a weld run, gradually move the electrode round and slowly pull it away, to prevent the formation of a crater at the end of the finished bead.

Most tests for welders include a section where the weld has to be stopped and then correctly restarted.

Weaving

Sometimes a wide weld bead is required. This can be obtained by **weaving** the electrode from side to side while moving the electrode forwards to advance the weld (Figure 6.10).

There are a number of patterns. To practise weaving, deposit two straight runs of weld with a gap between them and fill in the gap with a weave. Try practising the different patterns shown in Figure 6.10. The weave should be no wider than three times the diameter of the electrode.

Different welders prefer particular types of weave pattern. Type (b) is probably the most widely used, while the 'figure of eight' pattern (c) is preferred by other welders.

Some patterns are easier to do with certain types of electrode. However, the beginner should practise weave patterns with all types of electrode, as the experience will be valuable in the future when different types of welded joint are attempted.

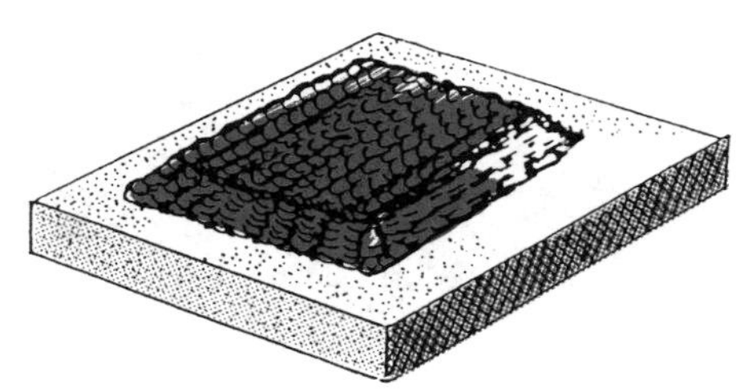

Figure 6.11 The pad weld.

Figure 6.12 Pad welding being used to deposit a layer of hard-surface material. (Courtesy of TWI, UK)

The pad weld

Sometimes a component needs a build-up of weld: perhaps as a repair, or to deposit wear-resisting material. Such a build-up of material is called a **pad weld** (Figure 6.11).

As the pad weld is made by placing straight runs on top of each other, it is often used as a practice piece. Each run of weld must be thoroughly chipped off and wire-brushed, otherwise slag inclusions will form inside the pad, which will weaken it.

The usual test carried out after visual inspection of the completed practice weld is to saw it through and give one surface a **macro-etch examination**. This method is described in Chapter 23.

Mechanised welding is sometimes used for large pad welds, and Figure 6.12 shows a layer of hard-surface material being deposited using **flux-core wire** (wire electrode with flux on the inside instead of the outside) so that it can be fed through the machine. Note the use of localised fume extraction.

Plate edge preparations: flat position

In arc welding, just as in gas welding, as the plates to be welded get thicker they will require different preparation so that the electrode can reach the base of the joint and give root penetration and good fusion. Figure 6.13 shows typical edge prepa-

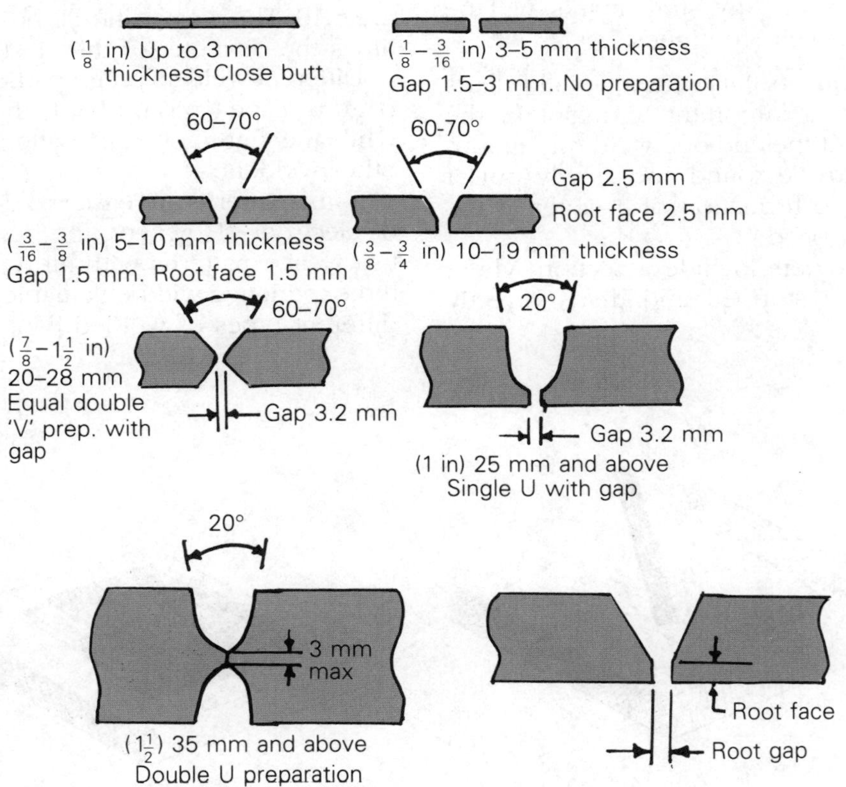

Figure 6.13 Plate edge preparations: flat position.

Figure 6.14 Floor turntable manipulator. Load capacity, 10 000 kg; table diameter, 1525 mm; overall length, 2000 mm; speed range, 0.1–2.0 rev/min; eccentricity, 300 mm; overall height, 550 mm; supply voltage, 240 V single phase; control, via remote pendant with forward, reverse, stop, speed and emergency stop. (Courtesy of MCE Co-Weld Ltd, UK)

rations for butt welds on different thicknesses in the flat position.

Most plate edge preparations can be achieved by the use of oxy-fuel cutting and/or gouging operations, by setting the nozzle at the required angle (see Chapter 10).

Manipulators

It is usually easier and faster to weld in the flat position whenever possible. You can achieve this using manipulators, which are mechanical devices that position the work.

Figures 6.14 and 6.15 show two types of manipulator, and Figure 6.16 gives examples of how simple manipulators can be made from scrap materials.

The main types of weld

There are two main types of weld: **butt welds** and **fillet welds** (Figure 6.17). All the variations of welds can be fitted into one or the other of these two categories: see Figure 6.18, which also shows some of the features of the various welds.

Figure 6.15 An electric arc welder using a roller bed manipulator. (Courtesy of MCE Co-Weld Ltd, UK)

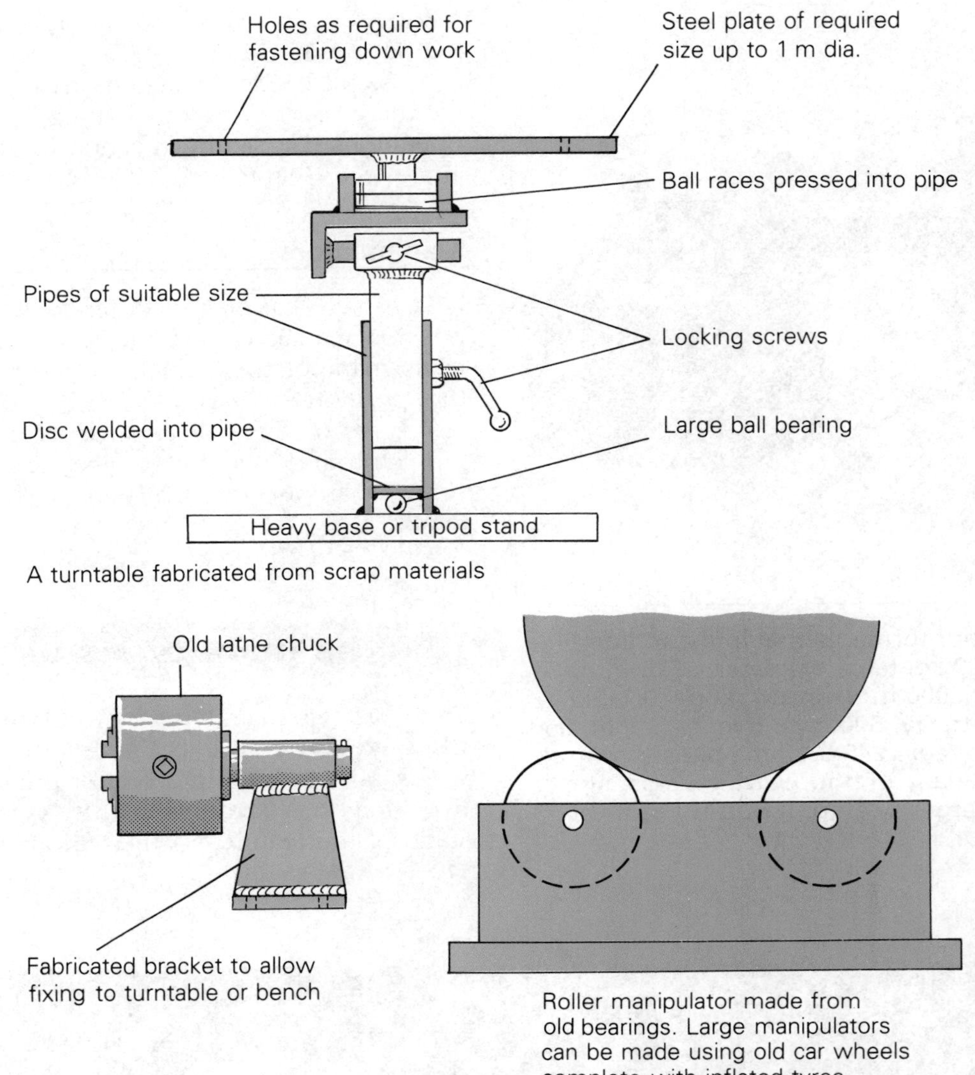

Figure 6.16 **Examples of simple welding manipulators made from scrap materials.**

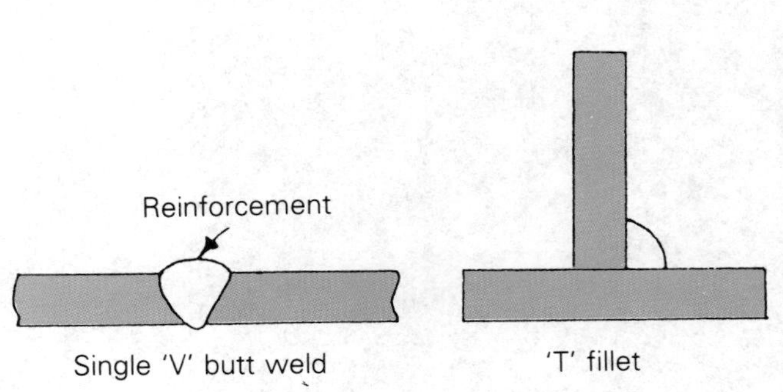

Figure 6.17 **The two basic types of weld.**

Making butt, lap and fillet welds in the flat position

Figures given in this section for bevelling and spacing are suggestions for average work. Exactness of preparation, the size of electrodes and their type, together with the skill of the welder, will influence all dimensions given. In most fabrication shops, such information will be given on the weld procedure and drawings.

Butt welds over 6 mm thick usually require preparation by bevelling. Figure 6.19 gives an example of welding plate of 10 mm thickness.

1. Prepare the plates with a 60° or 70° bevel (see the note above regarding exactness of prepara-

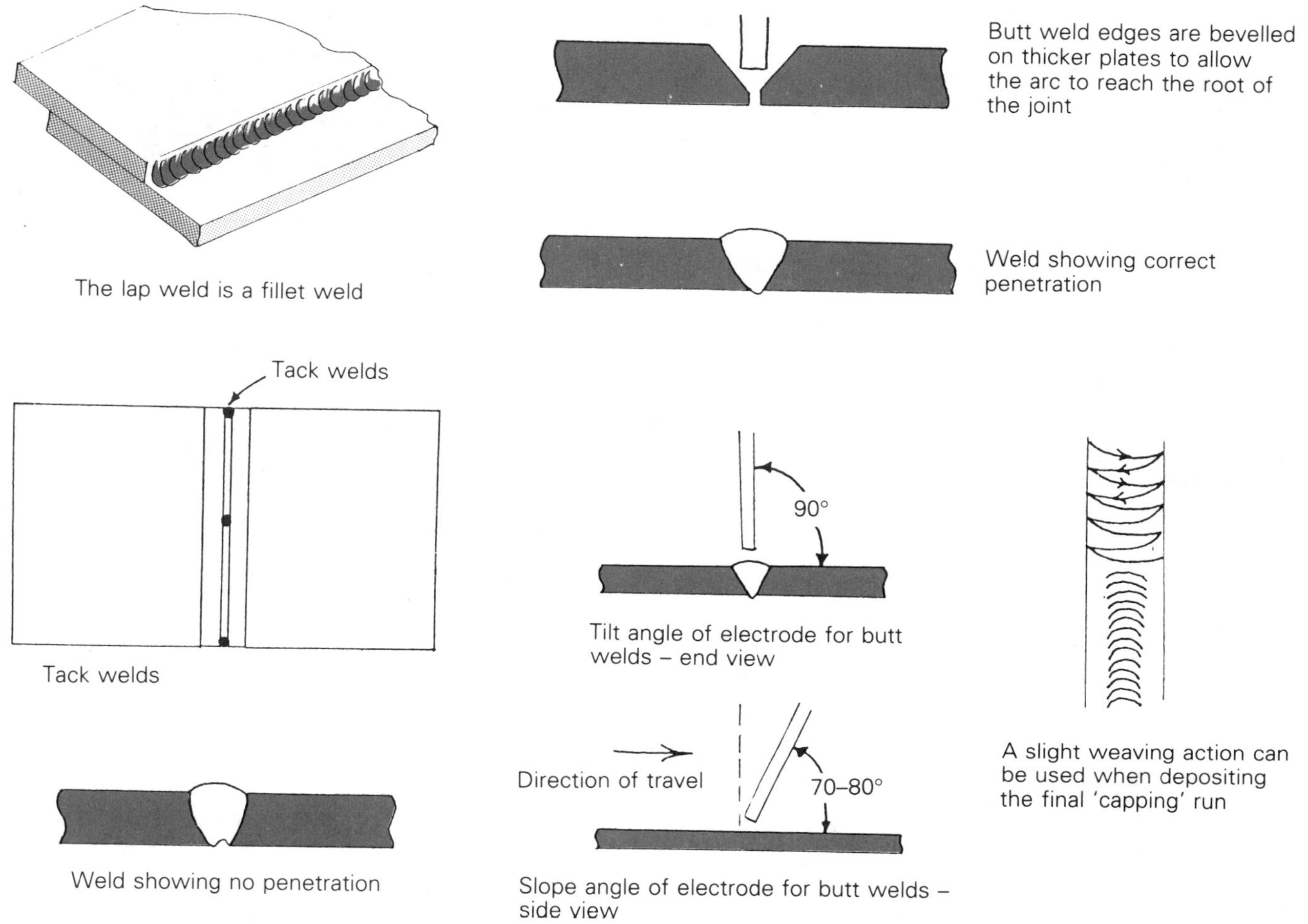

The lap weld is a fillet weld

Butt weld edges are bevelled on thicker plates to allow the arc to reach the root of the joint

Weld showing correct penetration

Tack welds

Tack welds

90°

Tilt angle of electrode for butt welds – end view

A slight weaving action can be used when depositing the final 'capping' run

Direction of travel

70–80°

Weld showing no penetration

Slope angle of electrode for butt welds – side view

Figure 6.18 **All the various types of weld are basically either butt welds or fillet welds.**

tion), and the required root face and gap setting.

2. Tack the plates together.
3. Deposit run 1, the penetration bead.
4. After cleaning with a chipping hammer and a wire brush, deposit run 2.
5. Finally, again after cleaning, deposit the capping run with a slight 'weave'. Allow the finished weld to cool down slowly.

A fillet weld is a joint made by two surfaces that meet at right angles. The procedure for fillet and lap welds is shown in Figure 6.20. Figures 6.21 and 6.22 show example test procedures for butt welds and fillet welds respectively.

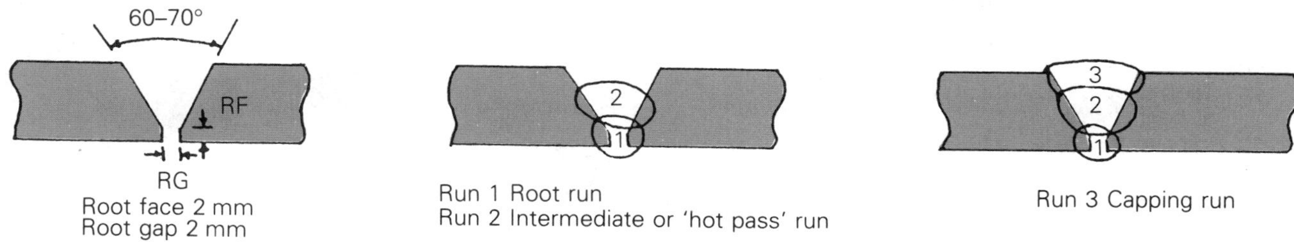

Root face 2 mm
Root gap 2 mm

Run 1 Root run
Run 2 Intermediate or 'hot pass' run

Run 3 Capping run

Figure 6.19 **Example procedure for welding plate of 10 mm thickness.**

A fillet weld in the flat position
Electrode angle of tilt
45°
70–80°
Fillet welds
Electrode angle of slope
Direction of travel
A fillet weld in the horizontal/vertical position
45°
70–80°
Lap welds
The electrode slope and tilt angles are the same for fillet and lap welds

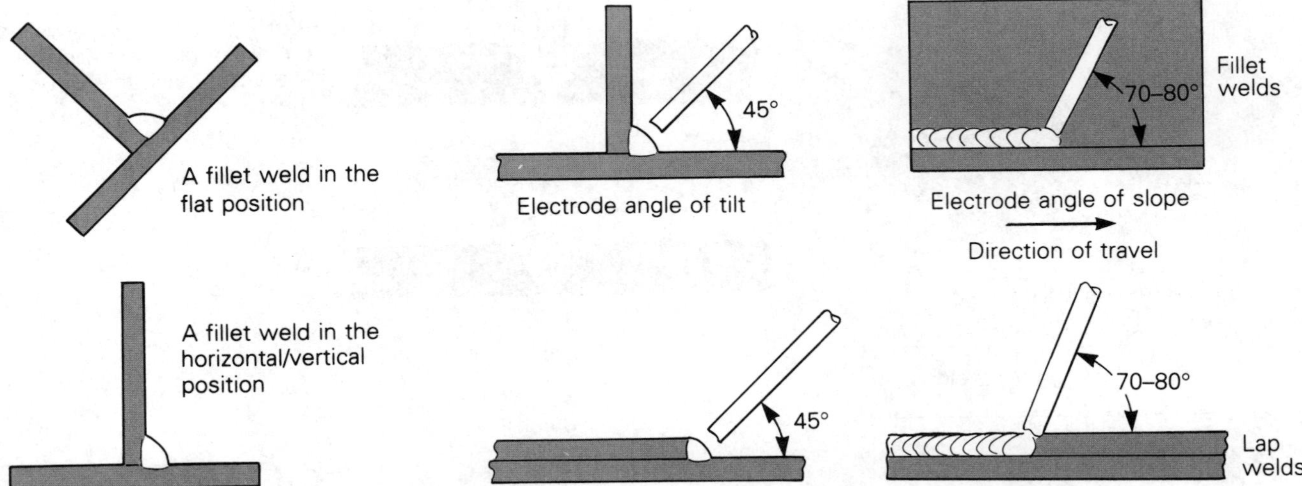

Figure 6.20 **Fillet and lap welds.**

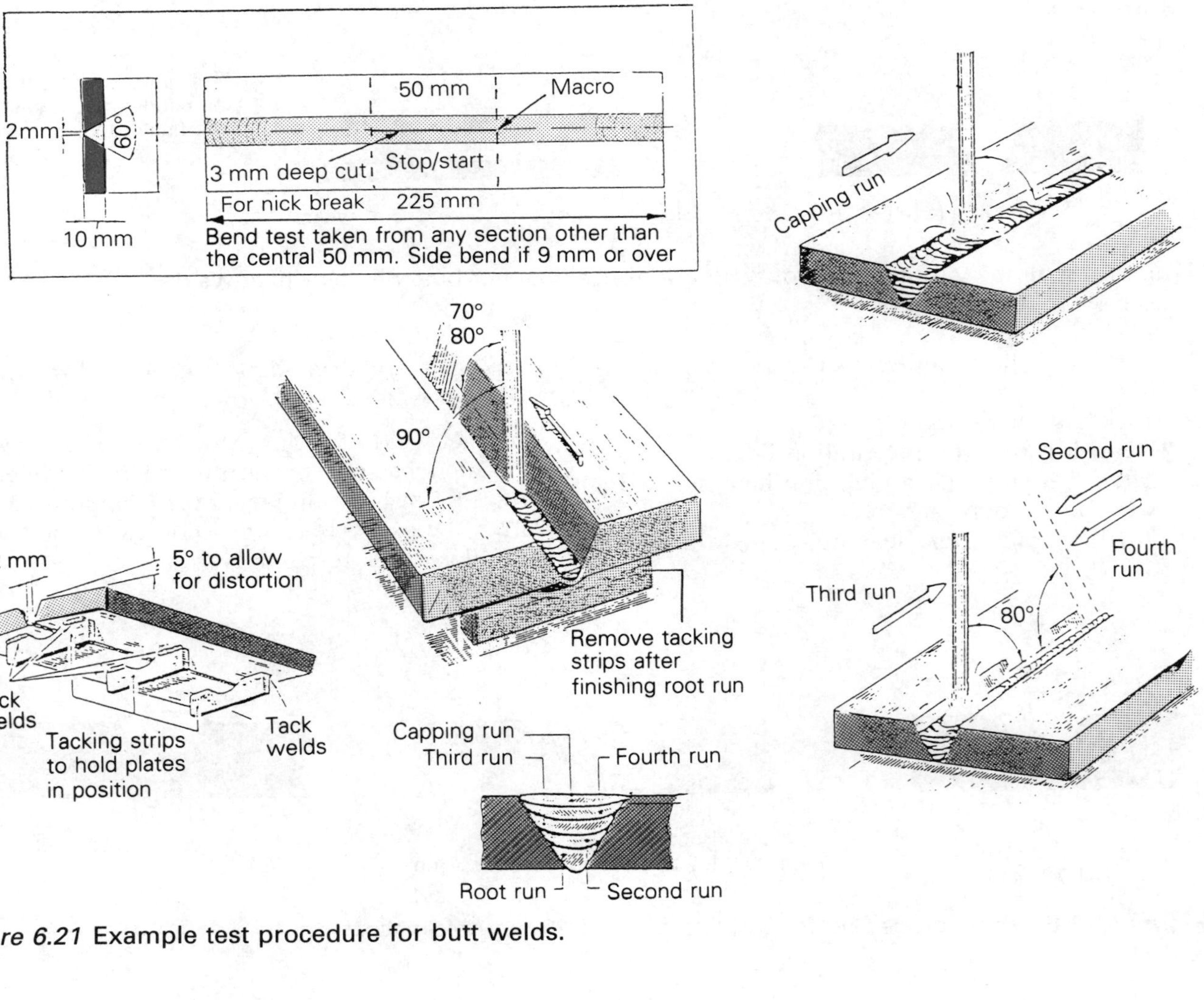

2mm
60°
10 mm
50 mm
Macro
3 mm deep cut
Stop/start
For nick break
225 mm
Bend test taken from any section other than the central 50 mm. Side bend if 9 mm or over
Capping run
70°
80°
90°
2 mm
5° to allow for distortion
Tack welds
Tacking strips to hold plates in position
Tack welds
Remove tacking strips after finishing root run
Capping run
Third run
Fourth run
Root run
Second run
Second run
Fourth run
Third run
80°

Figure 6.21 **Example test procedure for butt welds.**

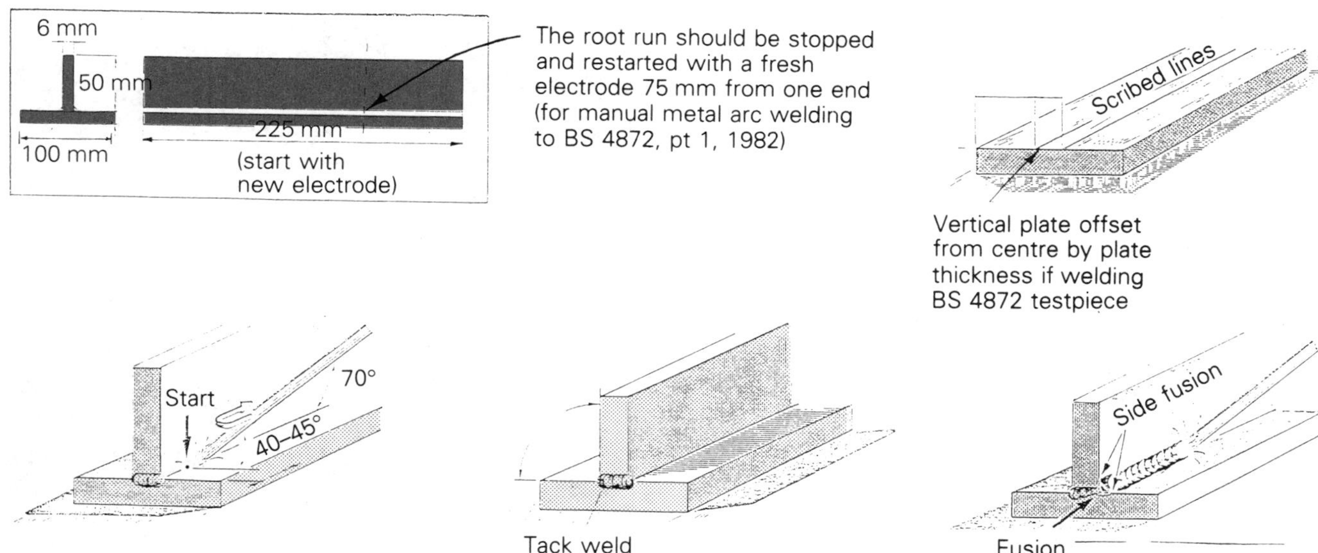

Figure 6.22 Example test procedure for T-fillet welds.

Welding in other positions

As was mentioned earlier, it is usually easier and therefore faster to weld in the flat position. This is where a manipulator can help. However, it is not always possible to turn the work, so on most welding courses, when you have fully mastered welding in the flat position, you will be shown how to practise welding in other positions.

Figures 6.23–6.30 give example procedures for welding in different positions, using both manual metal arc welding as described in this chapter, and some of the other processes described in this book.

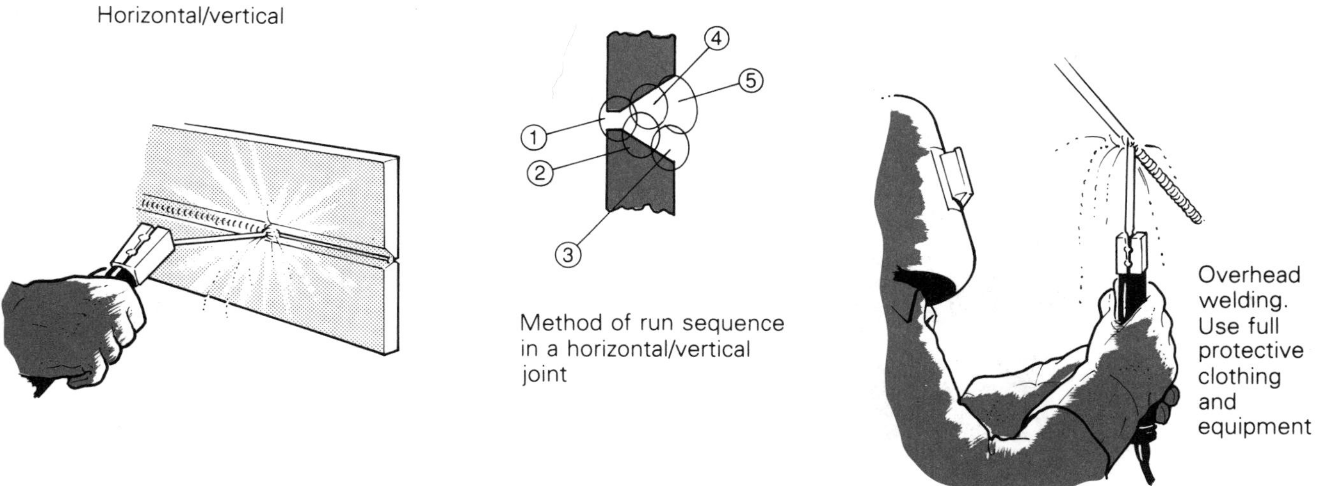

Figure 6.23 Welding in other positions.

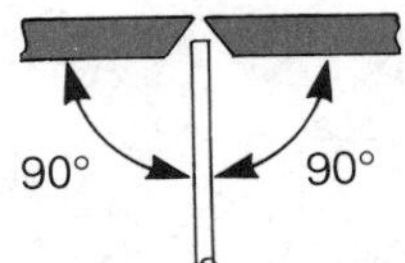

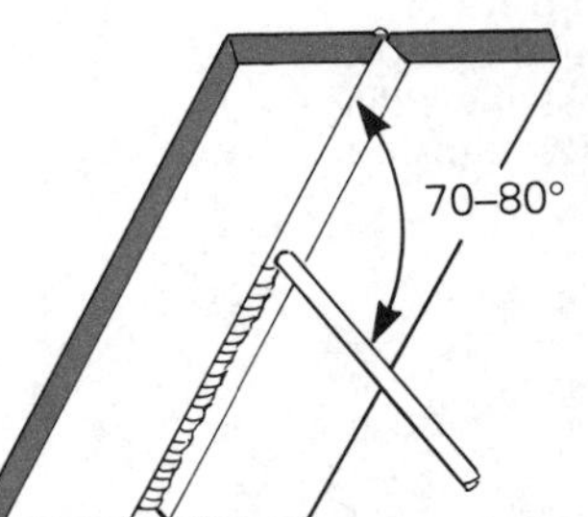

Figure 6.24 Overhead welding using the manual metal arc process.

Figure 6.25 Carrying out a repair using vertical manual metal arc welding on the chassis of a lorry. (Courtesy of UTP, UK and UTC, Nigeria and Ghana)

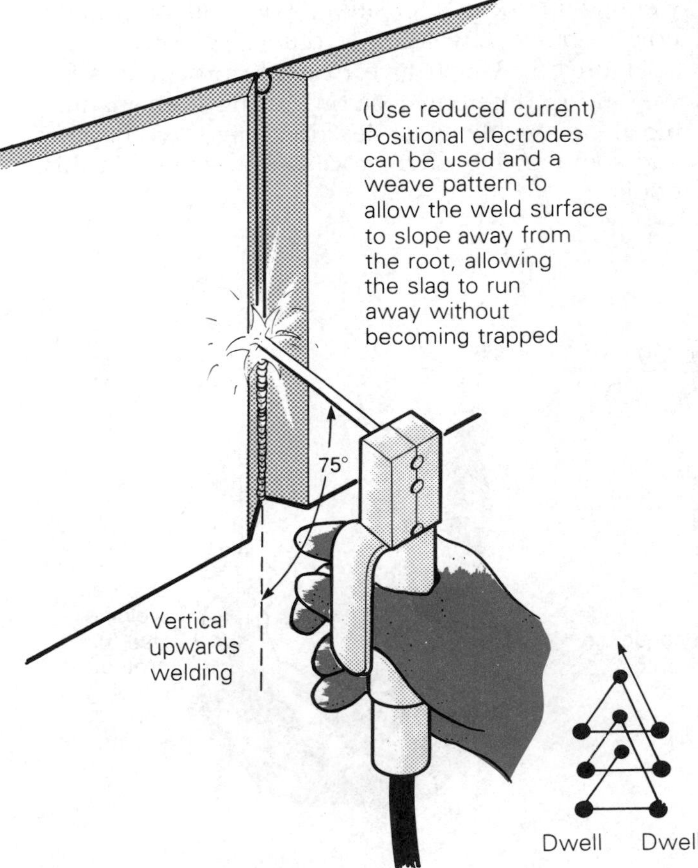

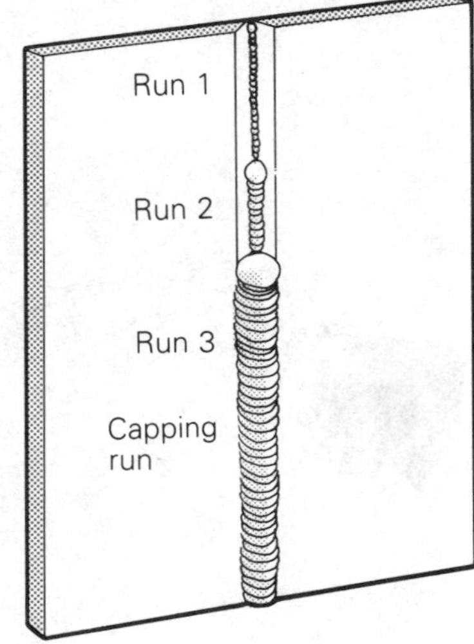

Figure 6.26 Vertical welding using the manual metal arc process.

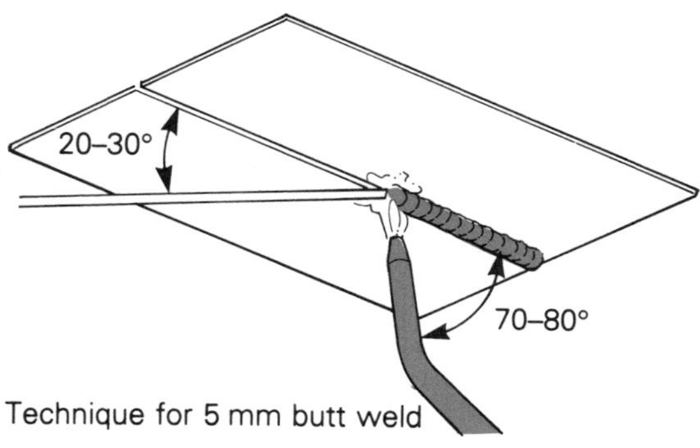

Figure 6.27 Overhead welding using the oxyacetylene process (see Chapter 4).

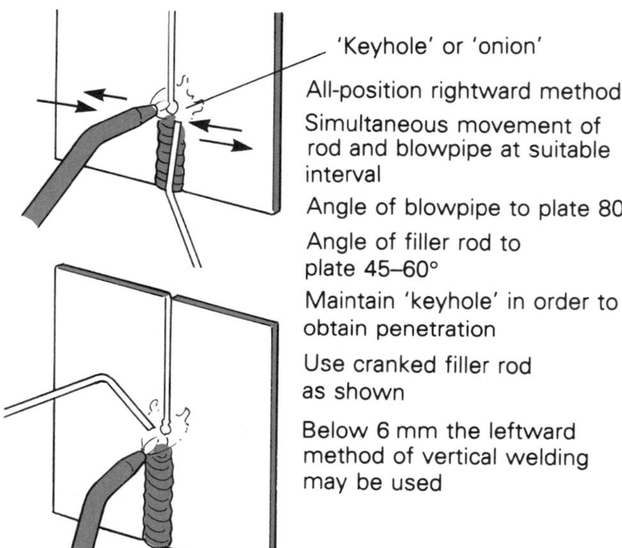

Figure 6.28 Vertical welding using the oxyacetylene process.

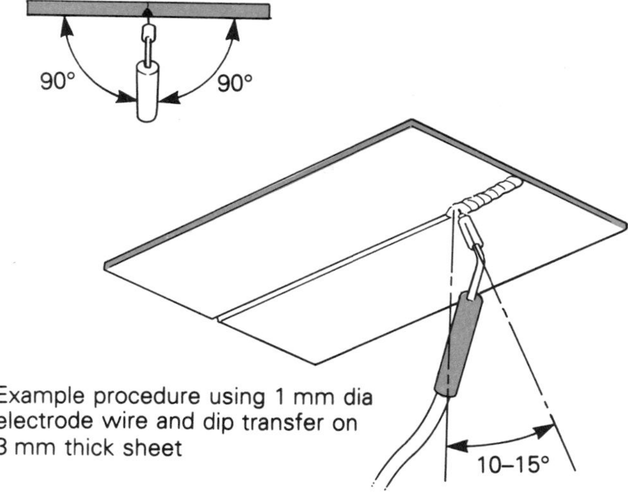

Figure 6.29 Overhead welding using the metal arc gas shielded (MAGS) process (see Chapter 8).

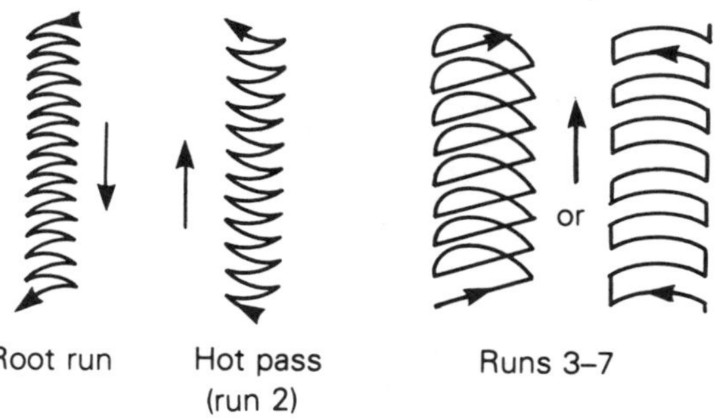

Figure 6.30 For MAGS welding vertically on low-carbon steel the root run is usually deposited vertically downwards, and any further runs vertically upwards.

Electrodes for manual metal arc welding

Figure 6.31 explain how to decode the information on electrode packet labels. The electrode classification is extracted from information given in British Standard BS 639 (1986). If you intend to continue your studies in welding, you should consult the complete document, as it explains the various tests carried out.

The United Kingdom is participating in the work of international standardisation and any proposed changes to future standards would take this work into account.

The general code is known as the **STC code**, as it covers strength, toughness and covering. Any additional coding is in brackets following the STC code.

Types of electrode flux coverings

Class C: cellulosic

These fluxes are manufactured from organic materials containing cellulose. These coatings produce a large gas shield. They give good penetration welds at high deposition rates and have an easily removable slag. They are often used for **stovepipe welding**: that is, depositing the first run (or stringer

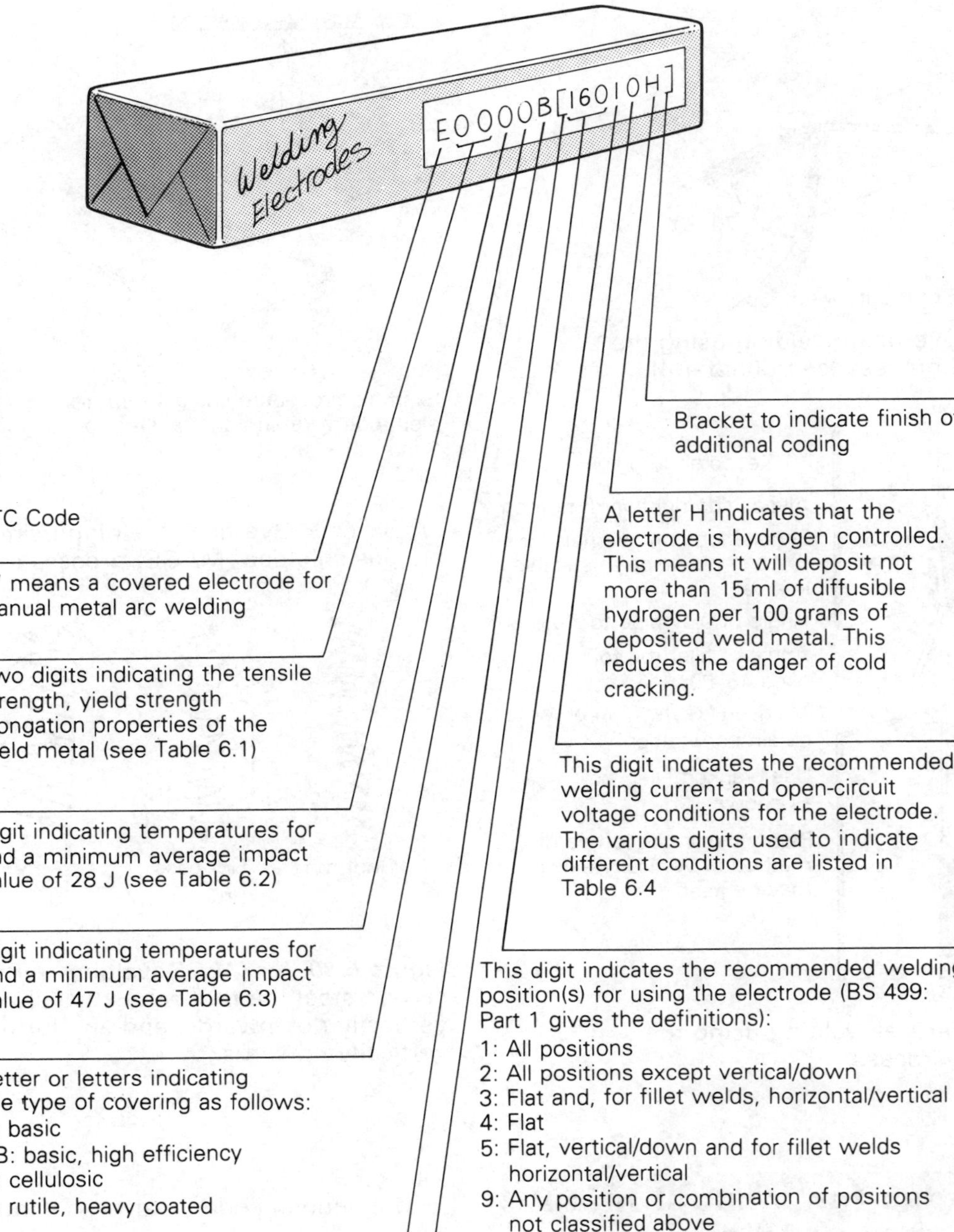

Figure 6.31 Electrode classification codes.

Table 6.1 Electrode classification: designation for tensile properties

Electrode designation digit	Tensile strength (N/mm^2)	Minimum yield stress (N/mm^2)	Minimum elongation (%)		
			When digit of Table 6.2 is 0 or 1	When digit of Table 6.2 is 2	When digit of Table 6.2 is 3, 4 or 5
E 43- - -	430–550	330	20	22	24
E 51- - -	510–650	360	18	18	20

bead) when pipe welding vertically downwards. The deposit can contain high levels of hydrogen. Cellulosic electrodes are suitable for welding steel with a.c. or d.c. electrode positive.

Class B: basic

These fluxes are manufactured from calcium carbonate, calcium fluoride and other carbonates, and are known as **basic coated**. The heat of the arc decomposes the calcium carbonate giving carbon dioxide, which provides the gas shield. The calcium oxide and calcium fluoride combine to form a slag with a low melting point.

These coatings help to produce a weld with a low hydrogen content. This makes them suitable for welding thick sections, as there is a reduced danger of cold cracking (see Chapter 22). The lack of organic material in the flux allows the electrode to be baked before use, thus further reducing the possibility of hydrogen in the weld.

The gas shield is relatively small, so a short arc should be maintained. The electrodes are suitable for use with a.c. or d.c. electrode positive. Always store these electrodes in warm dry conditions, and for best results bake them before using.

Class BB: basic high efficiency

These electrodes are similar to the basic class but have an addition of metallic material, usually iron powder, which melts in the arc along with the core wire, and which can raise the efficiency (amount of metal deposited) to 130 per cent and more (compared with an electrode without these additions).

These electrodes are used in the flat or horizontal/vertical position, as their high recovery rate makes them difficult to use in the vertical and overhead positions. They are suitable for use with either a.c. or d.c., and are usually made positive.

Class R: rutile

These are mainly titanium dioxide (rutile) but can contain other hydrated minerals and/or organic cellulose. They are very easy to use, giving a smooth finish with medium penetration. They are

Table 6.2 Electrode classification: first digit for an impact value

Digit	Temperature for minimum average impact value of 28 J, using 4 mm diameter electrodes only (°C)
E- -0- -	Not specified
E- -1- -	+20
E- -2- -	0
E- -3- -	−20
E- -4- -	−30

Table 6.3 Electrode classification: second digit for an impact value

Digit	Temperature for minimum average impact value of 47 J using 4 mm diameter and largest diameter electrodes submitted for classification (°C)
E- - -0-	Not specified
E- - -1-	+20
E- - -2-	0
E- - -3-	−20
E- - -4-	−30
E- - -5-	−40
E- - -6-	−50
E- - -7-	−60
E- - -8-	−70

Table 6.4 Electrode classification: welding current and voltage conditions

Digit	Direct current	Alternating current
	Recommended electrode polarity	Minimum open circuit voltage
0	Polarity as recommended by manufacturer	Not suitable for use on a.c.
1	+ or −	50
2	−	50
3	+	50
4	+ or −	70
5	−	70
6	+	70
7	+ or −	80
8	−	80
9	−	80

suitable for use with either a.c. or d.c. The fluid slag and fast-freezing weld metal make them ideal for positional work, although high levels of hydrogen in the weld deposit limit their use.

Class RR: rutile heavy coating
These are very similar to the rutile class, but again have additions of iron powder, raising the efficiency to 130 per cent or more. Their increased rate of metal deposition tends to make them unsuitable for positional work. The efficiency is indicated by a three-figure digit at the start of the additional coding.

Class S: other types
This class includes electrodes that do not fall into any of the above classes. The range therefore covers flux coatings that are seldom used, and also newly developed types.

> Packets of electrodes carry a manufacturer's health warning, which gives advice about their safe use. This warning stresses the need for adequate ventilation.

Try decoding the two electrode classifications to BS 639 (1986) in Figures 6.32 and 6.33; then check your results with the next page.

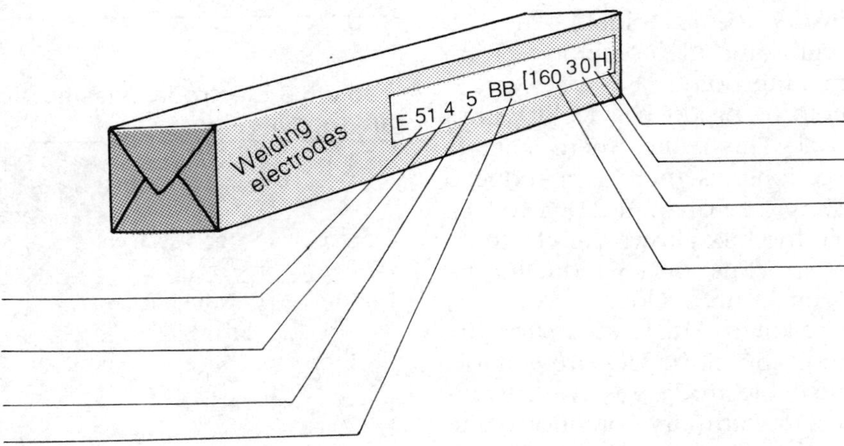

Figure 6.32 Example electrode classification.

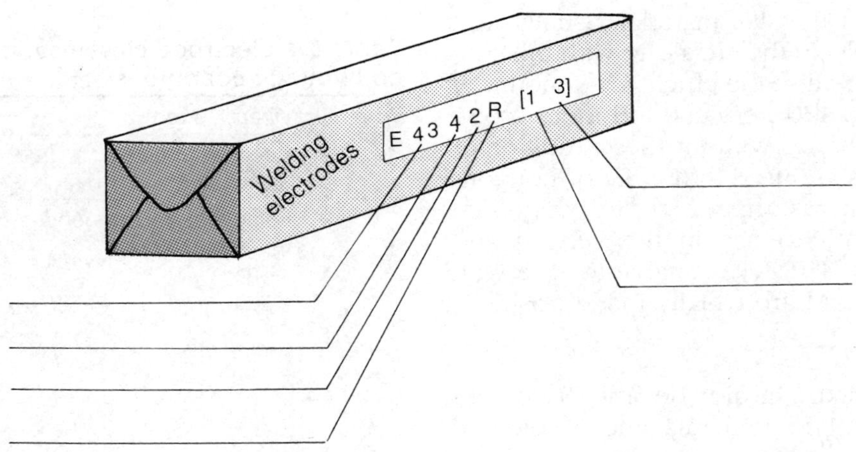

Figure 6.33 Example electrode classification.

The classification of the electrode in Figure 6.32 is:

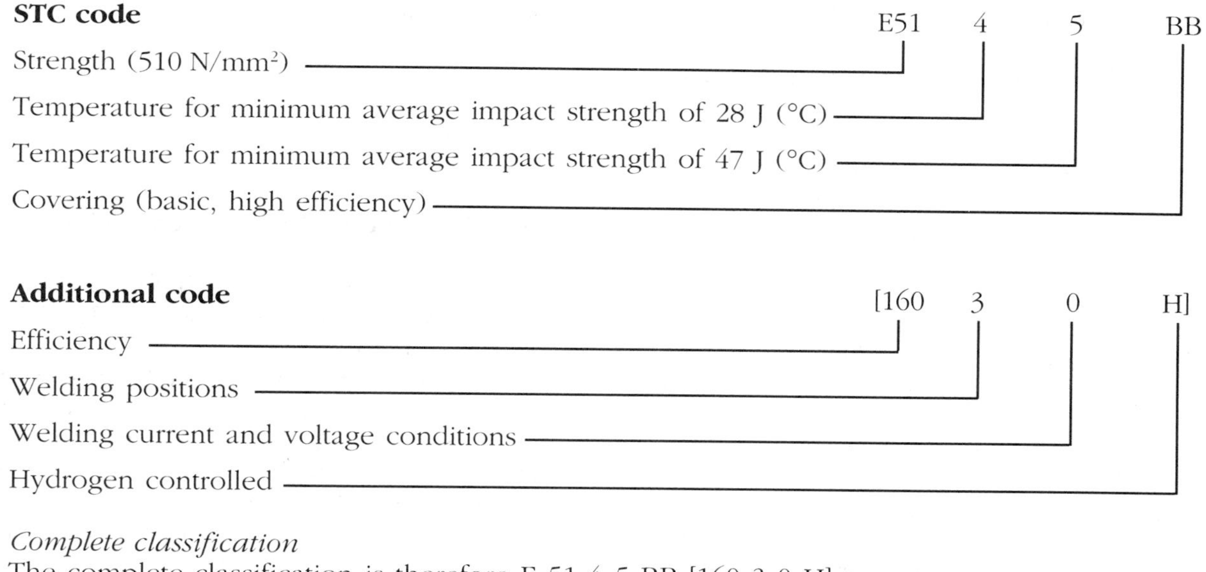

Complete classification
The complete classification is therefore E 51 4 5 BB [160 3 0 H]

The classification for the electrode in Figure 6.33 is:

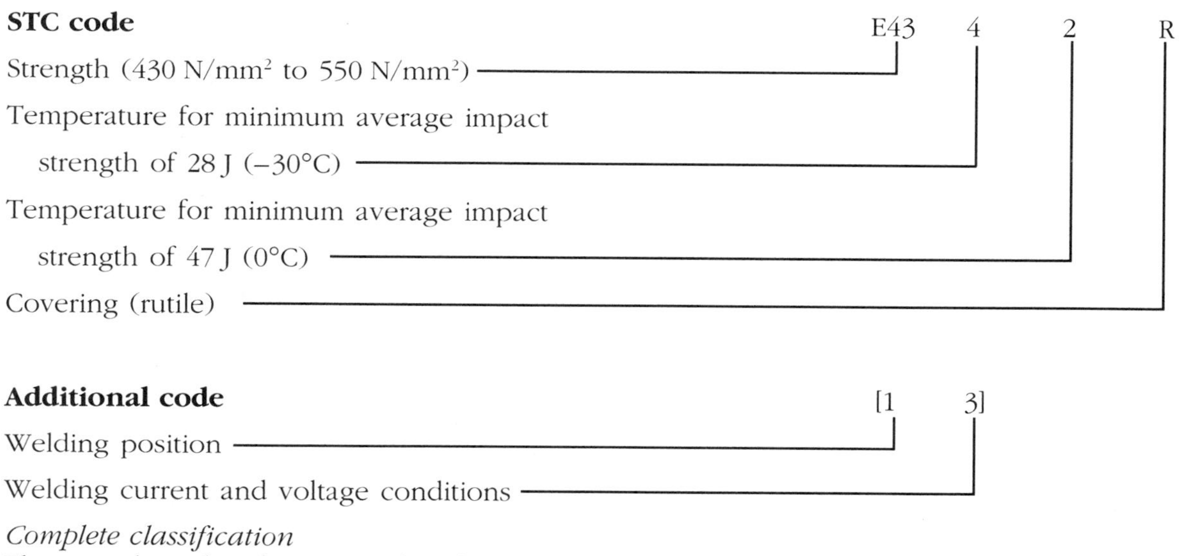

Complete classification
The complete classification is therefore E 43 4 2 E [1 3]

CHECK YOUR UNDERSTANDING

- The heat for welding is obtained from an electric arc maintained between the work and the end of a movable, flux-coated filler rod called the electrode.
- Electrodes are made in different sizes to suit different types of weld joint and plate thickness.
- Particular care must be taken when starting or restarting a weld and also in finishing a weld, as defects are most easily formed at these points if the correct procedure is not followed.
- Plate edges can be prepared as the material to be joined increases in thickness. Edge preparations allow access of the electrode to obtain fusion and penetration.
- Welding is usually easier and faster in the flat position, so where possible position work to allow this. Mechanical devices called manipulators or positioners are often used on smaller fabrications. Work can be turned by crane for larger items. Where work cannot be positioned, positional welding must be carried out.
- There are two main types of weld: butt welds and fillet welds.
- Electrodes for manual metal arc welding arc classified to conform to various standards. The classification is given on the packet in writing and as a letter and number code.

REVISION EXERCISES AND QUESTIONS

1 Why are electrodes made in different sizes?
2 Draw a cross-section sketch of a single 'V' butt joint preparation.
3 Draw a sketch of the manual metal arc process, naming the following components: welding power source, welding cable, return cable and clamp, electrode holder, electrode, electric arc, work and earthed connection.
4 How is the electrode classification given on the packet?

(Further practice questions can be found on page 202.)

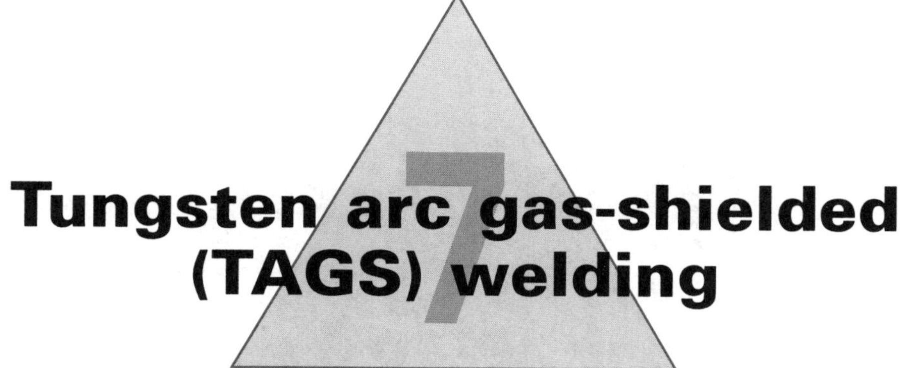

Tungsten arc gas-shielded (TAGS) welding

Introduction

Welding of aluminium and magnesium had always been a problem with conventional manual metal arc and oxyacetylene processes. Corrosive fluxes had to be used to remove the oxide film from the material surface and molten pool.

To overcome this problem, and to eliminate atmospheric contamination during welding, inert gas was first employed as a shield in the early 1930s.

The first gas-shielded process used a tungsten electrode and helium shielding gas. It was called the **tungsten inert gas** (TIG) process. Direct current with electrode positive was used. With this system, the tungsten electrode tended to overheat and transfer fragments of tungsten to the weld unless a low current was utilised.

It was found that overheating could be avoided by making the tungsten electrode negative. This made the process suitable for welding stainless steel but unsuitable for aluminium and magnesium.

The development that allowed these materials to be welded was the use of alternating current, with a high-frequency, high-voltage current superimposed over the basic welding current to stabilise the arc. Using a.c. gives the perfect answer for welding aluminium and magnesium. When the electrode is positive, a cleaning action takes place on the surface of the weld and plate area; particles of oxide are lifted up electrically, leaving an oxide-free area. On the next half-cycle, the electrode becomes negative, allowing it to cool slightly and preventing overheating. As the cycle repeats, the alternating current gives the perfect balance of oxide removal and electrode cooling; the inert gas shield prevents further contamination until the molten pool has solidified.

The process can be called TIG (tungsten inert gas) or **TAGS (tungsten arc gas-shielded)** welding. In this textbook TAGS is used, as the term also covers the use of gas shields that may not be strictly inert.

> TAGS welding uses an inert (non-reactive) gas shield, usually argon or helium, to surround a non-consumable tungsten electrode, thus protecting the electrode and molten pool area from the atmosphere. This means that welding can be carried out without the need for a chemical flux.

The welding heat is created by an electric arc formed between the end of the tungsten electrode and the work. Tungsten is used as the electrode because it has a very high melting point (about 3400°C).

As in oxyacetylene welding, a filler rod is used to add extra metal. So skills obtained in gas welding can be transferred to this process (Figures 7.1, 7.2).

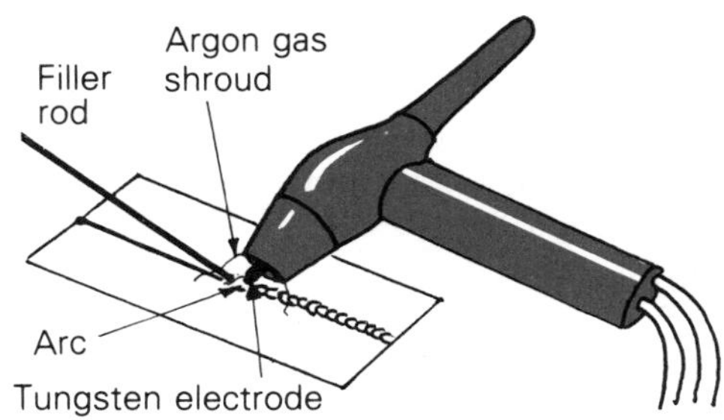

Figure 7.1 Basic principle of tungsten arc gas-shielded welding.

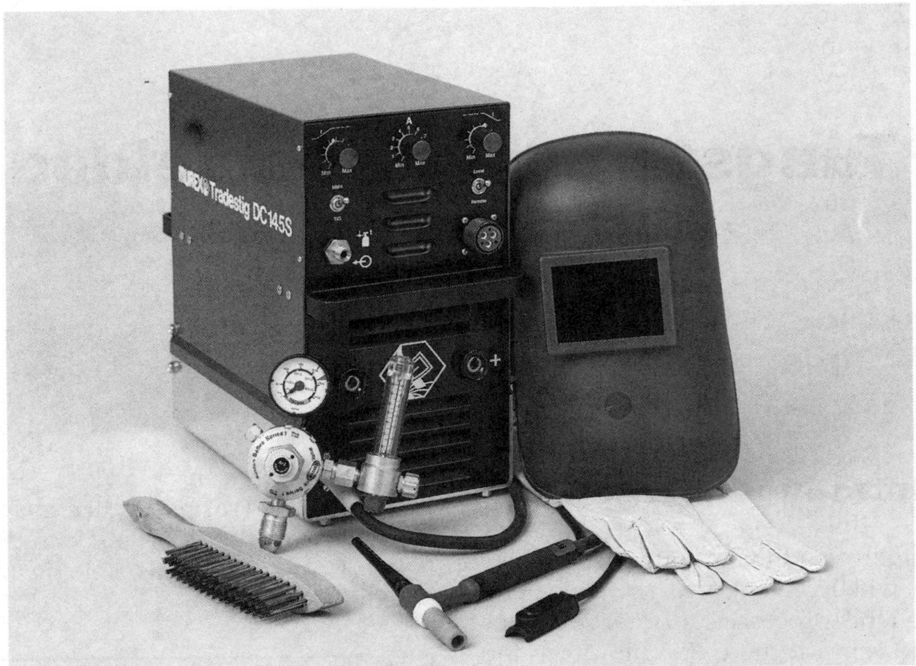

Figure 7.2 Small compact power source for use as a manual metal arc set or for TAGS welding. (Courtesy of Murex Welding Products Ltd)

Safety considerations

The precautions for protecting the skin from arc burn and the eyes from arc eye are the same as for other welding processes. All skin surfaces should be adequately covered and shields or helmets should have filters to BS 679 specification and of the correct shade.

The light radiated from a tungsten arc is more intense than that from metal arc welding.

Electric shock and burns

Keep all electrical equipment clean and free from dust.

Take special care with equipment that is water-cooled. If you notice any leakage, shut the equipment down immediately and report the fault for repair.

As with other processes, keep all hoses and cables clear of hot or sharp metal and rough surfaces.

Always switch the welding current off when you are either changing or making adjustments to the tungsten electrode.

Dangers from high frequency

Most modern equipment uses a high-frequency system to start the arc without the need to touch the work. When the welding current is on, take care that the electrode does not come near exposed skin, as a high-frequency spark may be formed between the tungsten electrode and the skin surface, causing a severe burn and shock.

Take care also to ensure that the filler rod is in contact with the parent metal.

In general, the amount of sparks and spatter is less with TAGS welding than with other arc welding processes. The protective clothing can therefore be lighter. The gloves, for example, are usually made from lighter leather than those for manual metal arc and MAGS welding. This makes it easier to control and manipulate the TAGS torch and filler wire.

Fumes

As with all welding processes, good ventilation and fume extraction are required. Take care not to disturb the protective argon gas shroud by too strong a draught.

Argon is heavier than air, and can accumulate at a low level in confined spaces. This gradually reduces the oxygen level and increases the risk of suffocation.

See also Chapter 3 for more information on fume extraction, and on the dangers involved when working with degreasing agents.

Applications and type of equipment

TAGS welding is widely used in many industries, particularly aircraft, food processing, chemical, brewing and nuclear, where the advantage of not requiring a corrosive flux and the deposition of a high-purity weld can be used to full advantage. It is also used extensively for depositing root runs in pipework to coded standards in mild and alloy steels.

Because of this wide variety of applications, the power sources are usually designed to provide both alternating and direct current supplies. This usually means that they can also be used for manual metal arc welding.

This choice of a.c. or d.c. is made possible by combining a transformer and a rectifier, or a transformer and an inverter, into one unit. The inverter can change a.c. into d.c. by using very fast-acting switches called **thyristors**. These units are lighter in weight than the transformer–rectifier types but they are also more expensive, so the transformer–rectifier is the most commonly used type at present (Figure 7.3).

Supply to the arc

Both alternating and direct current supply is used in TAGS welding, depending on the type of material being welded.

D.c. is normally used for the TAGS welding of stainless and heat-resisting steels, mild and low alloy steels, copper, titanium and other metals and alloys that do not contain aluminium or magnesium.

A.c. can be used on steels, but generally gives inferior weld quality to d.c.

With d.c. the tungsten electrode must be connected to the negative terminal, as two-thirds of the arc heat is generated at the positive pole. A tungsten electrode connected positive would quickly

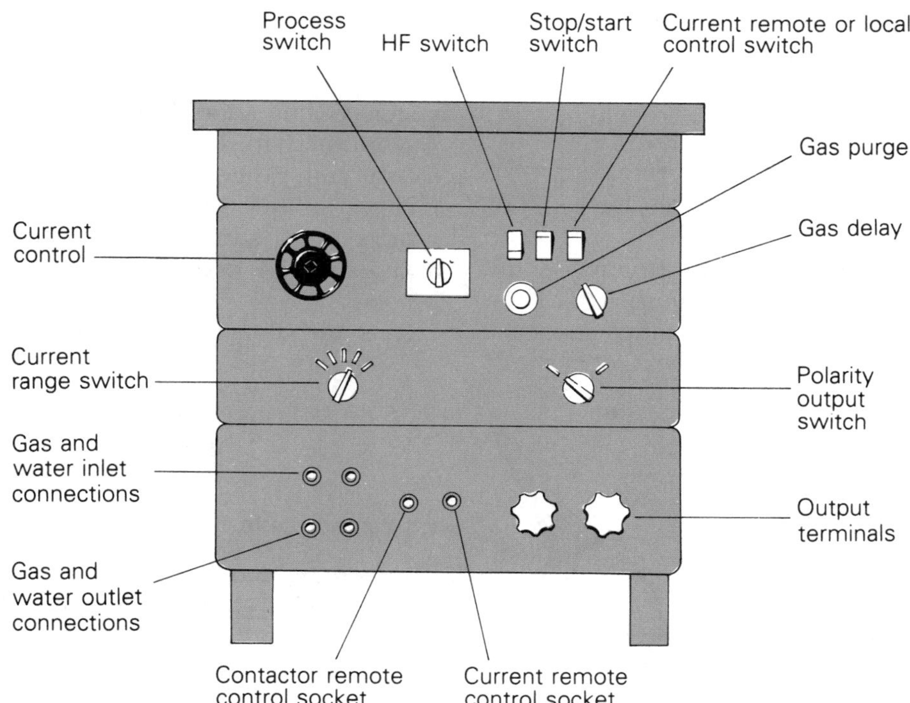

Figure 7.3 Typical layout of a single-phase transformer–rectifier unit. It can provide either a.c. or d.c. output as required.

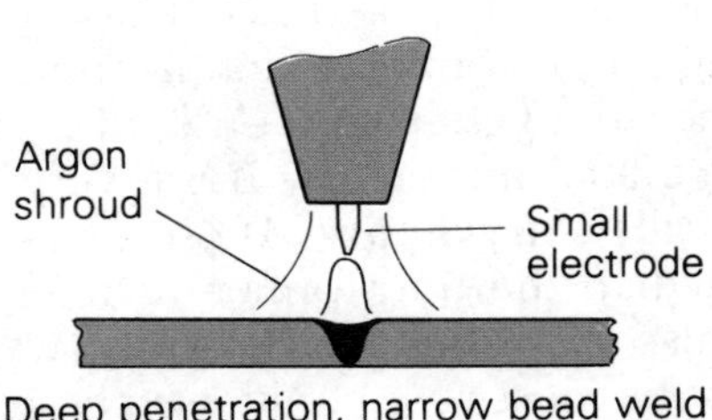

Figure 7.4 TAGS welding with d.c. supply and negative electrode.

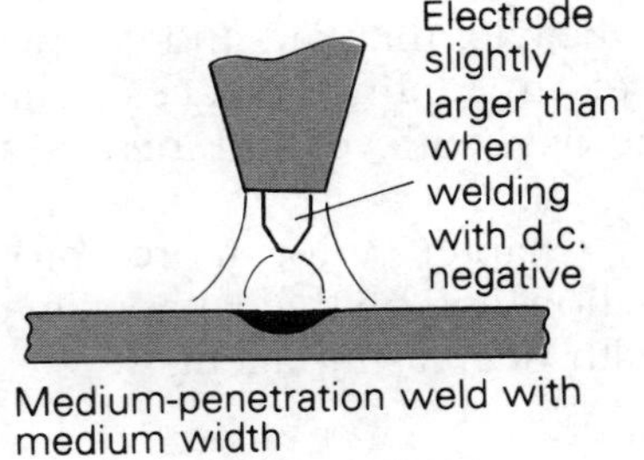

Figure 7.5 TAGS welding with a.c. supply.

overheat and melt. Figure 7.4 shows the characteristics of d.c. TAGS welding.

A.c. is necessary for TAGS welding of aluminium and magnesium alloys. This is because the surface oxide on these materials is removed automatically by the electrical action of the arc each time the electrode becomes positive, which is 50 times per second. This makes chemical fluxes unnecessary. The alternating polarity with a.c. results in equal heat distribution at both poles. D.c. would be unsuitable because, as stated above, if the tungsten electrode were connected positive it would rapidly overheat; if negative it would not remove the oxide film.

Because of the polarity changes, a larger-diameter electrode is needed for the same welding current. The depth of penetration will be less than that of a weld done with a d.c. electrode negative (Figure 7.5).

Torches

There are many designs available, but they all fall into two main categories.

The lighter **air-cooled torches** are made for welding thinner sheet sections (Figure 7.6). They are usually in three sizes – up to 50 amps capacity, 75 amps capacity or 100 amps capacity – but these ratings can vary with different makes.

Water-cooled torches are designed for more heavy-duty welding of thicknesses up to approximately 12 mm (Figure 7.7). They can have current capacities from 100 to 500 amps. They usually incorporate a fuse system to cut off the current supply and to save damage to the equipment should there be a water supply failure.

Figure 7.8 shows an automatic variation of the TAGS process.

A foot or hand control unit (on the torch) can be used for gradually reducing the current towards the end of a weld run. This allows the build-up and elimination of the end crater while maintaining the protection of the argon gas shield.

Ceramic nozzles are used with both the air- and water-cooled torches up to about 200 amps. However, above this amperage, metal nozzles with water cooling should be used.

Various shapes and sizes of nozzle are available to suit all ranges of work (Figure 7.9). These include shorter nozzles for working in confined spaces, transparent nozzles for improved visibility, and extended nozzles for welding in deep recesses.

Gas turbulence in the nozzle can sometimes

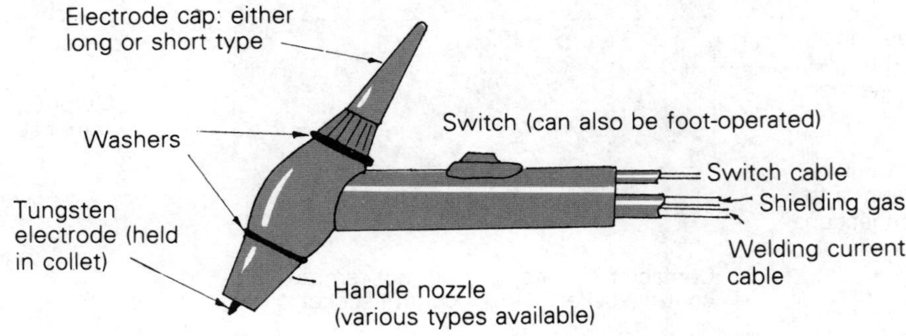

Figure 7.6 A typical air-cooled torch.

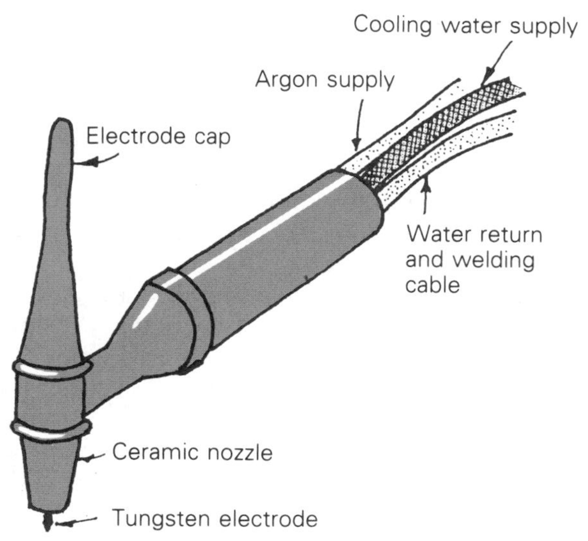

Figure 7.7 A typical water-cooled torch.

result in poor shielding of the weld area. This can be prevented by using a **gas lens** (Figure 7.9). The metal gauze helps to increase shielding gas coverage and allows welding to be carried out with greater extension of the tungsten electrode beyond the ceramic nozzle, to gain access in difficult weld preparations.

The use of a gas lens can also help to reduce the amount of gas required when using a normal electrode extension/projection, and to allow for greater variation of torch angle in positional welding.

Figure 7.8 Hot-wire TAGS welding: an automatic variation of the process. (Courtesy of TWI, UK)

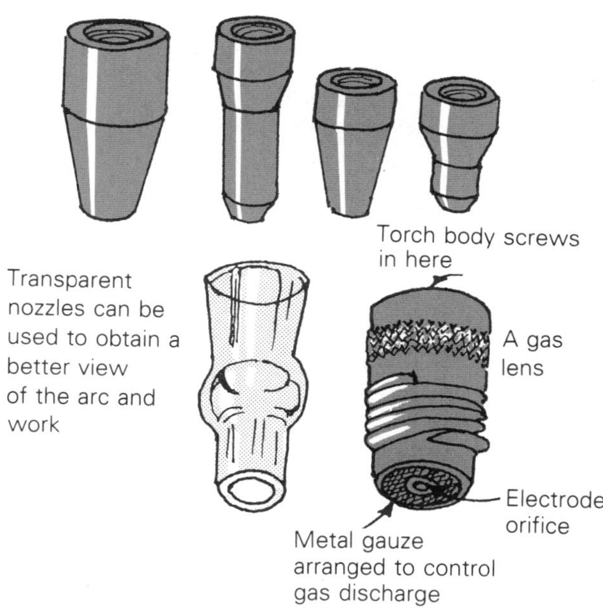

Figure 7.9 Various types of nozzle.

Gas nozzles are not particularly strong and the effect of constantly being heated and then cooled can make them brittle. You should therefore handle them with care in order to obtain maximum usage.

Tungsten electrodes

To improve the quality of tungsten electrodes, certain additions can be made during manufacture. The main elements added are either zirconium or thorium. These help to reduce tungsten inclusions in the weld, which increases the current-carrying capacity and the life of the electrode while also giving improved arc stability.

Thoriated electrodes are used mainly for d.c. welding with electrode negative for stainless and heat-resisting steels, mild and low alloy steels, copper, nickel, titanium and other metals. They can be used with a.c., but this is not recommended for aluminium and its alloys, as zirconiated electrodes give better arc characteristics with these materials.

Zirconiated electrodes have been specially designed for use on a.c. welding and are not as

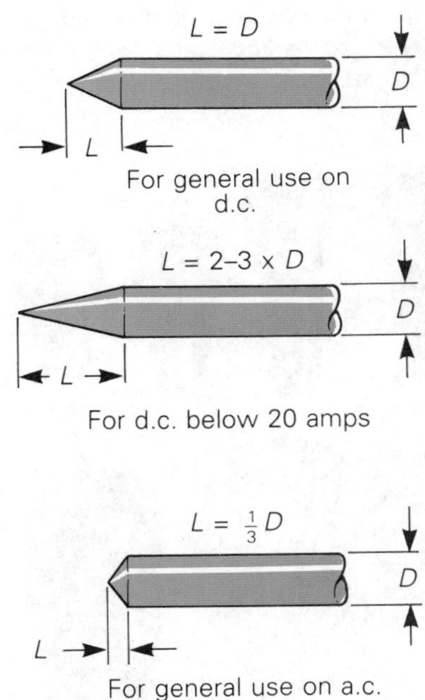

Figure 7.10 Preparation of tungsten electrodes (approximate dimensions).

efficient on d.c. Zirconium electrodes are especially suitable for welding of aluminium, magnesium and their alloys. (See also Chapter 19.)

Tungsten electrodes are prepared for use by grinding to the required shape. Figure 7.10 shows approximate dimensions.

Always use localised dust extraction when grinding tungstens.

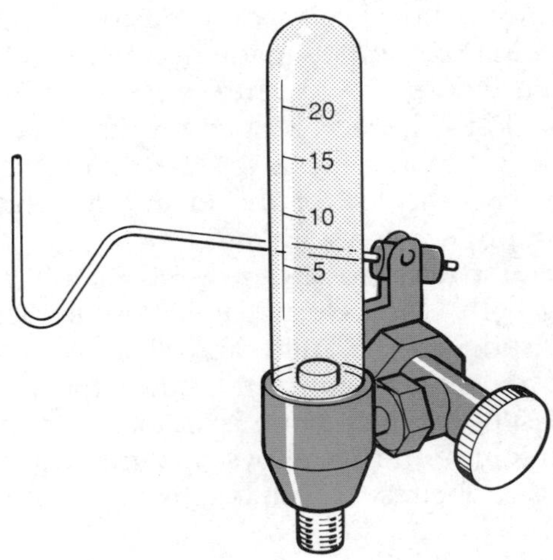

Figure 7.11 Flowmeter and gas economiser.

Shielding gas

Welding-grade argon is supplied in steel cylinders painted light blue. The usual size of cylinder is 8.5 m^3 charged at a pressure of 172 bar (2500 lbf/m^2).

Take care that the cylinder pressure does not fall too low, as the moisture level of the gas can rise as the cylinder pressure falls.

The flow of shielding gas can be controlled and measured by a valve and flowmeter. A simple bobbin-type flowmeter is shown in Figure 7.11. This type is also fitted with a gas economiser, similar to the type used in oxyacetylene welding. It has a lever (the contactor) on which the TAGS torch can be hung, to stop the flow of shielding gas.

Some equipment contains automatic flow controls for both shielding gas and water cooling. They can operate in conjunction with the contactor and allow argon to flow for a preset duration before and after welding.

Initiating the arc

When TAGS welding was first developed, the simplest way to start the arc was to touch the tungsten electrode to the workpiece. This caused the current to begin to flow. The electrode was then simply raised until the required arc length was obtained for the particular welding application.

This method was called **touch** or **scratch starting**. Instead of striking the arc directly on to the workpiece and risking electrode contamination, a carbon block was used. The carbon block was placed near the start of the weld. Once the arc was established on the block, it could be moved down the side of the block to the workpiece.

The development of special arc-starting circuits eliminated the need for touch starting and the problems of tungsten contamination.

High-frequency starting and the high-voltage spark gap oscillator

In high-frequency (or HF) starting, a supply at high voltage (3000–5000 volts) but very low amperage (a couple of amps) is combined with a high-frequency oscillation (up to a million or more hertz) and connected across the arc gap. The high voltage ionises the gas in the arc gap to establish a starting spark. In a.c. welding, it also helps to reignite the arc at the beginning of the positive half-cycle.

The high-frequency spark oscillator consists of a transformer with a high-voltage secondary winding, a capacitor, a spark gap and another transformer which has one coil in the high-voltage circuit and the other in the welding circuit (Figure 7.12). The capacitor is charged every half-cycle to 3000–5000 volts, and discharges across the spark gap in a series of spark oscillations. This discharge, on every half-cycle, sets up oscillatory currents in the circuit, and these are superimposed on the welding current through inductance in the second transformer. The discharge is timed to occur at the start of each half-cycle, although in order to aid reignition, it is needed only at the start of the positive half-cycle.

HF stabilisation with a.c. allows TAGS welding to be used for welding aluminium, as partial rectification can be reduced. Adequate suppression is required when using HF to avoid radio and TV interference.

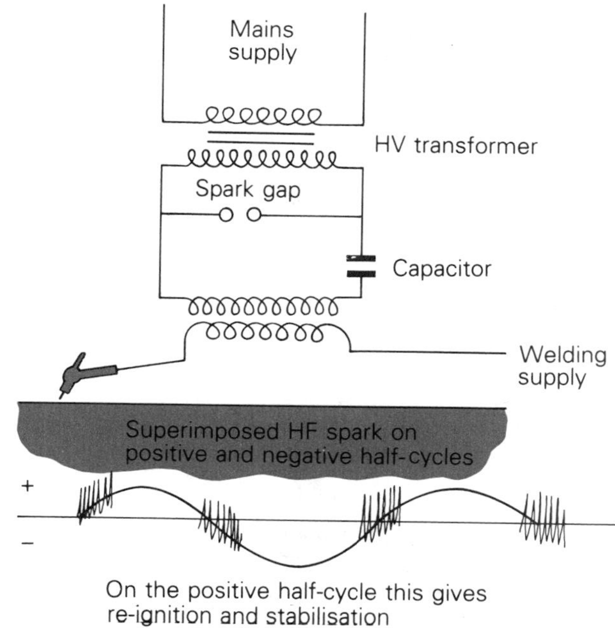

Figure 7.12 **High-frequency starting circuit with high-voltage spark gap oscillator.**

Surge injector unit

The surge injector unit supplies a pulse surge of about 300 volts, which is phased to come in at the exact point when the negative half-cycle changes to the positive half-cycle. The surge injector does not produce a high-frequency spark oscillation, and therefore does not interfere noticeably with radio or TV transmissions.

Machines fitted with a surge injector usually consist of a rectifier unit supplying d.c. to a circuit containing resistance and capacitance. A surge valve supplies the short high-voltage pulses controlled by a trigger valve, which releases the pulses into the welding circuit at exactly the right time, aiding the start of the positive half-cycle.

The surge injector is therefore an alternative method to the spark gap oscillator for maintaining the arc on the positive half-cycle. It will not usually be able to start the arc, however, so sets using this system have a high-voltage spark gap oscillator, which is taken out of circuit automatically once the arc is established.

Suppression of the d.c. component in the a.c. arc

Even with the use of HF, there is still an imbalance between the positive and negative half-cycles, and a d.c. component will flow. This can cause the transformer core to become 'saturated' magnetically, and overheating can develop.

Banks of capacitors connected in series with the welding circuit will allow the a.c. through but block the d.c. component. They will also charge up on the negative half-cycle (because of the greater charge, resulting from the imbalance) and discharge on the positive half-cycle. In fact, at open-circuit voltages above 100 volts they will reignite the arc on each half-cycle, so that HF is needed only for starting. The resulting increased voltage on the positive half-cycle improves the form of the a.c. waves, making each wave more equal. This equals out the heating effect between the electrode and the work, and removal of the oxide film will be increased.

Because of the cost of large banks of capacitors, and because of the associated high voltages, most modern welding plant uses another method called **thyristor control** or **silicon-controlled rectification** (SCR). Sets using this method are fitted with the latest solid-state components to enable one control knob to be used. The welder sets the current control to the required value and a sensor in the outgoing welding supply checks this against the setting. The output of the SCR is thus constantly adjusted to that set by the welder.

Welding technique

This section gives an example procedure for welding 1.5 mm thick mild steel plate.

Use a filler rod complying with British Standard 2901 A15. Set the argon flow to 5.6 litres/minute. Set the welding current in the range of 60–75 amps.

1. Hold the torch between the forefinger and thumb of the right hand. The handle of the torch should lie on the top of the hand and the hose assembly should be supported by the forearm.
2. Lower the torch at an angle of about 70–80° until it is about 25 mm from the sheet surface at the right-hand end. With the welding current on, allow the argon to purge the hose of air and switch on the high-frequency start.
3. Position the welding shield and lower the torch gently towards the sheet. As the tungsten gets close to the sheet, a train of high-frequency sparks will initiate the arc and the high frequency will cut out.
4. Lower the torch to maintain an arc length of about 1.5 mm.
5. Once the molten pool has been formed, the technique is very similar to gas welding. Hold the filler rod in the left hand between the fingers and thumb, and feed it into the molten pool at an angle of approximately 10–20° (Figure 7.13).
6. Always keep the end of the filler rod within the argon shroud, making contact with the weld pool but not touching the electrode.
7. If the filler touches the electrode, or the electrode touches the work, it can be contaminated and will have to be reground to shape.

As with gas welding, practise producing neat straight beads of weld on scrap plate before you attempt to join two pieces of plate together.

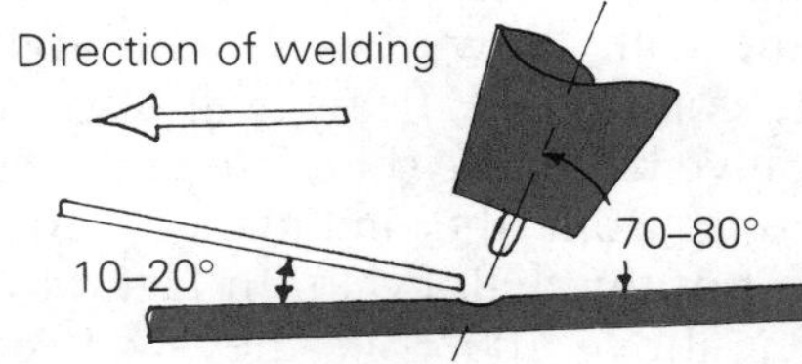

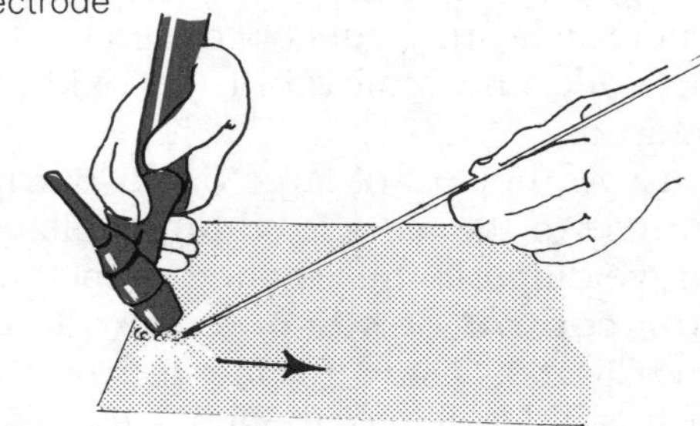

Figure 7.13 TAGS welding of mild steel sheet in the flat position.

Plasma arc welding

Plasma is ionised matter that carries an electric current. It makes up the arc of any arc welding process used in air or within a shielding gas.

Plasma arc welding (PAW) is a variation of TAGS welding. As shown in Figure 7.14, the main difference between TAGS welding and PAW is that the PAW process has an inner nozzle for the gas to form the plasma and an outer nozzle for the shielding gas. So two gas cylinders are needed for PAW.

There are two types of plasma torch: the **non-transferred arc**, in which the arc strikes between the tungsten and the nozzle, and the **transferred arc** (as shown in Figure 7.14), in which the arc is between the electrode and the work. Because PAW is hotter than TAGS, deeper-penetration welds can be made with fewer passes. Because of the formation of a 'keyhole' right through the work (Figure 7.15), which is surrounded by molten metal that

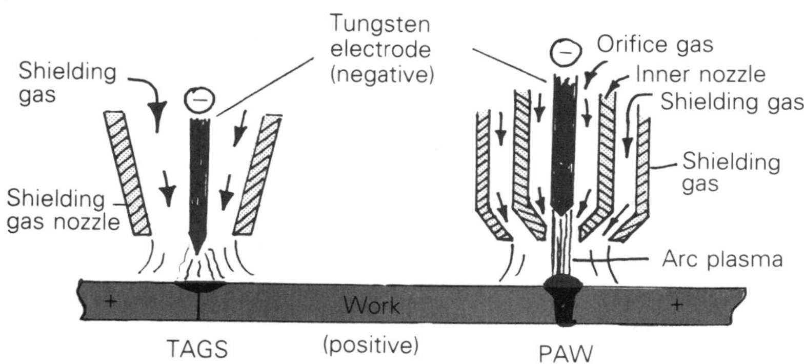

Figure 7.14 Comparison between TAGS welding and PAW.

flows back into the gap, poor fit-up joints can be welded more easily.

CHECK YOUR UNDERSTANDING

- Tungsten arc gas-shielded (TAGS) welding uses an inert (non-reactive) gas shield, usually argon or helium, to protect the non-consumable tungsten electrode and molten pool area from the atmosphere.
- The general precautions are the same as for manual metal arc welding. The light intensity can be greater with a tungsten arc. Take care that the electrode does not come near to exposed skin; when high-frequency starting devices are used, a spark between the tungsten electrode and any skin surface can give a severe burn and an electric shock.
- Alternating current is required for welding of aluminium and its alloys, as the oxide is removed electrically when the electrode is positive. The next half-cycle allows the electrode to cool slightly when it is negative, thus giving a balance between oxide removal and preventing the electrode overheating.

Figure 7.15 Close-up of keyhole plasma welding. (Courtesy of TWI, UK)

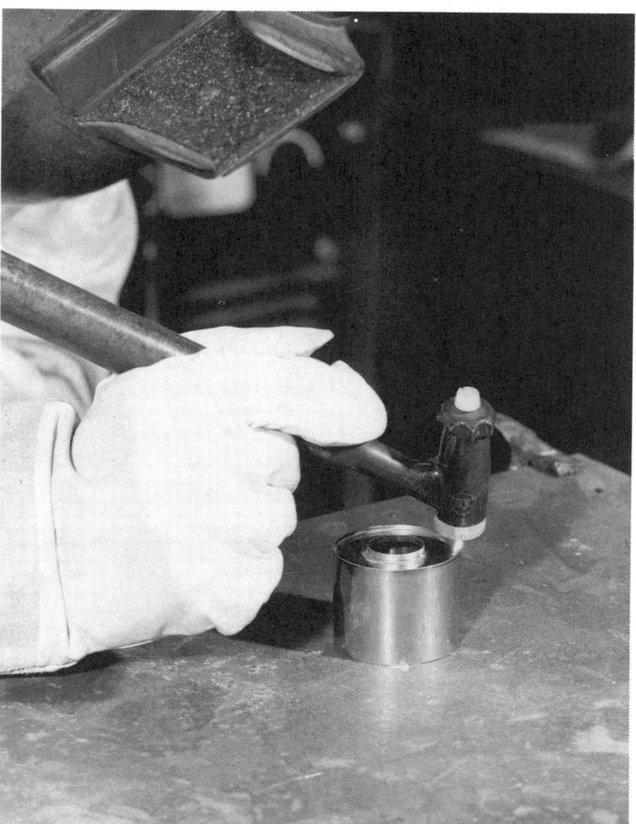

Figure 7.16 Microplasma welding. (Courtesy of TWI, UK)

- It is common to employ equipment that can provide both direct current or alternating current, as d.c. is employed on steels. Having both a.c. and d.c. available makes it possible to weld a range of materials.
- Various types of ceramic nozzle are available. Transparent heat-resisting glass nozzles allow greater visibility of the molten pool; a gas lens can allow greater extension of the tungsten and therefore aid welding in awkward situations.
- Tungsten electrodes can have additions. Thoriated tungstens are used mainly on d.c. and zirconiated tungstens on a.c. Use dust extraction when grinding tungstens.
- High-frequency starting avoids having to touch the tungsten to the work to establish the arc, and so reduces the risk of electrode contamination.
- Plasma arc welding (PAW) and cutting is a variation of TAGS welding.

REVISION EXERCISES AND QUESTIONS

1 In TAGS welding, how is the weld protected from atmospheric contamination?
2 Why are the recommended welding screen filters darker in shade than those used for manual metal arc welding using the same amperages?
3 Why is a.c. required for the TAGS welding of aluminium?
4 When might a gas lens be needed?
5 Which type of tungsten is recommended for use on d.c.?
6 Why is it better to have equipment fitted with high-frequency starting?

(Further practice questions can be found on page 202.)

8 Metal arc gas-shielded (MAGS) welding

Introduction

These semi-automatic and automatic processes have found increasing use in recent years. They have replaced the use of oxyacetylene and manual metal arc processes on certain types of fabrication.

The process is known by different names, such as MIG (metallic inert gas), CO_2 welding (when a carbon dioxide gas shield is employed), metal active gas welding and, in the USA, gas metal-arc welding. In the UK, the most widely accepted name is **MAGS (metal arc gas-shielded welding)** because this term covers shielding gases other than inert gases, and also gas mixtures.

Because the MAGS process is semi-automatic, it is suitable for full automation on certain types of work, and is used quite widely in robot form.

The process

A continuous consumable wire electrode is fed through a welding gun fitted with a concentric gas nozzle. The arc is struck between the workpiece and the wire, which acts as both electrode and filler. The arc and the weld pool are shielded from

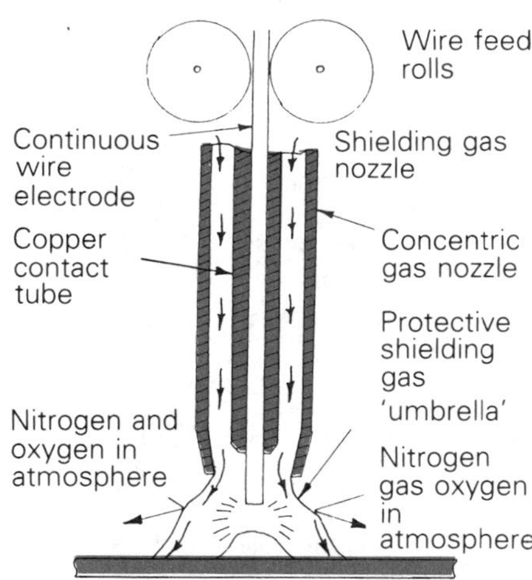

Figure 8.1 Diagram of welding nozzle and gas shield for metal arc gas-shielded (MAGS) welding.

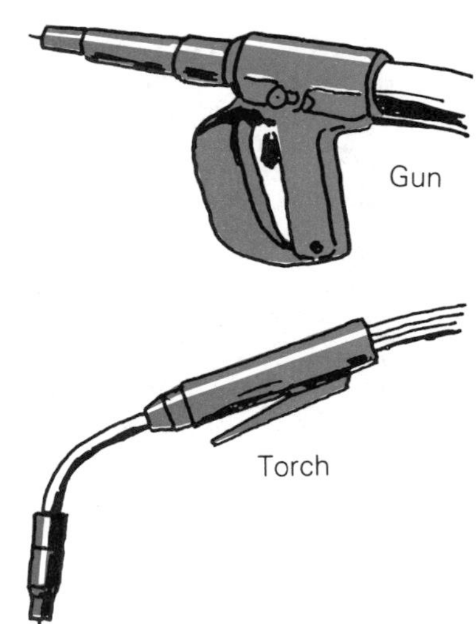

Figure 8.2 MAGS welding gun and welding torch. Some guns can have an outer nozzle attachment for fume extraction. This has to be carefully set so as not to disturb the gas shield.

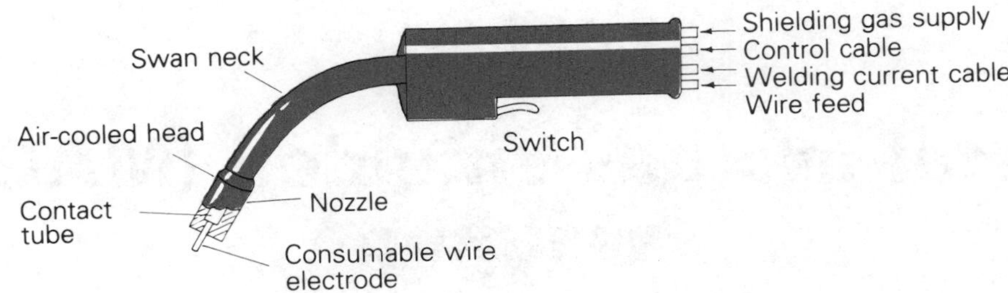

Figure 8.3 **Air-cooled welding torch.**

atmospheric contamination by passing a suitable gas through the nozzle to form a protective shield around the welding area (Figures 8.1–8.3).

For non-ferrous metals, pure argon is usually used as the gas shield. Other gases can be used, such as helium or (for copper) nitrogen. For ferrous metals, the gases used include carbon dioxide, argon and oxygen, argon and CO_2.

> The arc is self-adjusting, which means that any variation in the arc length made by the welder produces a change in the burn-off rate of the electrode, and the arc rapidly returns to its original length.

Figure 8.4 shows the basic set-up for MAGS welding.

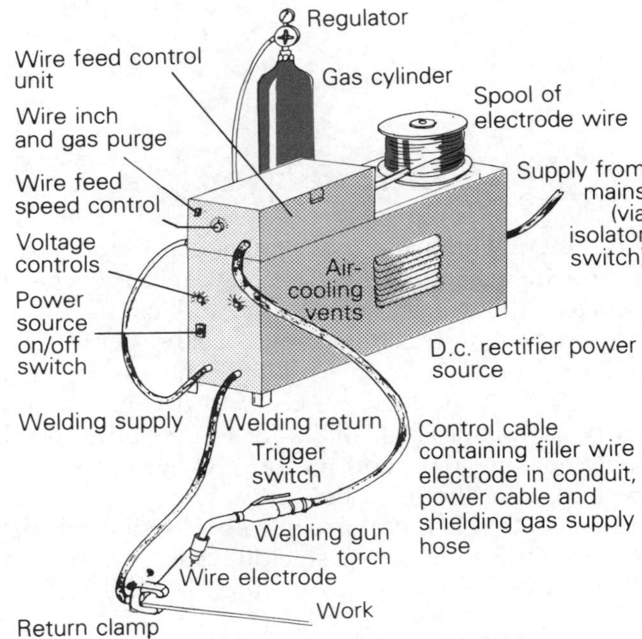

Figure 8.4 **Basic set-up for MAGS welding.**

Figure 8.5 MAGS welding a T-fillet testpiece. (Courtesy of TWI, UK)

Figure 8.6 A MAGS welder at work on a mild steel fabrication. (Courtesy of TWI, UK)

Applications

The process was developed from TAGS welding, with the tungsten electrode replaced by the continuously fed consumable wire. It was first used only on aluminium with argon as the shielding gas.

When the use of carbon dioxide was developed as a cheaper shielding gas, the process began to be used for welding steels. The MAGS process (using a variety of gas mixtures) can be used on steels of all thicknesses, aluminium, copper and many alloys, including stainless steel (Figure 8.6).

Safety precautions

The general safety precautions that apply to other arc welding processes also apply to MAGS welding. Pay special attention to the section on fumes in Chapter 3, as good ventilation is essential with all gas-shielded processes. Note that normal overhead fume extractors may not work effectively when shielding gases heavier than air are used. This is especially true of CO_2, but argon and other gases have also been known to build up to dangerous levels when special care was not taken.

The controlled arc system

In MAGS welding, the electrode melts and molten particles are detached and transported across the arc to the work.

Unlike TAGS welding, the MAGS process is usually used with a d.c. power source and the electrode positive. This gives fast melting of the relatively small-diameter electrode, which can then be fed at a speed sufficient to compensate for this 'burn-off' rate.

With an automatic welding head, the arc length can be controlled by a system that automatically speeds up or slows down the rate of wire feed as differences in arc length occur. This is called the **controlled arc system**.

In most semi-automatic machines, a system known as the **self-adjusting arc** is employed. In this system, the wire electrode is fed at a preset constant rate through the flexible conduit to the hand-held torch. If the arc length is increased, the voltage is increased with a corresponding decrease in current, which causes a decrease in electrode burn-off rate and restores the arc length. Likewise, if the arc length is reduced, the process is reversible; an increase in burn-off rate occurs, again restoring the required arc length. This system, therefore, easily compensates for the variations in electrode-to-work distances (arc length) that occur with a hand-held welding torch.

This self-adjusting arc feature is possible because MAGS welding power sources have a **flat characteristic** (Figure 8.7). Manual metal arc welding machines tend to have a **drooping characteristic** (Figure 8.8). With MAGS welding, if the arc is disturbed by a surface irregularity and the arc shortens by a small amount, the arc voltage will be

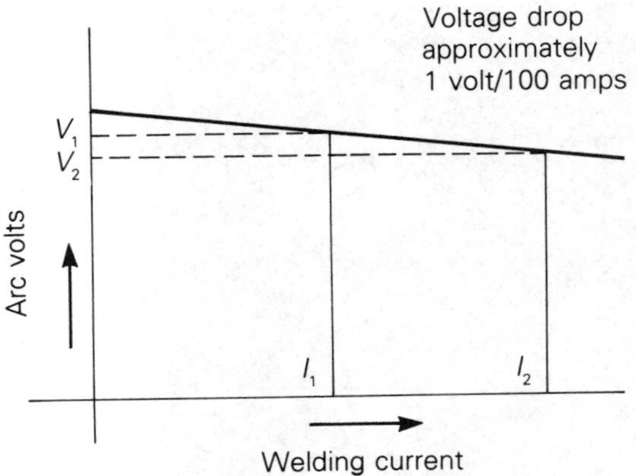

Figure 8.7 Volt–ampere curve of a constant-potential welding machine.

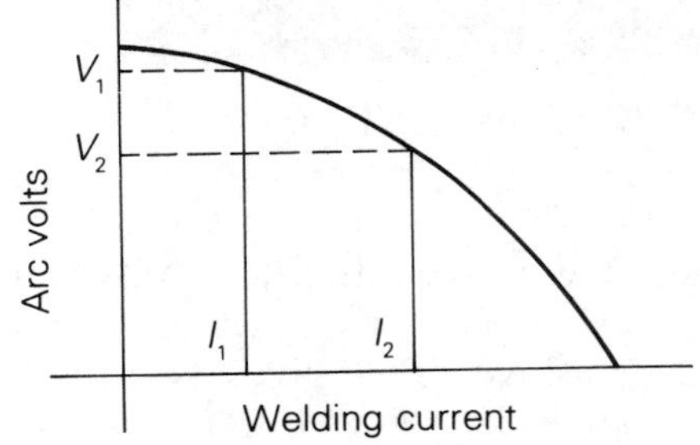

Figure 8.8 Volt–ampere curve of a 'drooping characteristic' welding machine.

decreased from V_1 to V_2, resulting in a considerable rise in current from I_1 to I_2. The burn-off rate of the electrode increases, so that the wire tip establishes the original arc length. The response rate of the flat-characteristic machine is therefore extremely rapid. Likewise, if the arc tends to lengthen during welding, this results in an immediate current drop. The electrode then burns off more slowly, again retaining the original arc gap.

With the drooping-characteristic machine (Figure 8.8) a small change in arc voltage produces a much smaller change in arc current. The rate of change of burn-off is therefore slower, which is less desirable for MAGS welding, but better for manual metal arc welding, when positional welding or filling in a gap.

Wire feed systems

There are many types of equipment available both for industry and for the DIY welder (Figure 8.9). The continuous electrode wire is driven by feed rolls, which are controlled by a variable-speed mechanism, housed in a control unit. This unit also contains automatic devices for starting and stopping the flow of shielding gas, cooling water (with some systems) and the drive motor for the wire

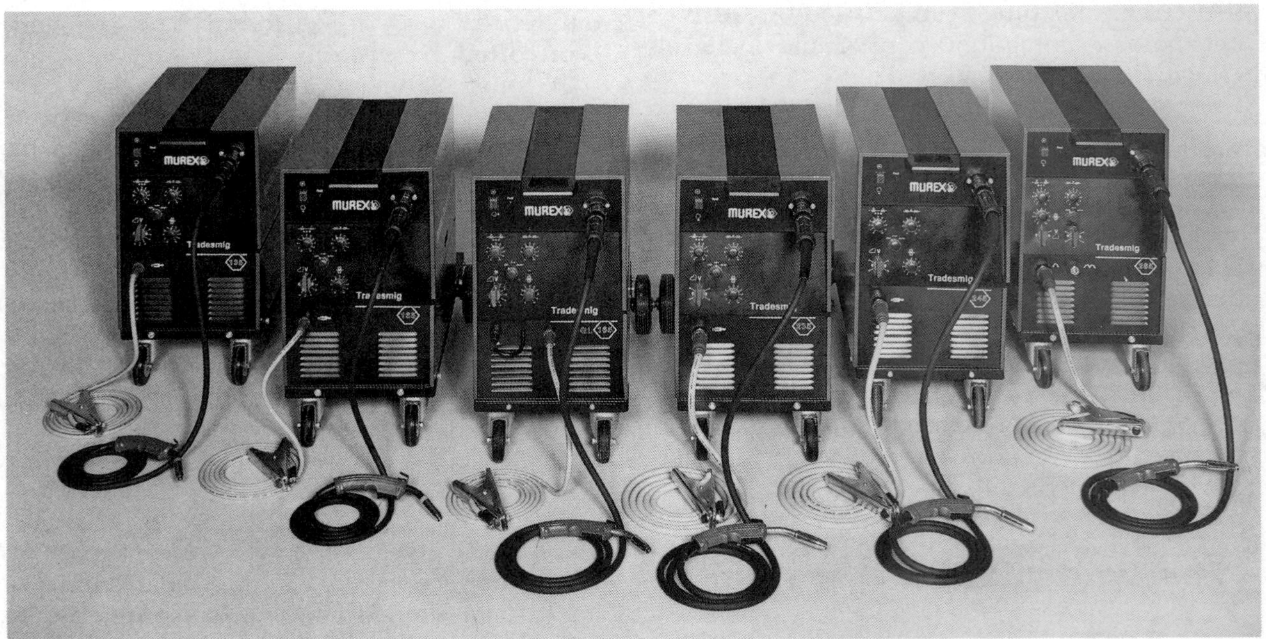

Figure 8.9 A range of air-cooled MAGS machines. The wire spool is placed vertically with this type of equipment. Access is obtained by lifting off the side panel. (Courtesy of Murex Welding Products Ltd)

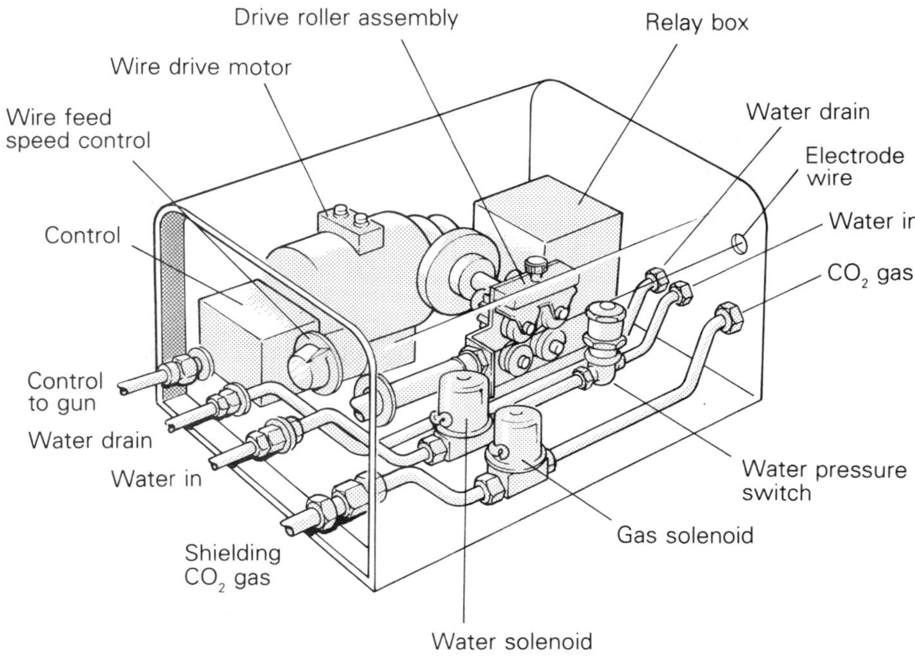

Figure 8.10 Typical MAGS welding control unit.

feed (Figure 8.10). The unit also contains the components for actuating the contactor in the power source, thus applying the welding current and voltage to the electrode.

Wire feeds may be either a push or pull type, or a combination of both (Figure 8.11). The push type uses two or more feed rolls, and a tensioning screw is used to adjust the pressure. This method is used for feeding bare soft wire with a diameter of 1.2 mm or more, and hard wire of diameter at least 0.6 mm. The combination type is usually used for flux-cored wires.

When the drive rolls are incorporated into the control unit, the wire is fed through a flexible conduit into the welding gun, and on through the contact tube. For soft or fine wires, the drive rolls and wire feed motor are located next to the gun for automatic welding heads, or in the handle for a

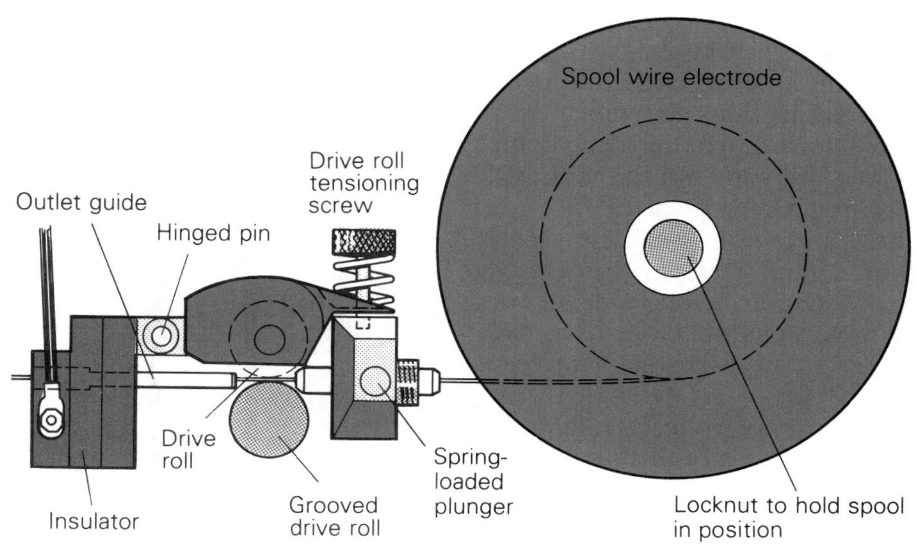

Figure 8.11 Wire drive unit: push type.

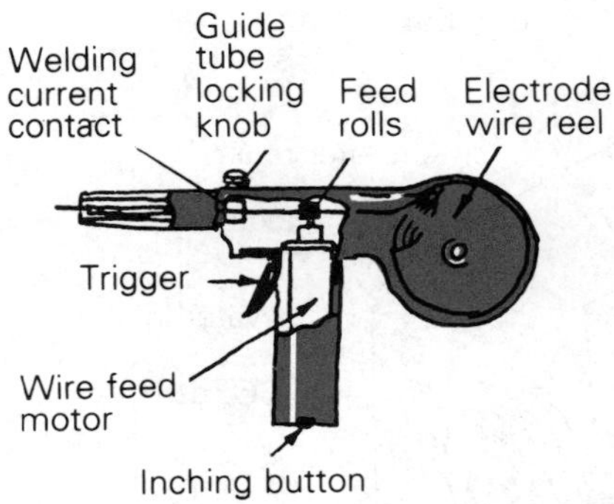

Figure 8.12 Reel-on-gun arrangement: pull type.

pistol-type air-cooled hand gun. The gun type also contains a mounting spindle that can hold a small reel of wire weighing from 450 grams to 650 grams, depending on the metal that the electrode is made of (Figure 8.12).

The feed rate is usually given in inches or cm per minute, and the general range is from 50 to 100 inches (127 to 254 cm) per minute. The wire feed speed on modern sets is usually controlled electronically. A mechanical governor can also be used, or a constant-speed motor through a variable-speed gearbox. Another design uses a valve-controlled air supply to increase or reduce the speed of a small turbine.

Drive roll systems can consist of one grooved roll (to suit the size of the wire) and one plain roll, or two grooved rolls. For smaller-diameter wires, only one roll may be needed. Larger-diameter and flux-cored wires may need both rolls to be driven, for a smooth and positive wire feed.

The rolls must be in good condition and the pressure must be set correctly. The contact tube at the gun nozzle has only a small clearance in its bore, for effective current pick-up. Too much pressure on the wire can deform it, making it jam in the contact tube. Too little pressure and the wire will slip, resulting in an irregular wire speed.

Large or very hard wires can sometimes leave the contact tube off-centre, resulting in lack of fusion or lack of penetration at one side of the weld. Some larger drive units therefore have two straightening rolls just in front of the wire feed rolls.

The electrode wire must not project too far from the contact tube when the arc is broken at the end of a weld, so an electronic control is therefore needed that is rapid enough to cut the drive motor, stopping the wire at the correct length.

The wire is fed from the drive rolls to the contact tube through a flexible Bowden cable. Nylon and plastic liners can also be used to provide a smooth feed for the smaller sizes of wire. Finer wires should be carefully supported, as a kink in the feeding cable can lead to extensive snarling of the wire. The feeding tubes should be regularly cleaned to prevent metal dust from building up and causing possible wire feed problems.

Shielding gas, cylinder types and contents

One of the shielding gases that can be used for the welding of steel is **carbon dioxide** (CO_2). It is suitable for use for dip transfer MAGS welding techniques (see the next section).

There are two types of cylinder in use. The first type allows CO_2 to come out as gas, which might contain moisture, on opening the cylinder valve. The second type, shown in Figure 8.13, is called a **siphon cylinder**. It draws liquid CO_2 from the

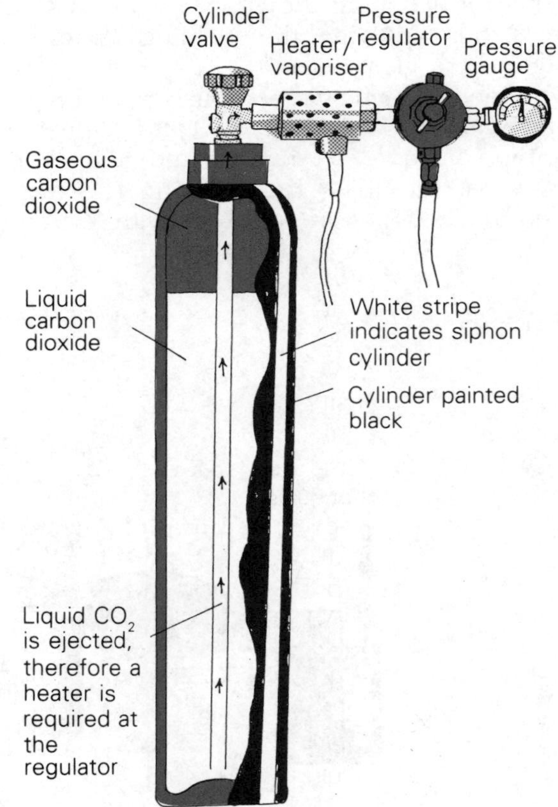

Figure 8.13 Cutaway view of a CO_2 siphon cylinder.

bottom of the cylinder, avoiding the problem of unwanted moisture. To prevent the regulator from freezing when the liquid CO_2 expands into gas, an electric heater/vaporiser unit has to be fitted between the cylinder valve outlet and the regulator.

Some other shielding gases are as follows:

1. Argon (inert gas): cylinder colour blue.
2. Helium (inert gas): cylinder colour brown.
3. Argon/oxygen mixture: cylinder colour blue with black band. The percentage of oxygen is indicated. About 1–2 per cent of oxygen is added for welding stainless steels and 2–5 per cent for welding mild steel by spray transfer. For pulse transfer, argon mixed with up to 2 per cent oxygen and up to 5 per cent carbon dioxide can be used for welding steels.
4. Argon/carbon dioxide mixtures: cylinder colour blue with green band (percentage mixture indicated). Dip and spray transfer techniques are possible with mixed shielding gas or argon and from 5 to 25 per cent carbon dioxide.

Metal transfer in MAGS welding

Figure 8.14 shows the three main types of metal transfer: spray transfer, pulsed transfer and dip transfer.

In **spray transfer**, droplets of metal are transferred from the end of the electrode in the form of a fine spray. It is usually used for welding thicker plate in the flat and horizontal/vertical positions.

Spray transfer requires the use of higher welding current and arc voltages. The resulting fluid state of the molten pool prevents it from being used for welding steels in positions other than flat or horizontal/vertical. Aluminium, however, can be welded in all positions using spray transfer.

There are two types of spray transfer. The true spray is obtained when the shielding gas is argon or argon/oxygen mixture. With these gas shields, the droplets in the spray are very fine and never short-circuit the arc. When carbon dioxide or an argon/carbon dioxide mixture is used, a molten ball tends to form at the end of the electrode. This can grow in size until it is bigger than the diameter of the electrode. These large droplets can cause short circuits to occur. This mode is known as **globular transfer**. With conditions that cause the short circuits to occur very rapidly, the mode becomes **short-circuiting** or **dip transfer**.

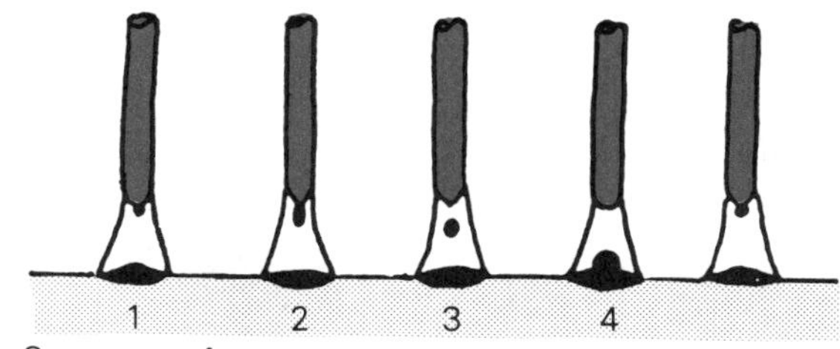

Spray transfer

1 Droplet forming
2 Droplet being 'pinched' off
3 Droplet in free flight
4 Droplet deposited in molten pool

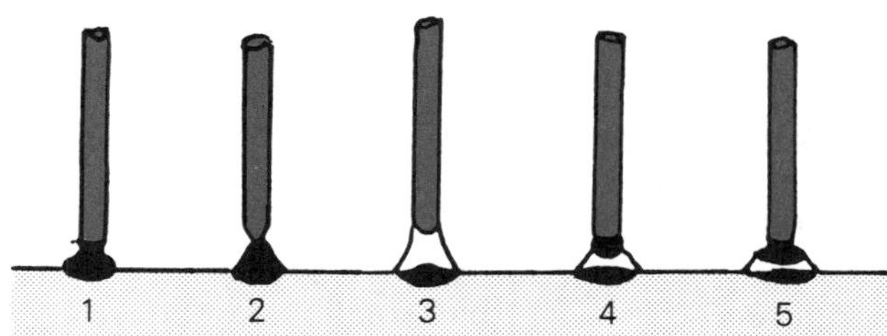

Dip or short-circuiting transfer

1 Electrode short-circuits
2 Current increases
3 Arc re-ignited
4 End of electrode heating up
5 Electrode about to short-circuit. Cycle repeats

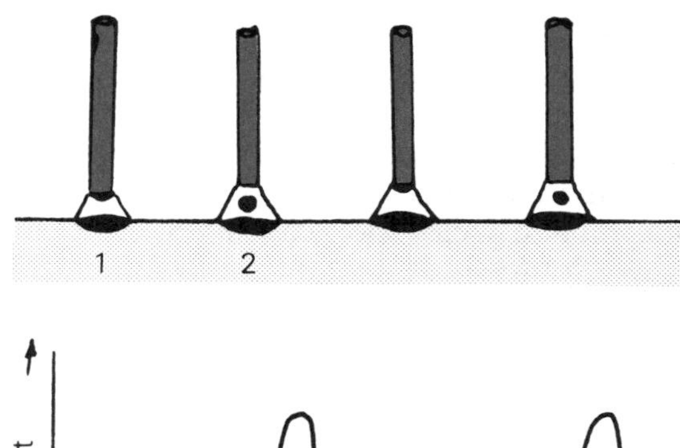

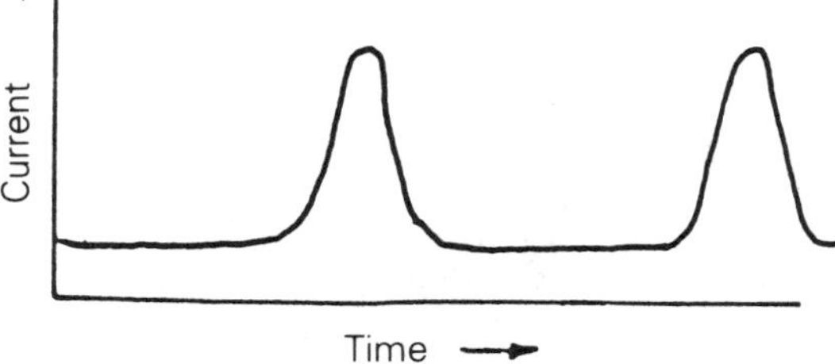

Pulsed arc transfer

1 Background current maintaining arc
2 Pulsed current projects metal droplet across the arc gap

Figure 8.14 The three types of metal transfer used in MAGS welding.

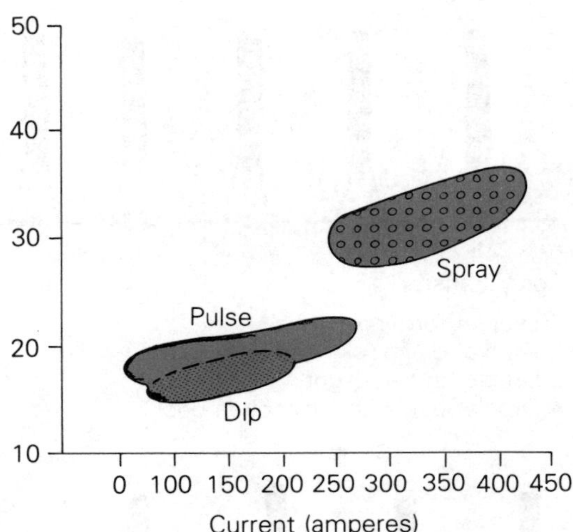

Figure 8.15 Approximate voltage and current ranges for spray, pulsed and dip transfer using 1.25 mm wire.

Figure 8.15 shows that smaller welding power sources below 200 amps will not be able to operate in the spray transfer range and so are usually confined to the dip transfer mode.

Pulsed transfer allows the droplets of metal to be controlled by using a regular frequency of pulses supplied by a special power source, which provides a background current to maintain the arc and adds the extra pulse at regular frequencies. This method reduces spatter and gives greater control of heat input to the workpiece. The amount of weld metal deposited can also be controlled much more closely.

In **dip transfer**, the wire electrode actually dips into the molten weld pool, causing a short circuit; the power source is designed to give an increase in current at this point. The molten tip then melts off the electrode into the weld pool and the arc is re-established. This process produces a weld pool that solidifies quickly, allowing positional welding and the welding of thinner sheet. Dip transfer is therefore useful for motor vehicle body repair and sheet metal constructions (Figure 8.16).

> ▲ When you are electric welding on a car, you should remove the battery. Depending on the area being welded, you may need to remove the petrol tank as well and store it away from welding operations. Disconnect alternators to avoid damage. Always have a fire extinguisher handy.

Operating procedures

There are a wide range of different types of welding machine for MAGS welding, so it is not possible to give specific instructions for all types. The following information is therefore for guidance only. It should provide the basics when you link it with the information for the specific machine that you are working on.

The plate edge preparations for MAGS welding are the same as those used for manual metal arc welding.

Arc voltage and welding current

It is best to set the open-circuit voltage to the lowest setting that gives the required arc voltage. If the arc voltage is too high, the arc will tend to be

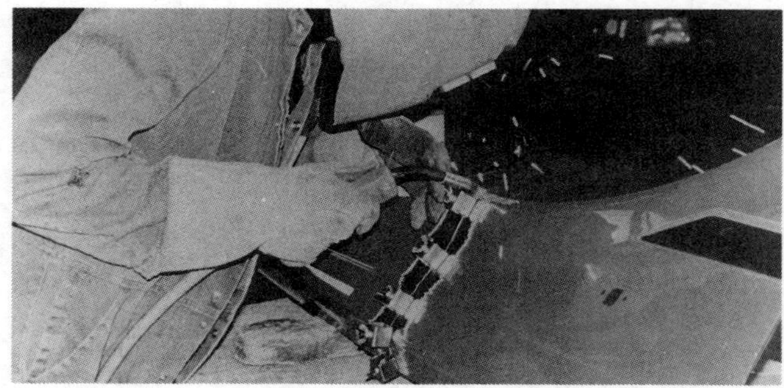

Figure 8.16 MAGS welding is ideal for thin sections such as car bodywork. Here a weld is being made between two halves of a front wing. Small clamps called 'intergrips' are being used to position the parts. (Courtesy of Frost Auto Restoration Techniques Ltd, UK)

too long, with irregular metal transfer and consequently poor deposit quality with excessive spatter. Too low an arc voltage can result in 'stubbing' of the electrode wire into the weld pool, or excessive penetration, or both. The detrimental effects of too high or too low an arc voltage will be more noticeable with dip transfer. The welding current is set with the wire feed speed control. This is calibrated in different ways on different makes and types of machine.

Electrode wire size

Generally speaking, the smaller-diameter wires will give greater current density, resulting in a fast burn-off rate and a tendency to give deeper-penetration welds.

Modern MAGS welding machines have an automatic inductance, but older machines may need a manual setting. The inductance is used for dip transfer welding. Increasing the inductance for a given open-circuit voltage produces a hotter arc, which results in quieter welding conditions with less spatter and a smoother weld finish. Decreasing the inductance produces a cooler arc that give out a distinctive 'crackling' sound, and a weld surface with a more pronounced ripple.

On machines that require manual adjustment, high inductance will be needed for thicker materials and low inductance for thin sheet.

Contact tips and nozzles

On some torches and guns, the positions of contact tip and nozzle can be adjusted to allow greater visibility of the welding area or accessibility to the particular joint, and/or to improve gas shielding. Table 8.1 lists the commonly recommended settings.

Always use the correct size of contact tip. A brief spray with silicon 'anti-spatter' solution before use and at regular intervals during use will make it easier to remove spatter from the nozzle and tip. Clean the nozzle and tip regularly.

Welding speed

Perfection with MAGS welding, as with the other processes discussed in this book, will only come with adequate practice under guidance.

When you are learning MAGS welding, you must pay special attention to obtaining the correct welding speed. Too fast a welding speed can cause excessive spatter and undercut. Shielding gas can get trapped in the quickly solidifying weld metal, causing porosity. Too slow a welding speed may cause excessive penetration.

Wire extension

The length that the electrode wire extends beyond the contact tip can also affect weld quality. With more wire protruding, the arc current will be reduced, and this will result in less penetration. Wire extension from the contact tip should be approximately:

1. For dip transfer: 3–6 mm
2. For spray transfer: 18–30 mm
3. For flux-cored wire: 30–45 mm

Purging the torch or gun

If the equipment has been left for any length of time, you should purge the gas hose and gun of any air before you use the welding equipment. Usually there is a gas purge button on the welding equipment. When you press this, shielding gas should flow through the hose and nozzle for approximately 15 seconds.

Table 8.1 Contact tip positions for MAGS welding

Mode of metal transfer	Recommended position of control tip
Dip	3–9 mm beyond the end of the nozzle to allow greater visibility/accessibility
Spray (on steels)	6–9 mm within the nozzle to give improved gas shielding
Spray (on aluminium)	9–12 mm within the nozzle to give improved gas shielding
Spray (using flux-cored wire)	9–18 mm within the nozzle to give improved gas shielding and contact tube protection

Possible problems and remedies

Sometimes, the electrode wire can fuse to the contact tube. This is called a **burn-back**. If it occurs, release the torch trigger at once; otherwise the drive rolls will continue to feed the wire and it will end up in a tangle around the wire feed mechanism.

You may be able to remove the fused piece of wire easily, but sometimes sawing or grinding may be needed to free it (Figure 8.17). Replace the contact tube or tip if it is badly damaged.

 Switch off the machine before you carry out this operation.

The cause of the problem should be traced and cured (with supervised help if necessary).

Many welding problems can be caused by using the wrong shielding gas or wire, or unclean plate, so check these points first if you are not getting good results.

The MAGS process does not produce a slag like that in manual metal arc welding, but it does form a thin silicate layer. This must be removed when you are carrying out high-quality multi-run welds, before depositing the subsequent run. If you do not remove this thin film, the result can be porosity and other defects, which will cause a weld to fail radiographic standards.

Lack of shielding gas will cause serious defects, as the weld will be a 'bare wire deposit' with no protection from the atmosphere. The nozzle should therefore be frequently cleaned of spatter deposits, and welding should take place in a draught-free area. Obviously you should also check that there is an adequate supply of gas in the cylinder.

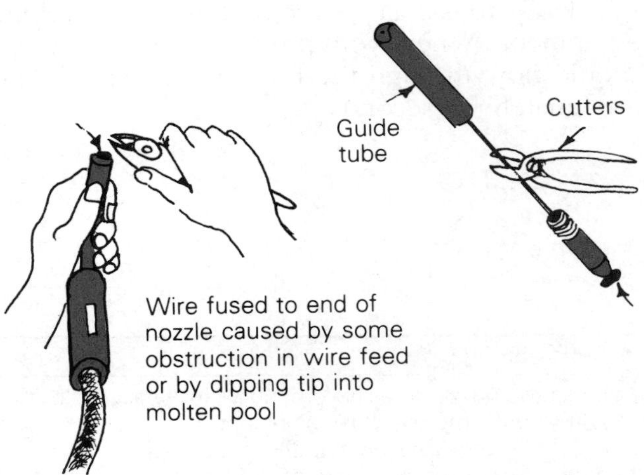

Figure 8.17 Dealing with a 'burn-back'.

Welding technique: example procedures

Bead on plate by dip transfer welding

1. Using either a 1.0 mm or a 1.2 mm diameter electrode, set the open-circuit voltage to around 25 volts.
2. Set the inductance (if fitted) to mid-point and the wire feed speed to about 4.25 metres per minute.
3. Set the carbon dioxide shielding gas flow at 9.0–12.0 litres per minute.
4. Take a piece of scrap 6 mm low carbon steel plate, and deposit a weld bead, holding the gun at the angles shown in Figure 8.18. The end of the nozzle should be about 10–15 mm from the work.
5. If the electrode stubs into the weld pool, increase the voltage slightly.
6. Examine the weld bead. If it is too small, increase the wire feed speed; if it is too large, decrease the wire feed speed.

If the wire bead is 'peaky' in appearance, increase the voltage. Lack of fusion at the edges of the weld can be cured by increasing the voltage and/or the inductance.

3 mm butt weld (close and open square edge) in the flat position

See Figure 8.19.

1. Assemble the plates using small tacks at the ends. The open square edge preparation should have a gap of 3 mm.
2. Adjust the distance of the contact tube to the work (electrode extension) and the travel speed, to control penetration. The electrode extension should not be greater than 1.5 cm.
3. Deposit the weld in one pass, at a speed fast

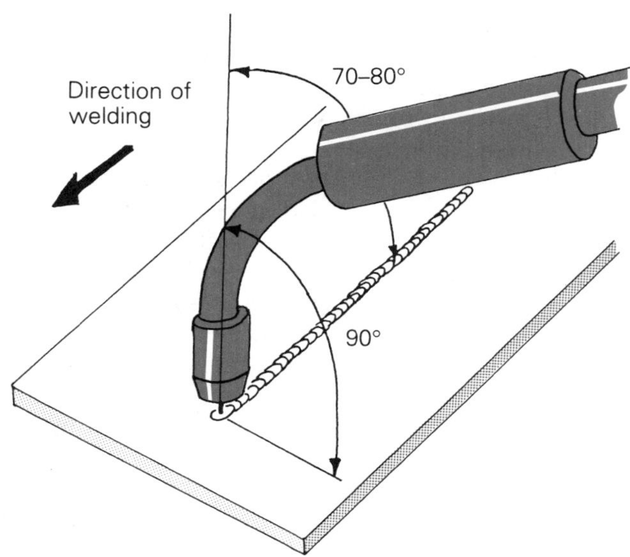

Figure 8.18 Recommended welding gun angles for forehand MAGS technique.

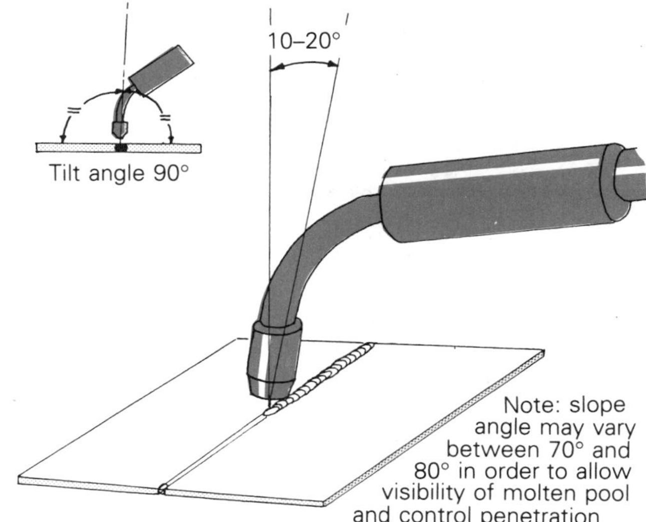

Figure 8.19 MAGS welding 3 mm low-carbon steel in the flat position.

enough to prevent weld metal flowing ahead of the arc.

4. If there is excessive reinforcement, reduce the wire feed speed and adjust the voltage and inductance to suit.

T-fillet and lap welds in the flat and horizontal positions

Assemble the joint without a gap at the joint line. Tack on one side and deposit weld on the untacked side of the joint. Keep the distance of the contact

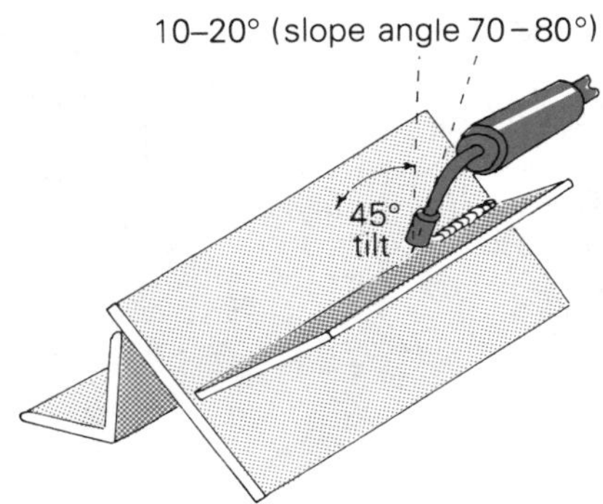

Figure 8.20 T-fillet weld in the flat position.

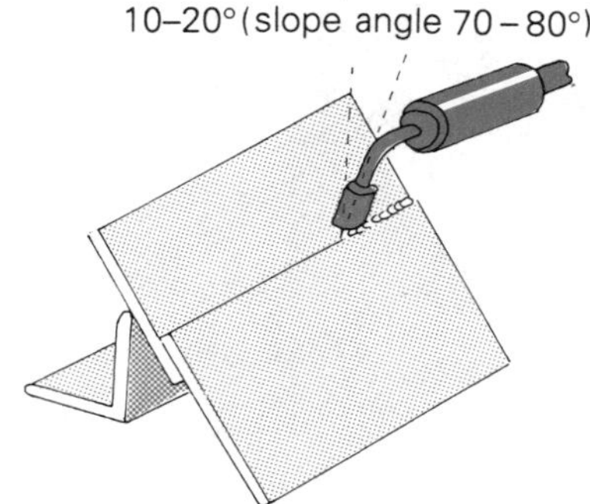

Figure 8.21 Lap weld in the flat position.

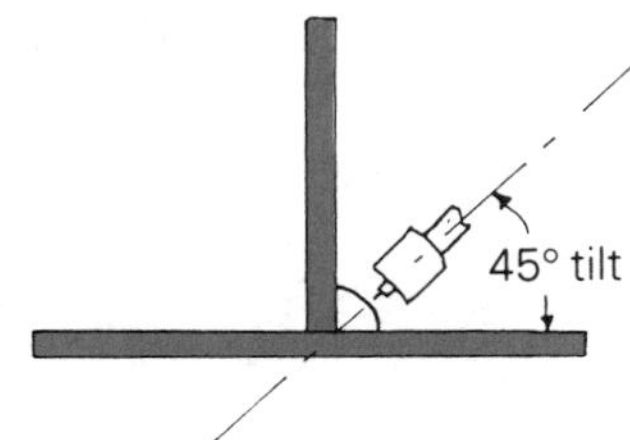

Figure 8.22 T-fillet weld in the horizontal/vertical position.

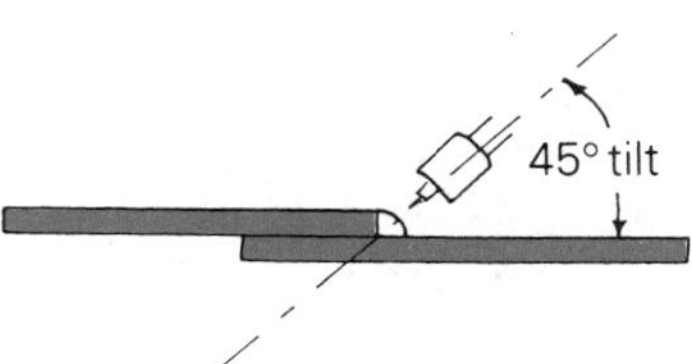

Figure 8.23 Lap weld in the horizontal/vertical position.

tube to the work at about 1.5 cm, and hold the gun roughly at the angles shown in Figures 8.20–8.23.

> Slope and tilt angles are the same for laps and fillets.

Tilting plates allows you to weld in the flat position. This means that, generally, you need fewer runs, you can use larger-diameter electrode wires, and you can complete the weld in less time. All these factors can help to reduce the overall cost of the job.

Automatic welding

Many automatic welding processes are used in industry. MAGS welding lends itself to robotics, in that a semi-automatic torch can be mounted on to a robot arm (Figure 8.24). In other applications, work can be moved beneath a fixed welding head or the head can be mounted on wheels and moved along a track alongside the work.

Resistance spot welding (see Chapter 9) has been widely automated and robotised in recent years for mass production work such as the manufacture of car bodies and domestic appliances.

One automatic process that has been in use for many years where high-quality welds are required is the **submerged arc process** (Figures 8.25, 8.26). In this process, the bare wire electrode maintains an arc with the parent metal. The whole of the welding area is submerged under a powdered flux, which melts as the welding progresses along the seam. The flux forms a slag over the completed weld, further protecting it from the atmosphere. Any unburnt flux is returned to the flux hopper for re-use, via a vacuum and filter.

Hand-held torches can be obtained for fillet and corner welds, but the process is more usually used in its automatic form for large high-quality welds on pressure vessels (where the work can be rotated beneath a fixed welding heat), and bridges and girder work (where the welding head can be moved along a track next to the work).

Figure 8.24 Robotic MAGS welding. (Courtesy of TWI, UK)

Figure 8.25 Close-up view of the submerged arc welding process. (Courtesy of TWI, UK)

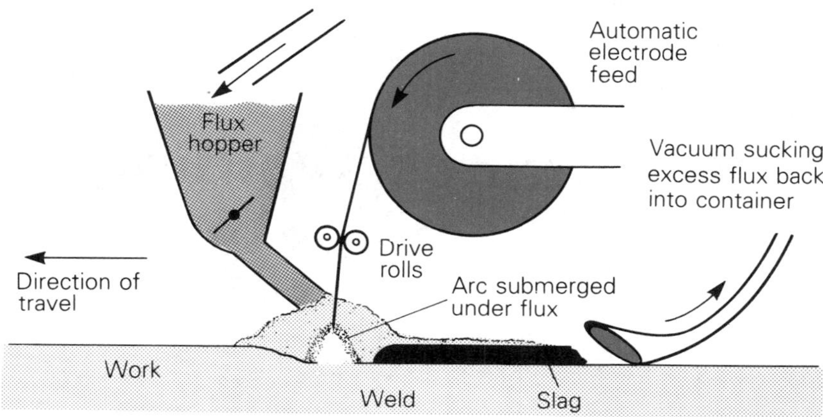

Figure 8.26 Basic principle of the submerged arc welding process.

CHECK YOUR UNDERSTANDING

- Metal arc gas-shielded (MAGS) welding is a direct development of TAGS. The non-consumable tungsten electrode is replaced with a consumable metal wire electrode. In some applications a flux-cored wire electrode can be used.
- The arc is self-adjusting. Any variation in the arc length made by the welder, or due to plate surface irregularity, produces a change in the burn-off rate of the electrode. This returns the arc rapidly to its original length.
- Unlike TAGS welding, the electrode in MAGS welding is consumable, and is required to melt off rapidly. For this reason, a direct current power source is usually employed, with the electrode connected positive.
- Various gas shields are used when welding different materials. For ferrous metals, carbon dioxide, argon and oxygen, argon and CO_2, helium and others are used.
- The electrode is in the form of a spool of wire. It is driven by feed rolls, which are controlled by a variable-speed mechanism.
- There are three usable types of metal transfer: spray, pulsed and dip.
- MAGS welding lends itself to automatic and robotic applications.

REVISION EXERCISES AND QUESTIONS

1. What type of power source is usually used for MAGS welding?
2. State the electrode polarity normally used when MAGS welding.
3. What is meant by a 'self-adjusting arc'?
4. Name two gas shields commonly used with the MAGS process.
5. Name the three types of metal transfer.

(Further practice questions can be found on page 202.)

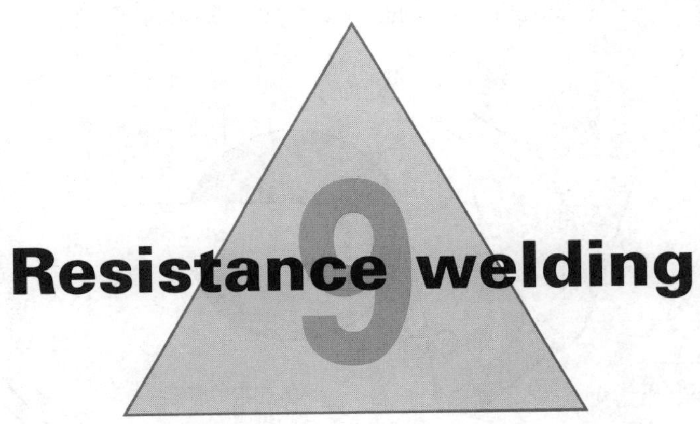

9 Resistance welding

Introduction

The basic principle of resistance welding is that heat is generated when an electric current passes through an electrical resistance. The amount of heat generated depends on the amount of **current**, the amount of **resistance** and how long the current flows (**time**).

This basic resistance welding principle is expressed by the equation:

$$H = I^2RT$$

in which

H = the heat generated, in joules
I^2 = the current flow, in amperes squared
R = the resistance, in ohms
T = the time the current flows, in seconds

Expressed in words, this means that the heat generated in a resistance weld is equal to the square of the current flowing through the workpiece, multiplied by the resistance of the workpiece, multiplied by the time that the current flows. From this you can see that if one of the three factors – current, resistance or time – is increased while the other two factors remain constant, the amount of heat produced is increased.

A factor K can be added to the formula to represent heat losses:

$$H = I^2RTK$$

where K has a constant value of 0.238.

The economy and speed of resistance welding are especially valuable in mass production. The automotive industry is a prime example. Articles manufactured for use in the preparation and serving of food and the aircraft industry are others.

It was Joule who apparently made the first resistance weld, in England in 1857. At that time, however, an adequate supply of electricity was not readily available, so it was not until 1886 that a suitable source of current allowed Thomson to develop the process.

Spot welding

In Figure 9.1 the two pieces of plate (or thin sheet) are lapped and placed between the copper electrodes. Pressure is applied to ensure good physical and electrical contact. An electric current is passed through the electrodes and through the workpiece. The greatest amount of resistance, and therefore heat, is generated at the interface directly in line with the electrodes. At this point, melting (in small areas) takes place. The molten area grows in size until the current is switched off. Electrode pressure is maintained until the molten metal cools. When it solidifies it forms a weld nugget. It is important to

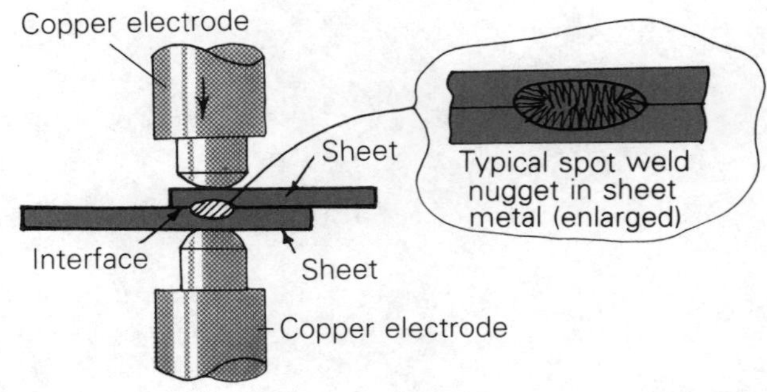

Figure 9.1 **Formation of a spot weld nugget.**

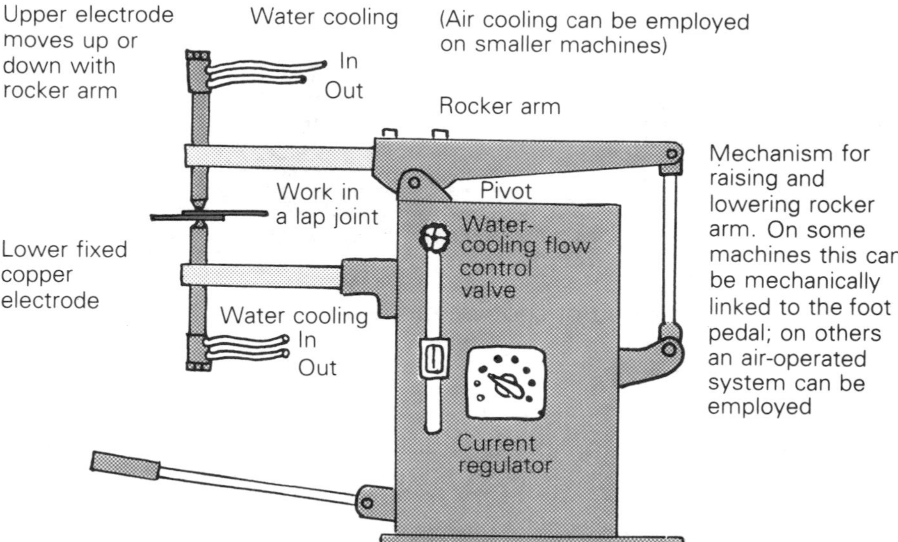

Figure 9.2 A typical rocker-arm spot welding machine.

Figure 9.3 Left: basic pedal-operated spot welder (17 or 25 kVA). Right: top-of-the-range 'Stronghold' spot welder with Micropak 16p control (17/100/150 kVA). (Courtesy of British Federal)

establish the correct pressure between the electrodes to maximise the current flow without deformation.

The metal to be joined is placed between the electrodes in the form of a lap joint. The foot pedal is depressed, bringing the top electrode down on the work (Figures 9.2 and 9.3). The electric current, while having a low voltage, can be up to 80 000 amps (some automatic machines can use currents of up to 200 000 amps). The minute air gaps between the two pieces of metal to be welded are sufficient to cause a resistance to the passage of electricity.

This resistance creates enough heat to melt the metal to form the spot weld.

Figure 9.4 shows the simplified principle of spot

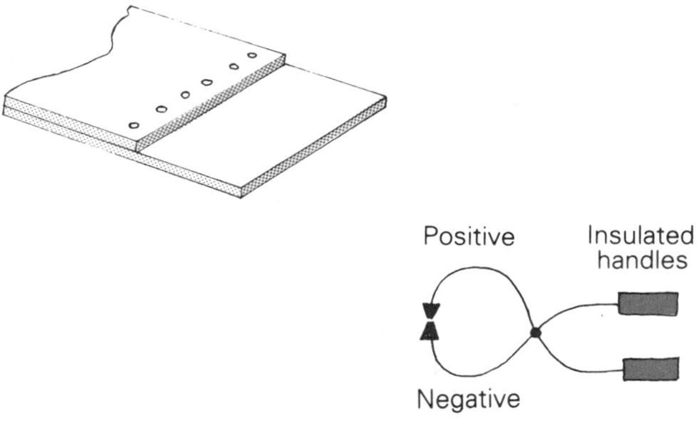

Figure 9.4 Simplified principle of spot welding pliers.

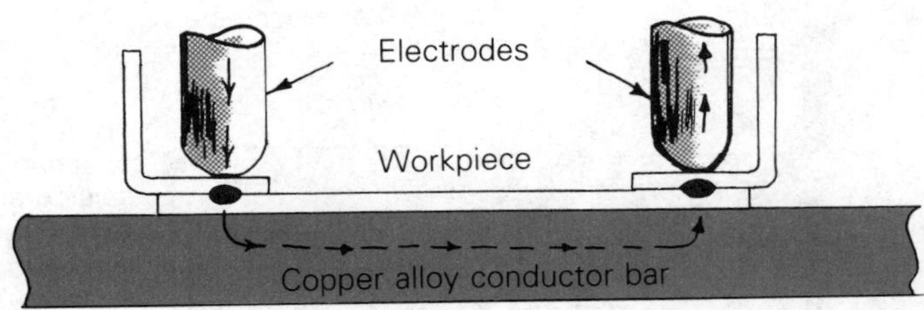

Figure 9.5 Series spot welding: a method of spot welding when only one side will show signs of welding.

welding pliers. Figure 9.5 illustrates the method of welding from one side only, by series spot welding. This method will leave no marks on the outer surface of the component.

Figure 9.6 shows some common defects in spot welding. These defects are usually caused by movement or sliding between the workpieces and/or the electrode, and incorrect alignment of the workpieces and/or the electrodes.

Lack of fusion can be due to the following causes:

1. insufficient current;
2. insufficient time;
3. insufficient pressure;
4. dirty work surfaces on plates to be joined, causing poor electrical contact and creating total current resistance.

Seam welding

With ordinary spot welding it is not possible to place welds very close to each other, as the current can pass through the first weld instead of through the interface to form the second weld. Seam welding is similar to spot welding, but the electrodes are a revolving set of wheels and the work is passed between them (Figure 9.7). A series of electrical impulses is sent through the electrodes, which causes a number of spot welds to take place very close together or half overlapping each other, if required, to produce an air-tight or liquid-tight joint (which is not possible with normal spot welding).

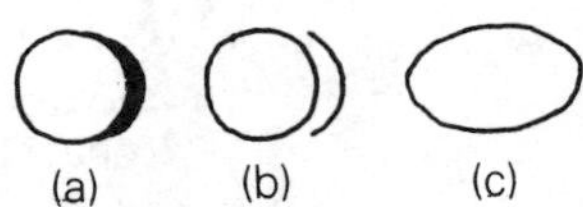

Figure 9.6 Common defects in spot welding: (a) skid; (b) eyebrow; (c) elliptical spot.

Projection welding

This process uses similar equipment to that used in spot welding, except that the electrodes are flat copper platens. It is common for three or four projection welds to be made at once. A weld will be made at each projection. The projections are either pressed into one of the components as a separate operation before welding, or are forged in manufacture, as in the nut shown in Figure 9.8.

Resistance butt welding

Resistance butt welding is similar to resistance spot welding, but the actual components to be joined become the electrodes (Figure 9.9).

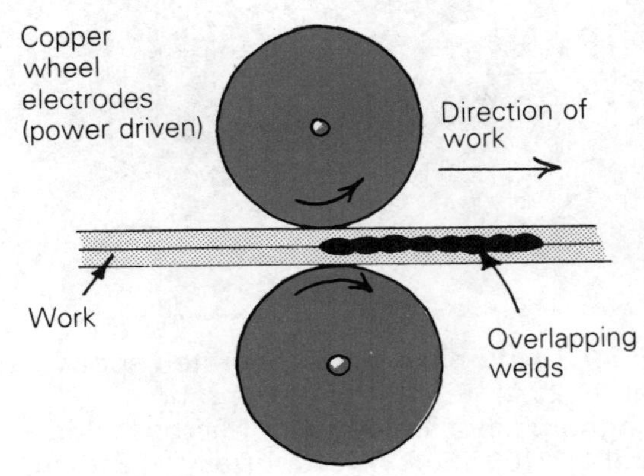

Figure 9.7 Seam welding.

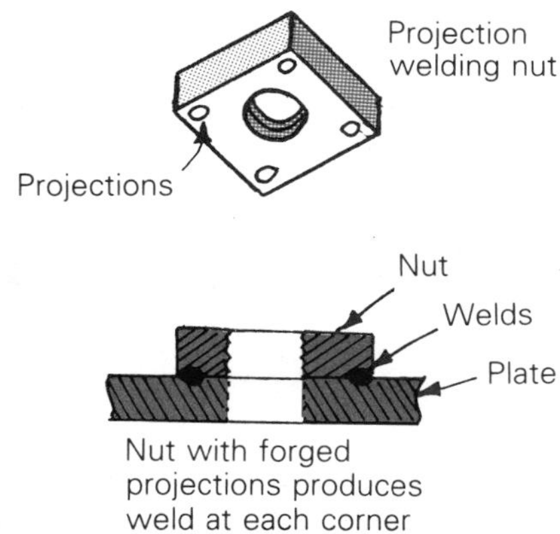

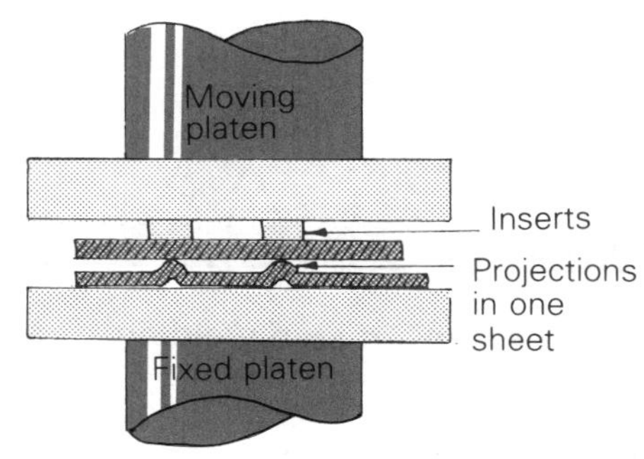

Figure 9.8 Projection welding.

The two components are placed in the jaws of a machine and pressed together. A large current is passed through the work, bringing the ends to be joined up to welding heat. At this stage, extra force is applied and the ends are pushed together. At the point of welding, an enlargement of section takes place. This is called an **upset**; it can be removed by machining if required.

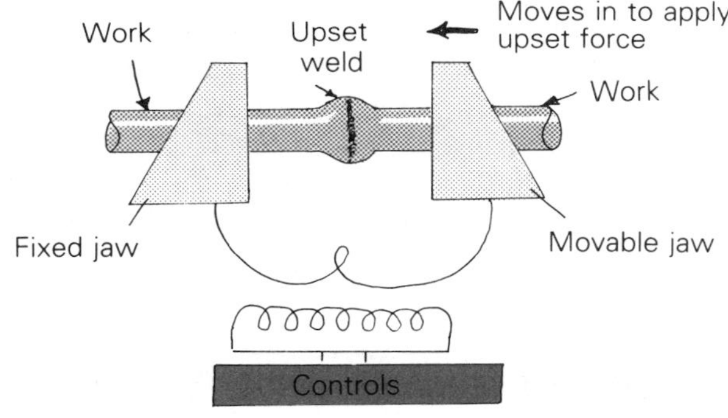

Figure 9.9 Resistance butt welding.

Flash butt welding

This is not strictly a resistance welding process, but it is usually discussed within such processes as it is similar to resistance butt welding.

The components are brought together and a current passing through them heats the ends to red heat (because of resistance). The components are then separated a short distance and an electric arc is established between the ends until melting begins. At this point, the components are pushed together under high pressure with the current still flowing. This forms a ridge or **flash** at the point of weld (Figure 9.10). Any impurities are forced out of the joint in the flash. The pressure and current are then switched off, although a post-weld heat treatment can be given after welding by again passing a controlled current through the work.

Flash butt welding is used throughout the world for joining railway lines, together with another process called **Thermit welding**. Thermit welding uses a chemical charge of aluminium powder and iron oxide to melt the ends of the railway lines. The molten iron then fuses with them and is shaped by preformed moulds fastened around the joint (see Chapter 27).

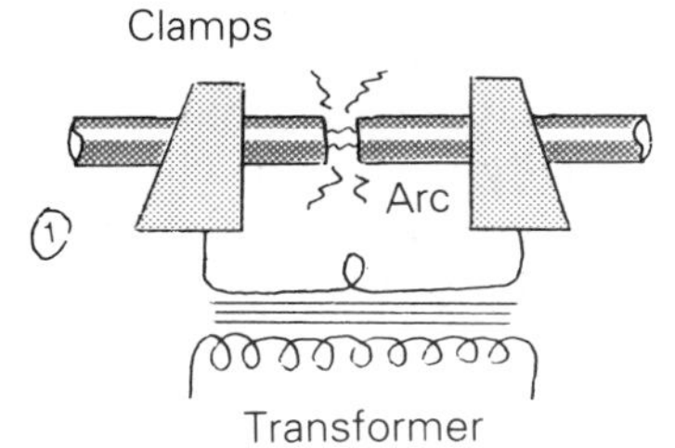

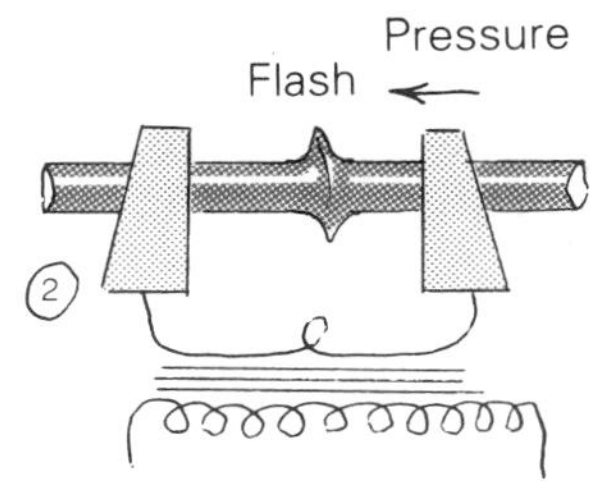

Figure 9.10 Flash butt welding.

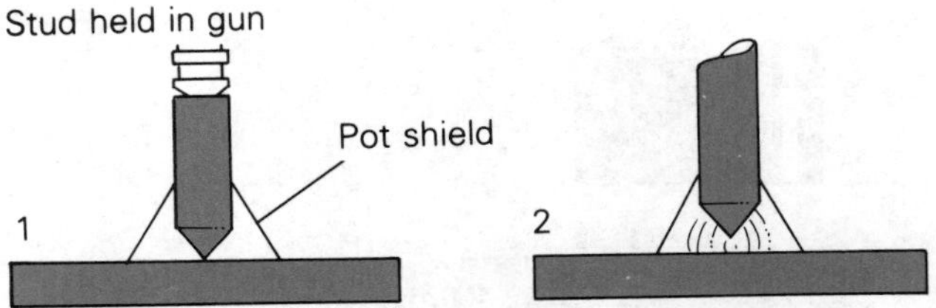

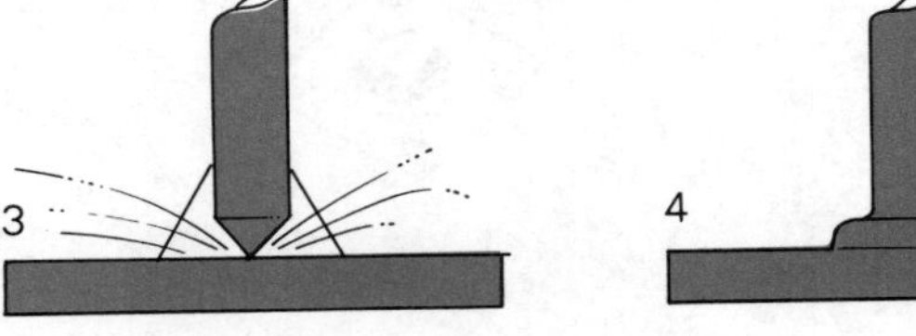

Figure 9.11 The four stages of stud welding.

Stud welding

This is a type of resistance welding used for attaching studs or pins to steel plate, sections, pipe or weldments quickly and without preparation of the base to which the stud is welded.

The resultant weld is stronger than the stud itself, and as the weld does not penetrate the plate, there is no possibility of leakage at the point of attachment.

Heavy components do not have to be moved to drilling machines for drilling and tapping operations. Studs can be applied at any convenient stage of assembly and access is needed to only one side of the job. Although the process is mostly used for steel studs, brass and copper studs can be welded to steel or copper sheet, and excellent results have also been obtained with aluminium bronze and silicon bronze studs.

The equipment consists of a 'gun' fitted with a chuck to receive the stud and a cable connected to a suitable direct current power source, such as a transformer rectifier specially designed for this purpose, or a direct current generator.

Figure 9.11 shows the four stages of the stud welding process, which uses a 'flash butt' technique.

1. The stud is held (in the gun) in contact with the plate. The end of the stud is covered with a pot insulator, which covers the welding operation and is broken off when the operation is complete.
2. The stud is raised, creating a pilot arc.
3. Full welding current is turned on, producing a power arc, which melts the end of the stud and the surface of the plate.
4. The stud is released, the current is turned off and the weld is completed.

The process is speedy and simple: apart from inserting a stud in the chuck of the gun, locating it and pressing the operating button, the entire process is automatic. The actual welding cycle takes less than a second to complete, and in a matter of seconds again, a new stud can be inserted in the gun ready to repeat the operation.

CHECK YOUR UNDERSTANDING

- The amount of heat generated in a resistance welding process depends on the amount of current, the amount of resistance and how long the current flows (time).
- The economy and speed of resistance welding make it especially useful where items are being mass produced.
- There are different types of resistance welding processes. These include spot welding, seam welding, projection welding, resistance butt welding and resistance stud welding. There is also flash butt welding, which is not truly a resistance process but is similar to resistance butt welding except for the fact that arcing takes place.
- Seam welding can be used to produce an air- or liquid-tight joint, which is not possible with ordinary spot welding.

REVISION EXERCISES AND QUESTIONS

1 What are the three main factors that cause heat to be produced for the resistance welding of metals?

2 Which type of resistance welding is suitable for producing an air- or liquid-tight joint?

3 What factors make resistance welding especially useful in mass production situations?

4 Why is flash butt welding not a true resistance welding process?

5 What are spot welding electrodes usually made of?

(Further practice questions can be found on page 202.)

Cutting and gouging

Introduction

During many manufacturing processes it is often necessary to cut metals to size or to shape their edges with a bevel ready for welding. This chapter describes the various processes that can be employed for this purpose.

Gouging is a method that allows removal of a layer of metal, forming a groove, without cutting all the way through. It is often used to remove a section of weld that contains a defect, in order that it can be re-welded.

Oxy-fuel gas cutting and gouging

For cutting and gouging, it is only necessary to raise the metal to a bright red heat before directing the stream of high-pressure oxygen at the hot metal. It is therefore possible to use fuels that provide a lower flame temperature than acetylene (see Table 12.1 in Chapter 12).

The basic precautions for this process are the same as those for gas welding, but you must take care to support work correctly, so that it will not collapse after being cut and cause injury. Cutting is often used in demolition work and for cutting up scrap, and so you should pay particular attention to what scrap containers may have contained, or may still contain. This is of course to avoid the risk of explosion when cutting up drums and tanks.

Nozzles for gas cutting have either six or eight holes, to give six or eight neutral preheating flames, and one central hole for the high-pressure oxygen, which is released when the cutting oxygen lever on the blowpipe is depressed (Figures 10.1 and 10.2).

Gas cutting is often used to prepare the edges of thicker plates for welding, by cutting to the appropriate level.

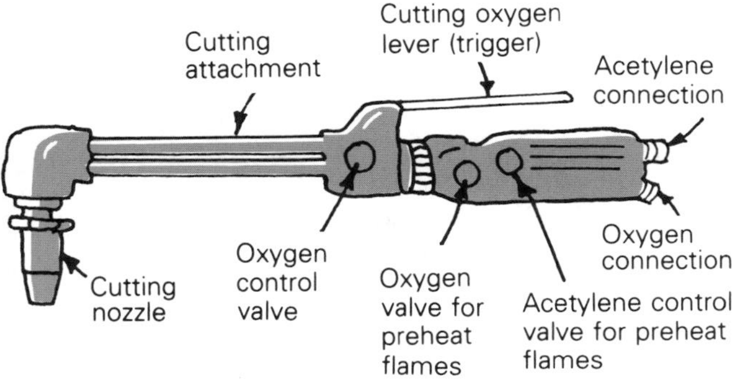

Figure 10.1 One type of cutting blowpipe, which is made by fitting an approved cutting attachment to the appropriate blowpipe shank.

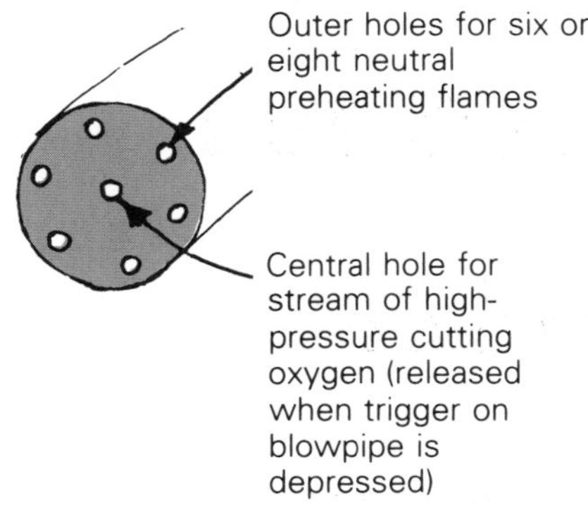

Figure 10.2 Sketch showing the end face of a typical cutting nozzle.

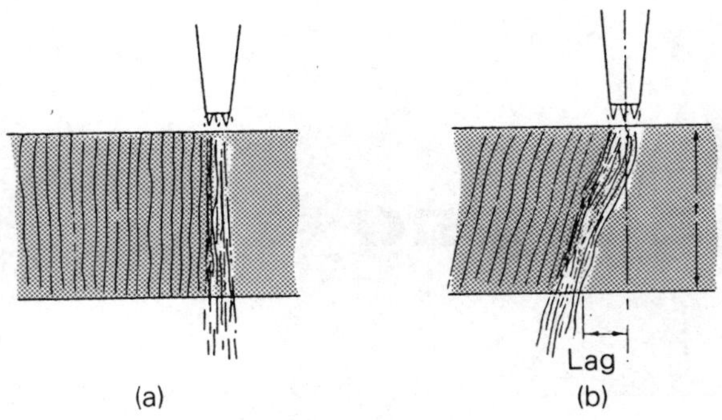

Figure 10.3 Drag lines on cut plate: (a) vertical lines – zero drag; (b) drag measured against plate thickness – for example, 10 per cent drag means a lag of 10 per cent plate thickness.

Operations involved in cutting

There are two operations involves in oxy-fuel cutting.

1. Heating flames are directed on to the metal to be cut, until it is raised to a bright red heat. This is called the **ignition temperature**: about 900°C.
2. A stream of high-pressure oxygen is directed on to the hot metal. This immediately oxidises the metal and, as the melting point of this oxide is below the melting point of steel, the oxide is melted and blown away.

The metal is therefore cut by a chemical action;

Good cut
Sharp top and bottom edges
Vertical drag lines
No adhering dross
Square face. Light, easily removed oxide scale

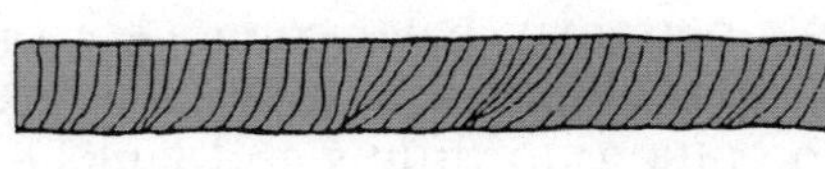

Cutting speed too fast
Top edge not sharp
Rounded bottom edge, which may not be completely severed
Drag lines uneven, sloping backwards.
Irregular cut edge

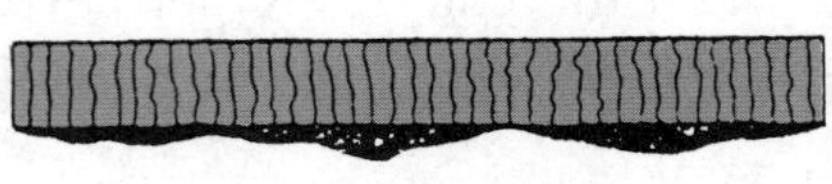

Cutting speed too slow
Rounded and melted top edge
Bottom edge rough. Dross on bottom edge difficult to remove.
Lower part of cut face irregularly gouged.
Heavy scale on cut face

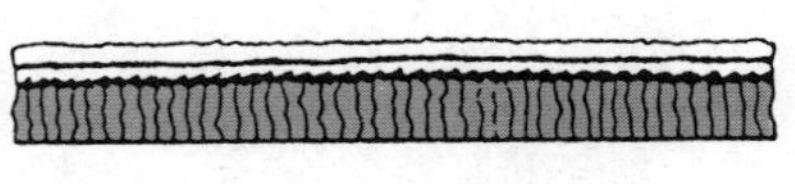

Nozzle too high
Excessive melting of top edge. Undercut at top of cut face

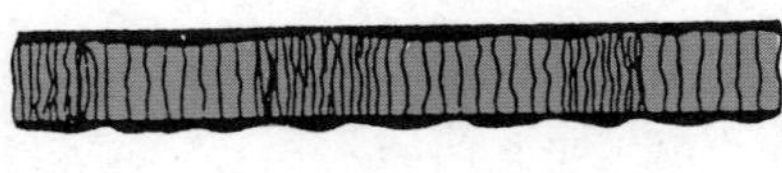

Irregular cutting speed
Wavy cut edge. Uneven drag lines

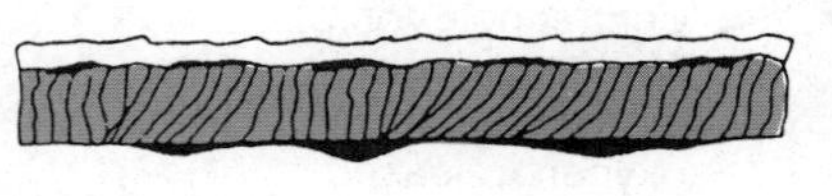

Preheating flame too high
Rounded top edge. Irregular cut edge. Melted metal falling into kerf.
Excessive amount of dross adhering strongly to bottom edge

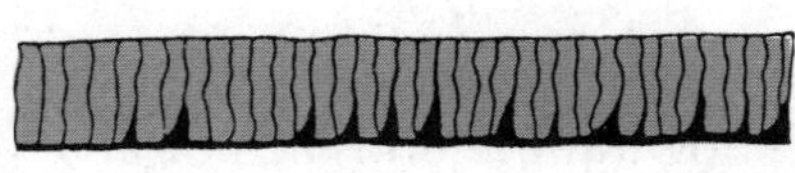

Preheating flame too low
Bad gouging of lower part of cut face.
Cutting speed slow

Figure 10.4 Examination of flame-cut edges.

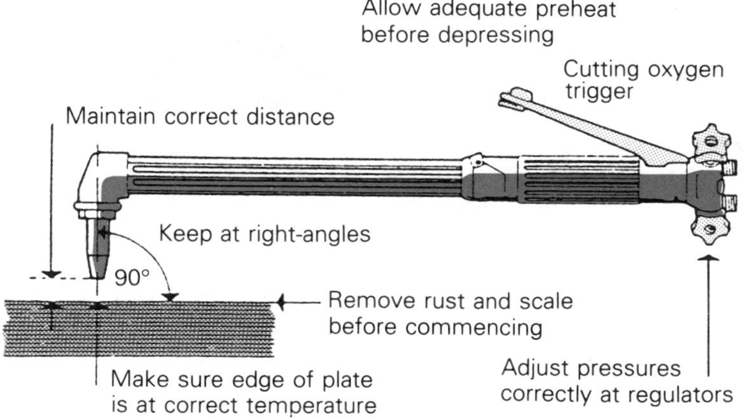

Figure 10.5 Some tips for achieving a good cut.

the iron or steel is not melted. The heat needed to keep the cut going is provided partly by the heating jets and partly by the chemical action.

Blowpipes are usually of the injector type, so that they can be used on both high- and low-pressure systems. The modern type of cutting nozzle has the mixing chamber incorporated in it, so that a 'blowback' usually only goes as far as the nozzle; the high velocity of the gas tends to prevent it from going any further.

The size of the cutting blowpipe varies with the thickness of work; special heavy-duty blowpipes are available. Nozzle sizes also vary to suit different thicknesses of plate.

Cutting machines, in which one or several cutting blowpipes can be employed, are faster and more accurate than hand cutting.

Because cutting is essentially an oxidising process, little or no steel is melted. The **kerf** (the width of cut) should therefore be quite clean, and the top and bottom edges should be square. On examining melted oxides after cutting, it has been found that they contain up to 30 per cent unmelted steel, which has been scoured from the sides of the cut by the high-pressure oxygen stream. This scouring can be seen if the sides of the kerf are inspected, because drag lines will be faintly etched on the faces of the metal. For an incorrect cut, these drag lines will be more pronounced (Figures 10.3 and 10.4).

Figure 10.5 shows some tips for achieving a good cut.

Oxy-fuel gas cutting by hand

It takes a fair amount of skill to maintain a constant rate of travel over the work (Figure 10.6). The general quality of cut produced with a hand-held cutting torch is therefore usually inferior to the quality of cut made with a correctly adjusted cutting machine.

Cutting guides can help to keep the torch on the correct line of cut. A roller attachment can be used to maintain the correct nozzle-to-work distance (Figure 10.7).

Stack cutting can be used to cut more than one plate at once, if the same shape is required (Figure 10.8).

Oxy-fuel gas cutting by machine

Modern cutting machines are capable of making high-quality cuts within close limits. Many machines prepare bevelled edges for welding without

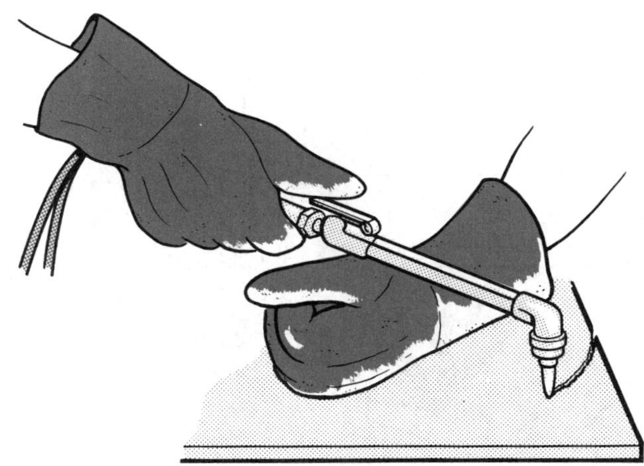

Figure 10.6 Oxy-fuel gas cutting freehand. This can be made much easier by the use of guides and attachments (see Figures 10.7–10.10).

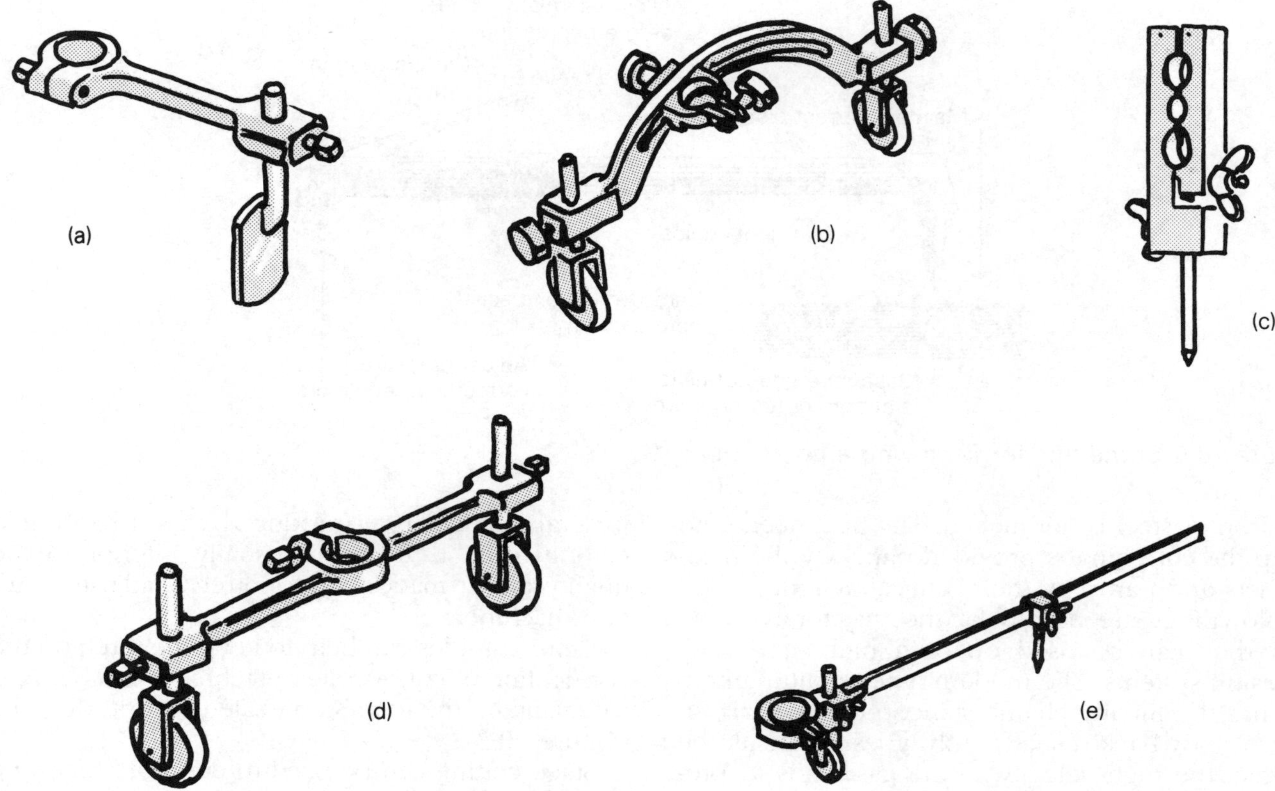

Figure 10.7 **Cutting guides and attachments: (a) spade guide; (b) bevel attachment: (c) small circle guide; (d) roller guide; (e) radius bar for cutting large circles.**

any additional dressing operations being required.

There are many different designs of cutting machine. Some machines have a single cutting torch, while others have many. One design moves the cutting torch or torches above the plate to be cut, while another design keeps the cutting head stationary and moves the work beneath it.

The simplest cutting machine is the **straight-line type**, which consists of a carriage, mounted on a track, containing the cutting torch. The carriage is traversed over the work by a variable-

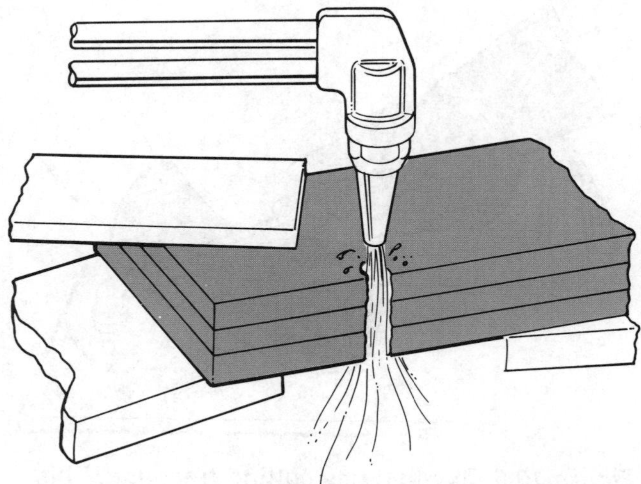

Figure 10.8 **It is possible to cut a stack of plates if they are clamped tightly together.**

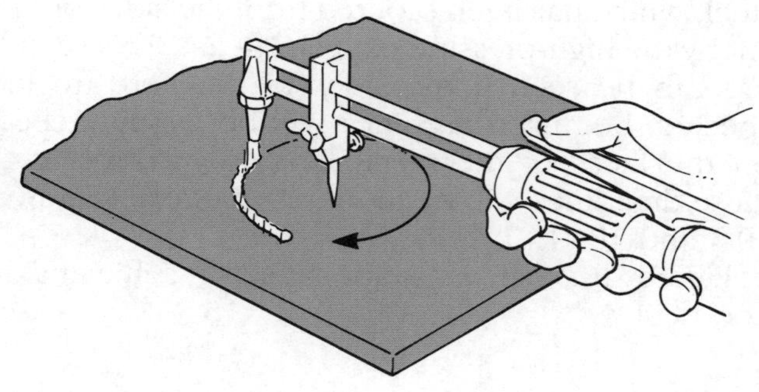

Figure 10.9 **Cutting a small circle using the attachment shown in Figure 10.7(c). Maintain the pivot point in the centre punch mark.**

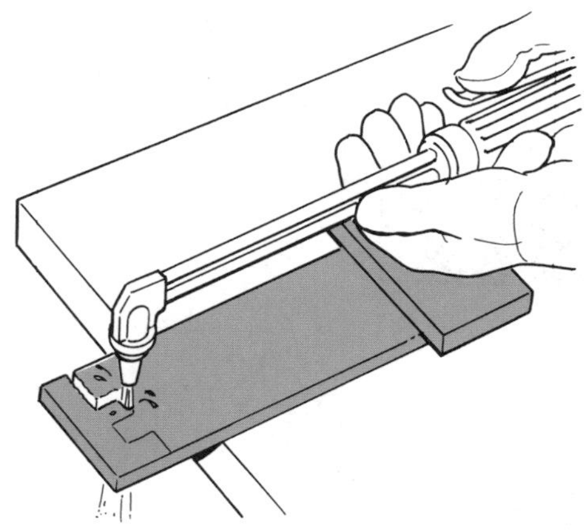

Figure 10.10 **Showing the position of the left hand when cutting out shapes (if right-handed).**

speed electric motor (Figure 10.11).

Other machines, often called **profiling machines**, can guide the cutting head or heads by following a template. Some guiding systems have a magnetic wheel device that will follow the outline of a steel template, while others contain a photo-electric cell that will follow the black outline of a drawing (Figure 10.12).

With all these machines, you should ensure that the work is correctly supported during cutting so that it will not collapse after being cut, thus reducing the risk of injury to the operator or damage to the machine.

Gouging

Gouging is often used to remove defects from welds, to prepare a 'U' groove, or to remove the heads from rusted rivets or bolts. Flame gouging uses a special curved nozzle (Figure 10.13) to modify the oxy-fuel cutting process into a process that will produce a groove in the surface of metal.

A cutting blowpipe is used in conjunction with this curved nozzle, designed to deliver a high volume of oxygen at relatively low velocity.

By using nozzles of different size and by varying the nozzle angle and travel speed, grooves of various width and depth can be produced. Figure 10.14 (a) and (b) shows the different angles required for starting gouging. Once the gouge commences, the angle of the nozzle should be lowered (Figure 10.14 (c), (d)).

Always ensure that sparks fall in a safe area, away from other people and away from anything that may catch on fire. This is particularly impor-

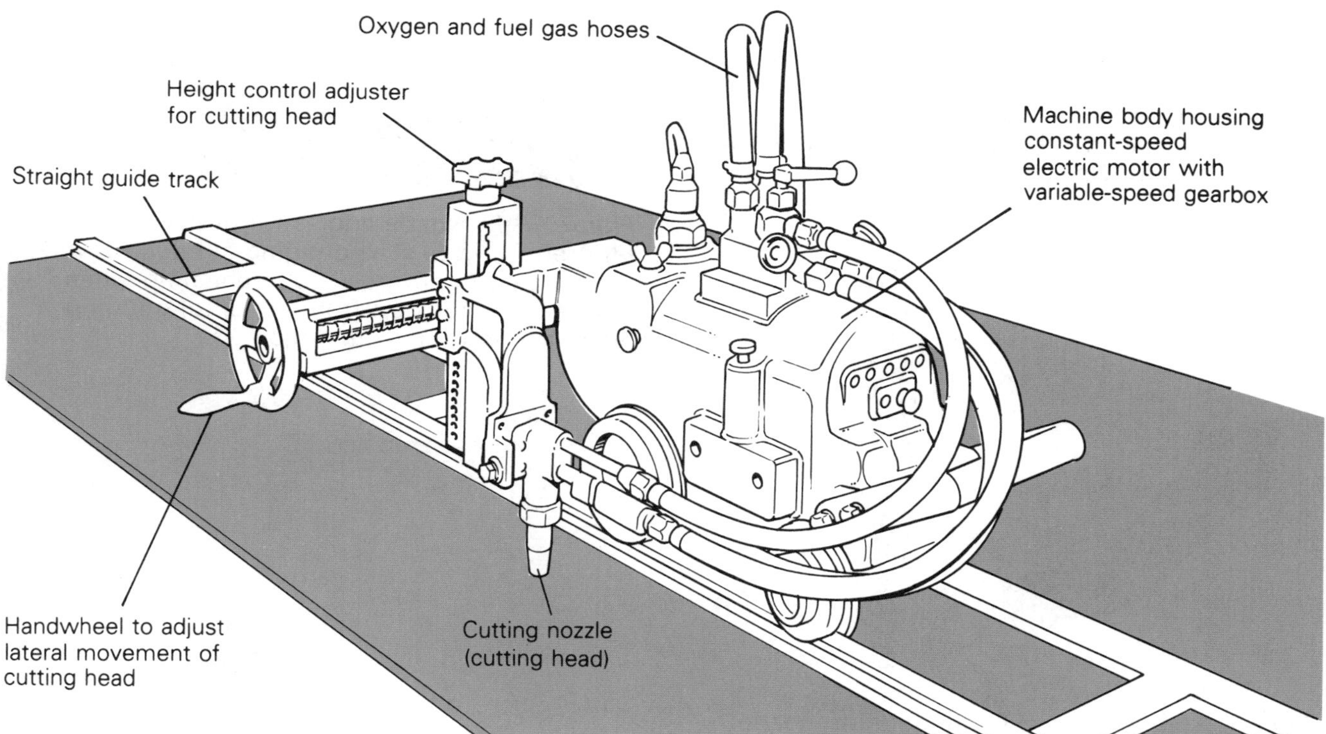

Figure 10.11 Typical straight-line and circle-cutting machine.

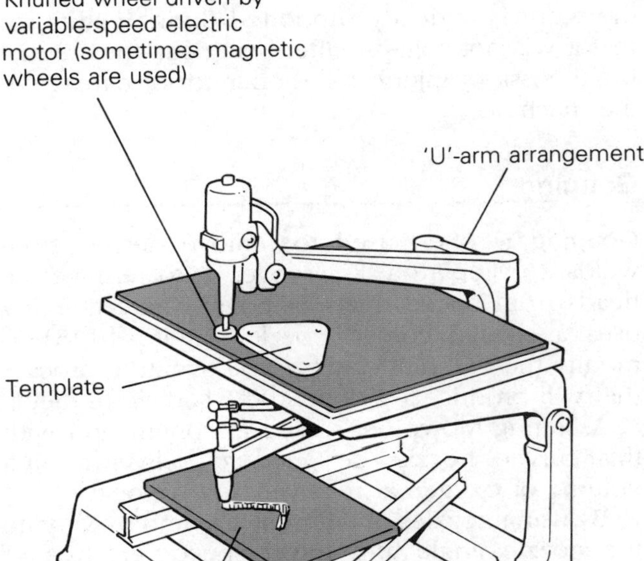

Figure 10.12 'U' arm type of profile-cutting machine. The wheel follows round the template on the upper table; the cutting head moves over the work on the lower table, cutting the same shape as the template. Alternatively a photoelectric cell can be used to follow the black outline on a drawing.

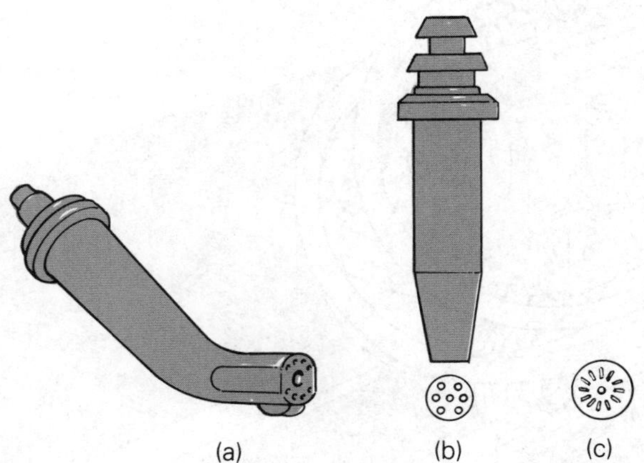

Figure 10.13 (a) Typical flame-gouging nozzle; (b) acetylene cutting nozzle and end face; (c) end face of a propane cutting nozzle.

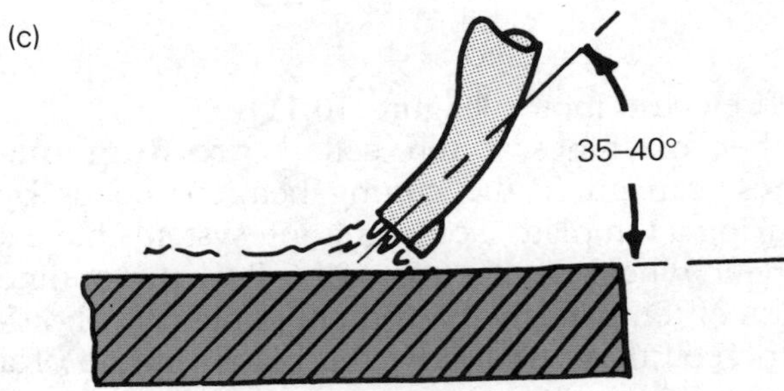

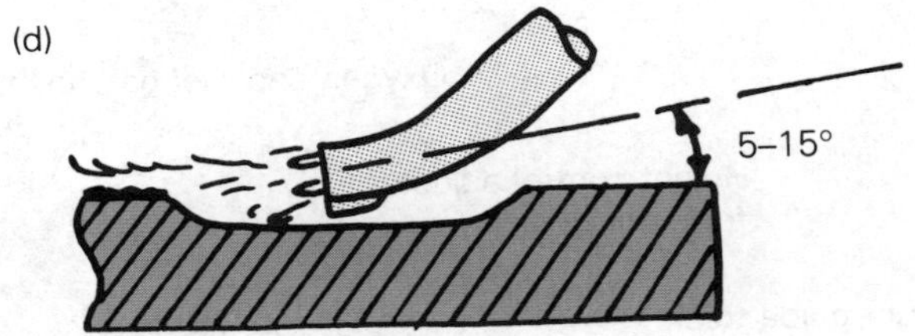

Figure 10.14 Nozzle angles for gouging: (a) preheating to start gouging at edge of work; (b) gouging in progress; (c) preheating when gouge does not start from edge; (d) gouging when not starting from edge.

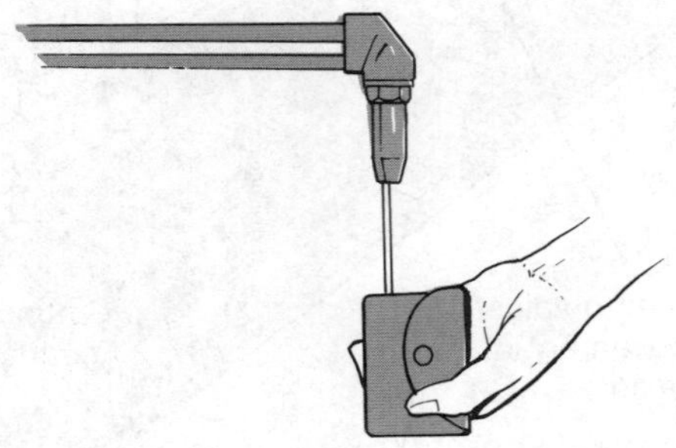

Figure 10.15 Always hold nozzle downwards when cleaning with nozzle reamers.

tant, as the sparks from cutting and gouging operations can travel a considerable distance from the actual workstation. Use nozzle reamers to keep holes clean (Figure 10.15).

The arc–air process

A d.c. arc welding power source is preferred for the arc–air process, although an a.c. power source can be used if suitable electrodes are available. Both d.c. and a.c. power sources should have a continuous rating for the current levels to be used. An output of 450 amperes is required for general-purpose arc–air cutting and gouging.

The electrode holder (Figure 10.16) is fitted with gripping jaws in a self-aligning rotating head. When the trigger is depressed, and the valve in the holder is opened, twin jets of compressed air are emitted parallel to the axis of the carbon electrode. The cable fitted to the electrode holder contains the power cable from the welding power source, and the tube carrying air from the compressor.

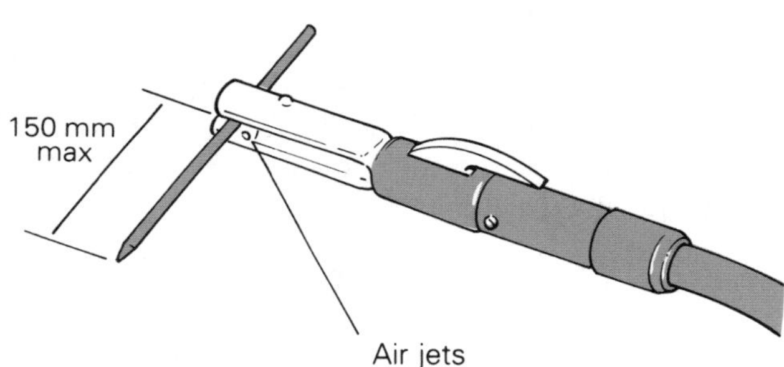

Figure 10.16 Arc–air electrode holder.

The electrodes are made from a mixture of carbon and graphite that has been bonded together and wrapped in a thin layer of copper. This thin copper coating reduces heat radiation and reduces tapering of the electrode. Electrodes for use with a.c. are designed to increase the electron emission and therefore improve the stability of the a.c. arc. Electrodes are made in standard 30 cm (12 in) lengths, in sizes from 4 mm (5/32 inch) to 20 mm (3/4 inch) diameter. The electrode holder should be connected to the positive terminal when using d.c. When the travel speed is correct, the process should give off a smooth and continuous 'hissing' sound (Figure 10.17).

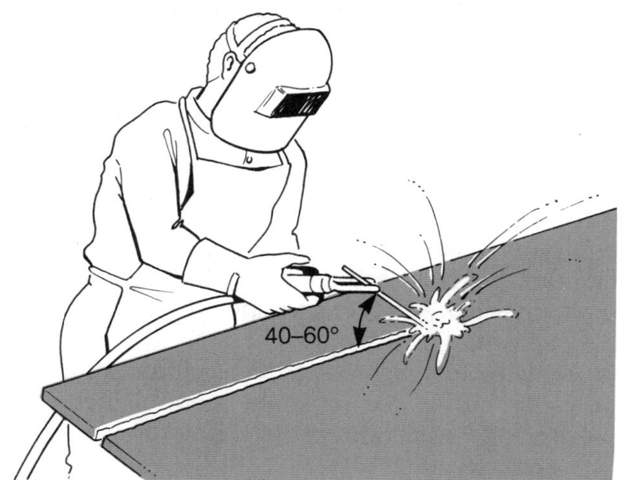

Figure 10.17 Hold the electrode at 40–60° to the plate when cutting. When gouging, start at an angle of 30–40° and then reduce to 20–30° during the gouging operation.

> ▲ Wear full protective clothing including safety boots. When cutting, ensure that the detached portion cannot fall, causing injury. Sparks can travel long distances; make sure they do not fall on anything that could catch on fire.

The oxygen–arc process

Either a.c. or d.c. manual metal arc welding power sources can be used, although d.c. will give a faster cutting speed. An output of up to 300 amperes with continuous rating is desirable. The oxygen supply is normally taken from a cylinder fitted with a high-pressure regulator, as used in the oxy-fuel gas cutting process.

The electrode holder is in the form of a gun (Figure 10.18) with a trigger to control the oxygen valve. The electrode is inserted through an oxygen seal washer, to ensure that there is a gas-tight seal between the oxygen supply tube and the end of the electrode.

Coated tubular steel electrodes are used. The cutting oxygen goes down the tube, with the coating helping to stabilise the arc. The usual sizes of electrode are 5 mm (3/16 inch) with 1.5 mm (1/16 inch) bore and 7 mm (5/16 inch) with 3.5 mm (1/8 inch) bore.

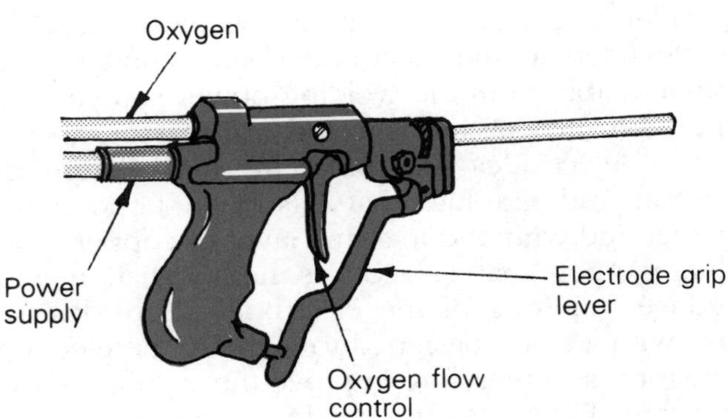

Figure 10.18 Gun electrode holder for the oxygen–arc process.

Portable screens should be used with both the arc–air and oxygen–arc processes. Any cutting guides used with these processes should be electrically insulated from the work. The oxygen valve is kept closed when striking the arc and then opened once the arc is established.

For cutting with oxygen–arc, point the electrode downwards and away from the body at an angle of 55–65° to the surface of the plate, bringing it vertical at the finish of the cut. Keep the heel of the electrode coating in contact with the plate surface. When gouging, commence the gouge with the electrode angle at around 30–40°, lowering it to around 5–15° during the gouging operation. Again, keep the heel of the electrode coating in contact with the plate surface.

The manual metal arc process

The equipment used for manual metal arc welding can be used for cutting and gouging. There are electrodes specifically designed for this purpose, but you can use Class 1 or Class 2 mild steel electrodes that have previously been dipped in water. (Take full protection against electric shock risk.)

When cutting, hold the electrode downwards and away from the body at an angle of 60–70° to the surface of the plate. Strike the arc in the normal manner. When the edge begins to melt, move the electrode down and up in a sawing movement. Make certain that the sawing movement is deep enough to cut through to the underside of the plate and keep the molten metal flowing away by the movement of the electrode and the arc force. When approaching the end of the cut, gradually increase the electrode angle until it is held vertical at the finish of the cut.

For gouging with this method, start with the electrode at around 20–30° and then lower it to around 10–15° once the molten pool has been established. Start the movement of the electrode immediately in the direction of the gouge, using the heat and force of the arc to push the molten metal and slag away. With this method, use a fairly rapid rate of travel, but do not attempt to gouge too deeply; the quantity of slag and molten metal can get out of control and cause difficulties.

Carbon arc cutting

A carbon electrode connected to the negative terminal of a d.c. power source can also be used for cutting operations. The electrode is held at the same angles as for manual metal arc cutting (60–70° during cut, bring to vertical at finish). When currents above 300 amperes have to be employed with this method, a water-cooled electrode holder should be used.

CHECK YOUR UNDERSTANDING

- The precautions and safety equipment in oxy-fuel gas cutting and gouging are the same as those used for gas welding. The precautions and safety equipment for arc cutting and gouging are the same as those employed when arc welding. Extra equipment like that for heavy-gauge welding operations, such as canvas or leather spats to cover the lower legs and feet, may be required for heavy-gauge cutting.
- Nozzles for gas cutting have either six or eight holes, to give six or eight neutral flames for preheating, and one central hole for the high-pressure oxygen.
- Gas cutting is often used to prepare plate edges for welding; gouging is often used to remove defects from welds, to prepare a 'U' groove, or to remove the heads from rusted rivets or bolts.

- There are two operations involved in oxy-fuel gas cutting and gouging:
  1. preheating the metal to be cut to ignition temperature, about 900°C;
  2. oxidising the heated metal with a stream of high-pressure oxygen.
- Various attachments can be used to assist oxy-fuel cutting by hand. However, modern cutting machines are capable of making high-quality cuts within close limits, and give high production rates. Stack cutting can be used to cut more than one plate at once, if the same shape is required.
- There are various arc-cutting processes. These include air–arc, oxygen–arc, the manual metal arc process using special cutting electrodes, and carbon arc cutting.

REVISION EXERCISES AND QUESTIONS

1 What are the two operations involved in oxy-fuel gas cutting?
2 Explain the term 'kerf'.
3 Describe the differences between a cutting nozzle and a welding nozzle.
4 What is meant by 'stack cutting'?
5 Describe two methods of cutting using an electric arc.
6 When might you use a cutting machine instead of a hand cutter?

(Further practice questions can be found on page 202.)

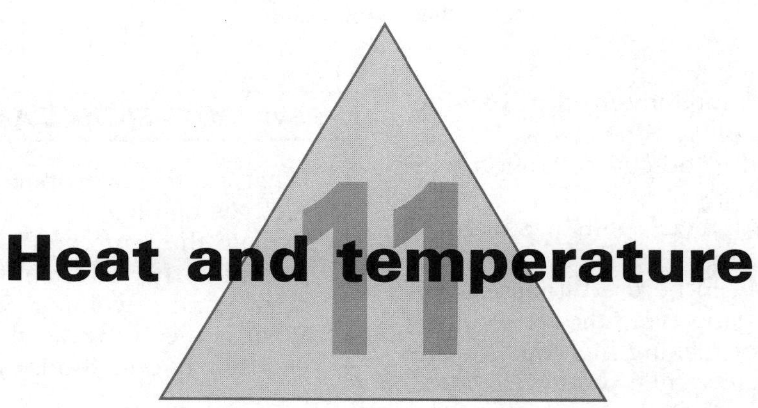

Heat and temperature

Introduction

We have now covered all the main welding techniques that you need to learn about in your studies. Before we move on to look at the applications of these techniques to particular materials, it is worth looking in more detail at what is going on in the welding process.

The next three chapters cover some of the basic science on which welding depends. We shall look at the structure of metals, to try and understand why they behave the way they do. However, we start with the one point on which all welding depends: heat, and its relationship to temperature.

Because fusion welding involves large amounts of heat and high temperatures, you need to understand the differences between heat and temperature.

In the welding workshop, the experienced welder can often judge the temperature of the work by the way the metal changes colour, or by using special crayon sticks that change colour at specific temperatures. For very accurate work, special temperature-measuring instruments called pyrometers can be used.

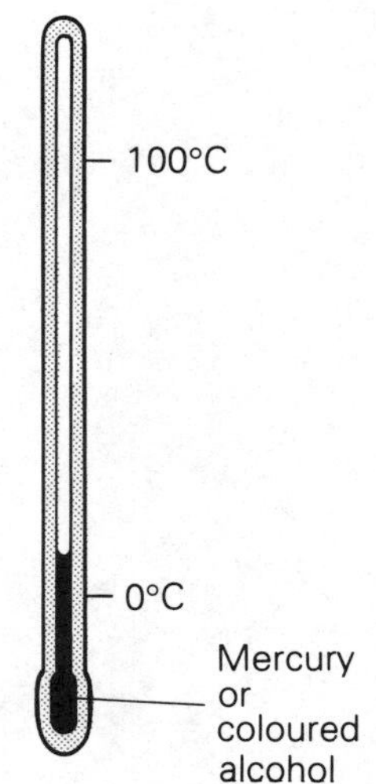

Figure 11.1 A Celsius thermometer.

> The point to remember is that when we measure the **temperature** of a substance, we are *not* measuring the amount of **heat** it possesses.

The molecules (see Chapter 12) in a hot substance move faster than those in a cold one, and temperature is a measurement of the amount of molecular motion in a substance. The amount of heat, however, is related to the mass of a substance or object, as well as to its temperature. A large mass of a substance at a low temperature could contain more heat than a smaller mass of the same substance at a high temperature.

In simple terms, if a pin head was heated to 650°C, the heat given off in a large room would go unnoticed. However, a block of steel 1 metre square at 550°C would be giving out a considerable amount of heat.

Scales of temperature

Figure 11.1 shows a Centigrade or **Celsius** thermometer, named after the Swedish scientist Anders Celsius, who in 1742 put forward his ideas of using the freezing point of water as 0°C and the boiling point as 100°C.

The simple glass thermometer works by the expansion of either mercury or coloured alcohol;

this rises or falls in the narrow tube, which has calibrations along the side. Glass thermometers have a limited range of use and would, of course, melt at welding temperatures.

In winter, when temperatures can fall below zero, they have to be shown on the Celsius scale as minus figures. To avoid this Gabriel Fahrenheit, a Dutch scientist, devised the **Fahrenheit** scale, which places the freezing point of water at 32°F and the boiling point at 212°F (a range of 180°). In 1848, Lord Kelvin suggested that the more logical starting point for a temperature scale would be absolute zero. All other temperatures could be measured from this point in degrees equal in magnitude to degrees Celsius. This scale is now the SI (Système International d'Unités) scale, and the unit of temperature is called the **kelvin** (K). On the kelvin scale, or absolute scale as it is sometimes called, absolute zero is 0 K, the freezing point of water is 273.16 K and the boiling point of water is 373.16 K.

Energy and work

> Energy and work are connected. **Work** is the expenditure of **energy**. They are therefore both measured in the same units.

The SI unit is the **joule** (J), named after James Prescott Joule, the British physicist who showed that different forms of energy could be converted into each other without loss or gain of energy.

Because heat is energy, it is measured in joules. As stated earlier, the amount of heat taken up by a substance depends on its mass and temperature. The final temperature will depend on the substance's **specific heat capacity**. Different substances have different specific heat capacities. You can measure this property by giving a substance of known mass a known amount of heat and measuring its rise in temperature.

For example, a piece of copper will gain 50 K in temperature when receiving the same quantity of heat that will produce a rise of only 5 K in the same mass of water. Copper therefore has a specific heat capacity ten times that of water.

Conduction, convection and radiation

These are the three ways in which heat can travel from one place to another. They are important because they are methods of producing heat in the area to be welded, and you need to understand them to appreciate how a weld loses heat.

Conduction

You have experienced conduction if you have ever burnt your fingers by picking up a piece of hot metal with your hand, or by touching some metal that has just been welded.

Conduction is the flow of heat through solids. If one end of a solid is heated, the molecules at that end will start to vibrate faster. If the heating is continued, this vibrating action gradually moves through the solid. Therefore, if you pick up a piece of metal that has just been welded with your fingers instead of using tongs, the heat will flow into your fingertips and give a burning sensation. The rate at which heat is conducted through a solid is called its thermal conductivity.

In welding, you can best understand the effect of thermal conductivity by considering two com-

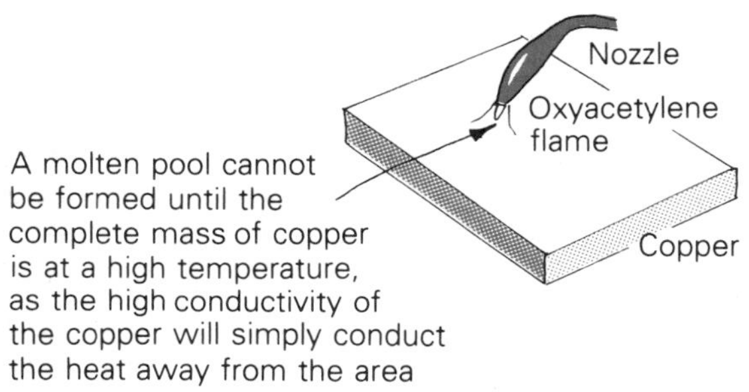

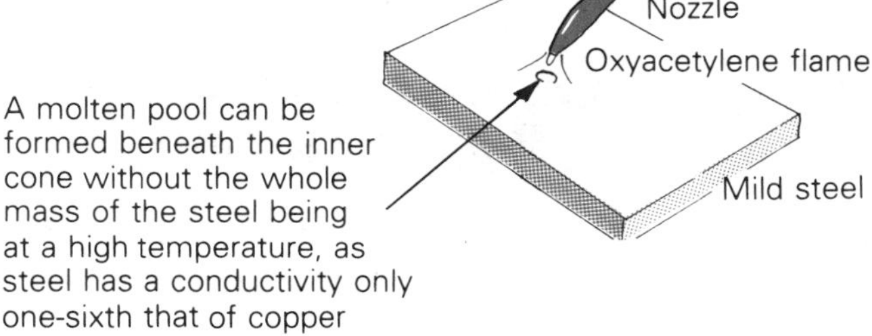

Figure 11.2 The difference between heating a block of copper and a block of steel of equal mass.

ponents of equal mass, one of copper and one of steel (Figure 11.2).

Convection

If you place your hand about 150 mm above a weld that has just been deposited, you will feel a lot of heat rising from it. This kind of heat transfer is known as convection. The new weld warms the air next to it. The air expands and becomes less dense than the surrounding air. It therefore rises from the hot weld and colder air will come in to replace it. This too will be heated and the cycle will be repeated until the weld cools down completely.

Convection also takes place in liquids. As you heat a pan of water, convection currents in the water stir it so that heating will automatically occur evenly throughout the water.

Radiation

A cooling weld will give off radiated heat energy, but the heat is transferred in a different way from conduction and convection.

Probably the best way of explaining radiation is to imagine standing in front of an open log fire. You will feel the warmth, but it is not by convection because the air heated by the fire will be rising up the chimney. It cannot be by conduction either, because there is an air gap between you and the fire. The heat, in this instance, is produced by heat rays from the fire moving through the air and warming everything that absorbs them.

An understanding of these three methods of heat transfer is essential when you are considering practical welding problems, such as heat input to control distortion, methods of controlling cooling rate, fume extraction systems, protective equipment for welders, and methods of cooling welding plant.

Temperature measurement in the welding workshop

The preheat temperatures used when welding certain types of alloy steel and casting must be measured accurately. You can estimate the temperature of low alloy, high tensile steels, medium and high carbon steels by the colours of the oxides on the surface. These are known as **temper colours**. If the surface has been freshly filed, these temper colours will show as listed in Table 11.1.

Table 11.1 Temper colours of surface oxides

Surface colour	Temperature (approximate) in degrees Celsius
Pale yellow	200
Straw	230
Brown	245
Purple	270
Dark purple	280
Blue	340

In the same way, you can estimate the temperature of iron and steels from the colour changes on their surfaces as you heat them with the preheating flame. The colour changes are as listed in Table 11.2.

Table 11.2 Surface colours for iron and steel at various temperatures

Colour	Temperature (approximate) in degrees Celsius
Faint red	500
Blood red	650
Cherry red	750
Bright red	850
Salmon	900
Orange	950
Yellow	1050
White	1200

When certain types of soap are rubbed on to the surface of a hot material they will change colour at definite temperatures. This idea was developed into **temperature-indicating paints** or **crayons**, which can now be purchased to measure temperatures accurate to one degree in stages up to 1370°C (Figure 11.3).

Seger cones are another workshop method of temperature measurement. They are small pyramid-shaped cones of clay and oxide mixtures, made to collapse at specific temperatures from 600°C upwards. When you are using Seger cones to determine a preheat temperature, it is best to use three: one that will melt below the required temperature, one that will melt at the required temperature and one just above the required temperature. In this way, when the first cone melts, you know that the right temperature is approaching, and you can be ready to start welding as soon as the second cone begins to start to bend. You should hold the temperature so that the third cone does not melt (Figure 11.4).

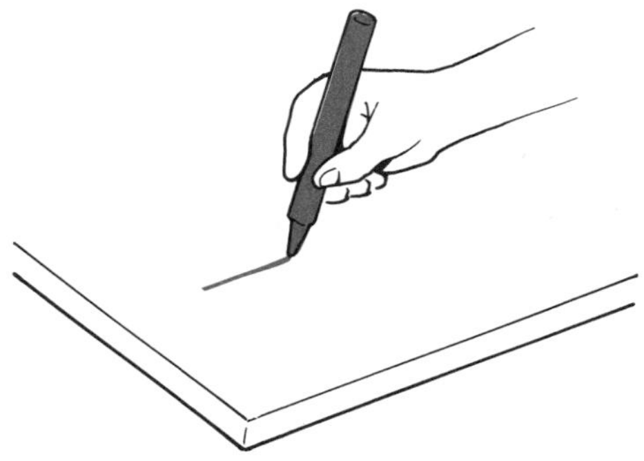

Figure 11.3 A temperature-indicating crayon.

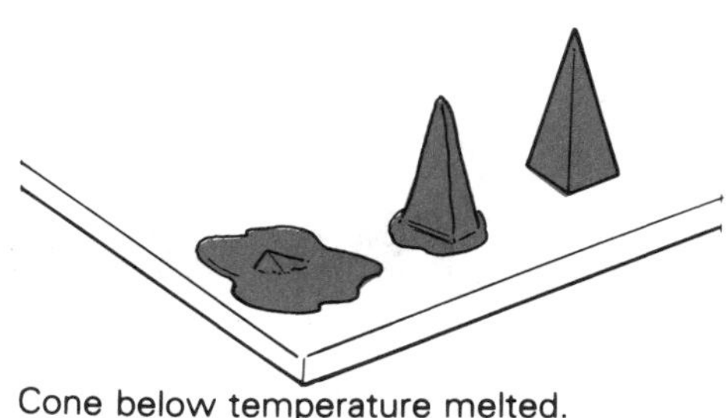

Figure 11.4 Seger cones.

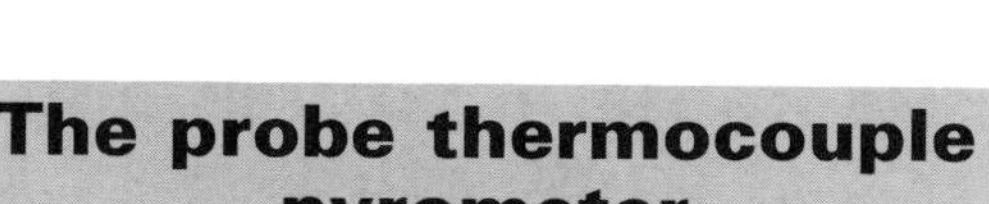

The probe thermocouple pyrometer

This instrument can measure temperatures up to around 1700°C and is a very useful workshop tool. It consists of a probe which is touched to the work. Inside the end of the probe is a joint between two wires made of different metals, known as the hot junction or **thermocouple**. The other ends of these wires are connected to a millivoltmeter to complete the circuit (Figure 11.5).

The electrical resistance of a metallic conductor varies with temperature, and the amount of this variation is different for different metals. So when the hot junction is brought into contact with a hot surface, an electrical pressure (or voltage) is set up, because there are dissimilar metals at the junction. This very small electrical voltage is measured on the millivoltmeter. The greater the temperature, the greater the voltage will be, and the voltage increase is proportional to the temperature rise.

The millivoltmeter can be calibrated in degrees Celsius, and the temperature of the surface can be read off directly.

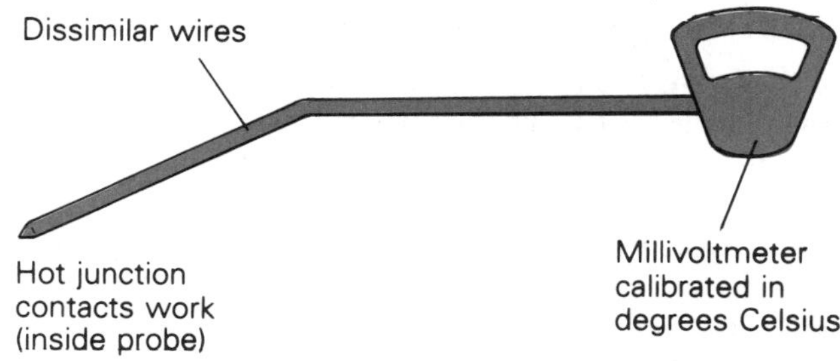

Figure 11.5 Probe thermocouple pyrometer.

CHECK YOUR UNDERSTANDING

- It is important to understand the difference between heat and temperature. If a pin head is heated to a temperature of 650°C, the heat that it gives off in a large room will go unnoticed. However, a block of steel 1 metre square heated to 550°C will give out a considerable amount of heat.
- The Celsius scale of temperature uses the freezing point of water as 0°C and the boiling point as 100°C. Higher temperatures can be measured by simply extending this scale.
- Energy and work are connected; work is the expenditure of energy. They are therefore both measured in the same units; the SI unit is the joule.
- Heat can travel from one place to another by conduction, convection and radiation.

REVISION EXERCISES AND QUESTIONS

1. How is the Celsius temperature scale calibrated?
2. What is the SI unit of energy?
3. State the three ways in which heat can travel.
4. Name two workshop methods of measuring temperature for welding applications.
5. Describe how the probe thermocouple pyrometer operates.

(Further practice questions can be found on page 202.)

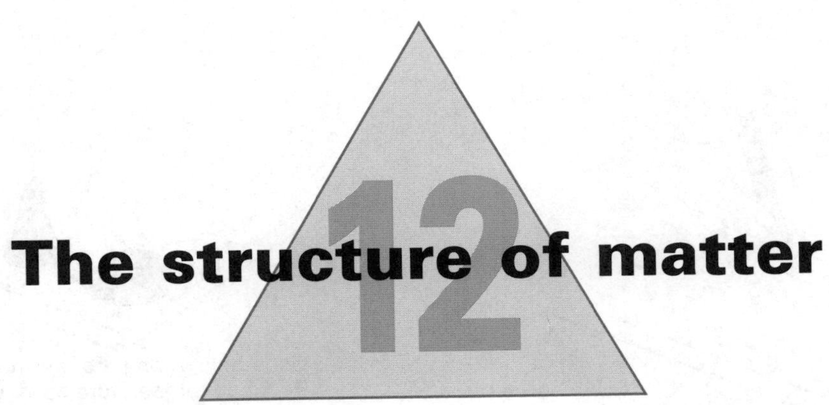

12 The structure of matter

Introduction

This chapter looks at the structure of materials, and at some chemical and physical changes that can take place.

A physical change in a substance is one that does not involve an alteration to its chemical composition.

We look at how some substances, called **elements**, exist in a state that cannot be broken down into a simpler substance. Chemical symbols are given for some of these metallic and non-metallic elements. (A more extensive extract from the table of elements can be found in Appendix 6.)

Elements can be mixed together without chemical action, or combined chemically to form new substances called **compounds**. We need to understand these points, because metallic alloys are made from mixtures or compounds or a combination of both.

It is also important that we understand how everything is made from **atoms** and that these in turn make up a **molecule** of a substance.

The way in which atoms are packed together determines whether a substance is a liquid, solid or gas, and this state can be changed by adding or taking away heat.

Important chemical reactions take place in the oxyacetylene welding flame and these are explained here in words and chemical symbols.

Elements, mixtures and compounds

Elements

> A substance that cannot be broken down into any simpler substances is called an **element**.

There are at present over 100 known elements, 92 of which occur naturally; some others are man-made. Substances such as iron, aluminium, copper, oxygen and argon are all elements.

The surface of the earth consists of approximately:

50%	Oxygen (in compound form)	O
26%	Silicon	Si
7%	Aluminium	Al
4%	Iron	Fe
3%	Calcium	Ca

Some common metallic elements are:

Aluminium	Al
Copper	Cu
Tin	Sn
Lead	Pb
Iron	Fe
Gold	Au
Silver	Ag

These are all pure metals.

Some common gaseous elements are:

Oxygen	O
Nitrogen	N
Hydrogen	H
Helium	He
Argon	A

The earth's atmosphere is made up mostly of nitrogen and oxygen (approximately $\frac{4}{5}$ N and $\frac{1}{5}$ O).

Some common non-metallic elements are:

Carbon	C
Calcium	Ca
Phosphorus	P
Sulphur	S
Silicon	Si

Appendix 6, at the back of this book, lists the atomic weights and melting points of the elements that are of most interest to the welder.

Mixtures

These are produced when two or more elements are mixed together without any chemical reaction taking place.

> A mixture maintains the chemical and physical characteristics of its component parts, such as their appearance, smell and taste.

A mixture can easily be separated back into its component parts. Examples are:

Mixture	*Method of separation*
Salt and water	Boil off water and condense. A residue of salt remains.
Iron and sulphur	Pass a magnet over the mixture to remove iron.
Salt and silica	Add water; the salt will dissolve into the water leaving the silica. Boil water to retrieve salt.

A substance that can be decomposed into two or more elements is known as a **compound**.

Compounds

> If elements combine chemically, they form new substances called compounds.

These can often have completely different chemical and physical properties from the original elements. For example:

hydrogen + oxygen → water
oxygen + silicon → sand
sodium + chloride → salt
carbon + hydrogen → acetylene

Some other common reactions are:

sulphur + iron + heat	→	iron sulphide
carbon + iron + heat	→	iron carbide (cementite)
calcium + carbon + heat	→	calcium carbide

In all these reactions, heat is needed. If no heat was present, the elements would not combine chemically and would remain as a mixture.

Iron + oxygen (Fe + O) will produce the compound Fe_3O_4 (rust) only if water vapour is present. The reaction will take place faster as the temperature is increased.

Metallic alloys

Metals in their pure state are often used when high electrical conductivity or maximum ductility (see Chapter 13) are required. However, mechanical properties such as tensile strength and hardness can be improved by blending metals (and non-metals) together to form alloys. For example:

Copper + zinc = brass
Iron + carbon = steel
Aluminium + copper = duralumin

Various percentages and additions of other alloying elements will vary the properties of alloys considerably.

Alloys can be mixtures of elements, or compounds, or both. The main component of any alloy is metal, but one of the most important alloying elements is a non-metal – carbon, which alloys with iron to form steel. We shall look at the structure of steel in Chapter 14.

Atoms and molecules

Atoms

> Everything is made from **atoms**. The atom is the smallest part of an element that can exist chemically.

Atoms are so small that if one atom was the size of your fingernail, then your hand would be big enough to hold the world (Figure 12.1)!

The atom is not solid, but mainly space, rather like a miniature solar system. It consists of a number

Figure 12.1 If every atom in your hand was the size of your fingernail, then your hand would be big enough to hold the world!

of negatively charged particles called **electrons**, which surround a small dense **nucleus** of positive charge (Figure 12.2). The electrons experience an attraction due to the positive charge of the nucleus and orbit in regions of space round the nucleus. The number of electrons in orbit around the nucleus determines the nature and stability of the atom, and the physical and chemical characteristics of the substance.

Chemical compounds are made up of atoms, and the properties of the compound are determined by the number, nature and arrangement of the atoms.

An atom is made up of three types of elementary particle: protons, electrons and neutrons

The **proton** is a positively charged particle with a charge equal and opposite to the charge on an electron. It forms a constituent part of the nucleus of all atoms. The simplest nucleus is that of the hydrogen atom, which contains one proton.

The **electron's** mass is 1/1836th of that of a proton. The electron's negative charge is equal but opposite to the charge on the proton. Electrons form a cloud around the nucleus and move within the electric field of the positive charge, being arranged in layers or shells. The electronic structure of an atom is responsible for its chemical properties.

The **neutron** has a mass equal to that of the proton but carries no electrical charge. It is a constituent part of all atomic nuclei except that of hydrogen.

The **atomic number** of an element indicates the number of protons in the nucleus. Because an atom in its normal state will exhibit no external charge, which means that the numbers of electrons and protons are equal, the atomic number is the same as the number of electrons in the shells. The atomic number therefore determines the atom's chemistry.

The **mass number** of an element is the total of protons and neutrons in its nucleus. For example, normal forms of carbon have six protons and six neutrons in the nucleus, which gives a mass number of 12.

Isotopes are forms of an element that possess some of the element's chemical properties but differ in mass number. Carbon atoms exist with either seven neutrons or eight neutrons in the nucleus. These are isotopes of carbon, and their mass numbers are 13 and 14 respectively. Heavy hydrogen or deuterium has a mass number of 2; this means that it has one proton and one neutron in its nucleus.

Molecules

A **molecule** is the smallest part of a substance that can exist in a free state and yet exhibit all the properties of the substance.

Molecules are composed of atoms, and the number of atoms in each molecule depends on the substance. For example, iron sulphide has one atom of iron and one atom of sulphur chemically combined. This would be written as:

$$Fe + S \rightarrow FeS$$

Molecules of some elements, such as iron, copper and aluminium, contain only one atom. Such elements are called **monatomic**. Other elements, such as oxygen, hydrogen and nitrogen, are called **diatomic**, because their molecules consist of two atoms. A molecule of the compound carbon dioxide contains three atoms, and other complicated compounds contain many atoms.

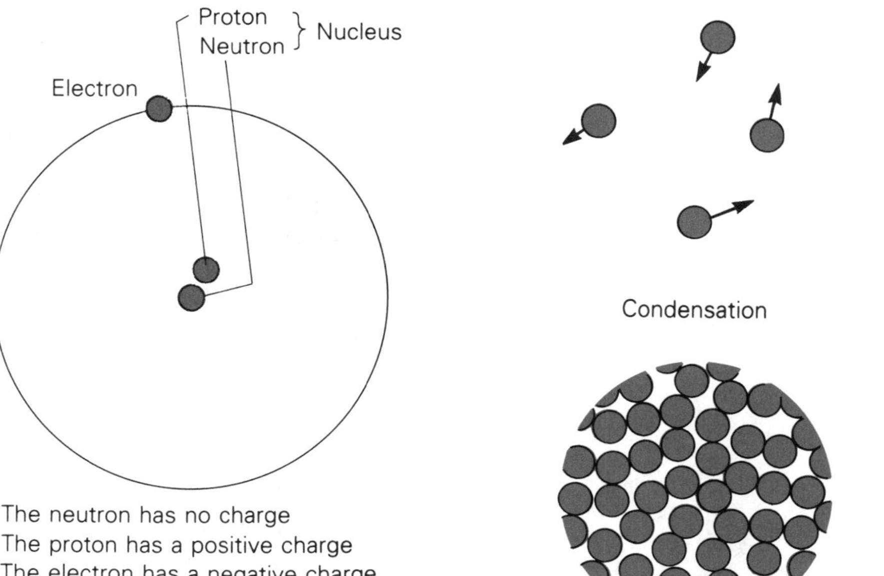

Figure 12.2 The atom.

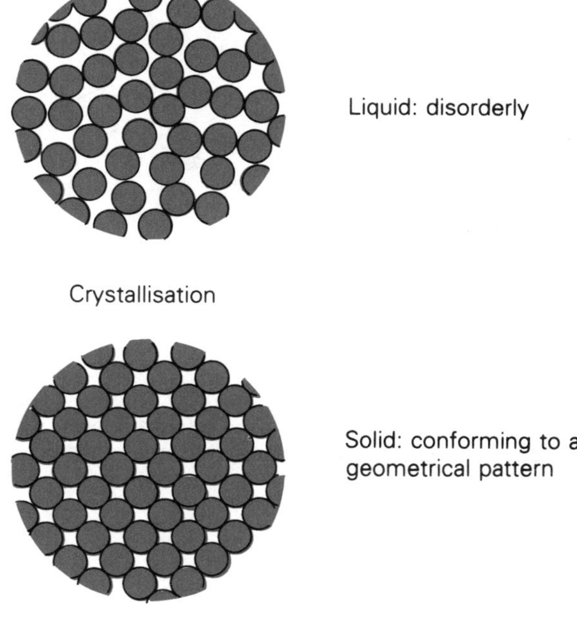

Figure 12.3 The arrangement of atoms in the three states of matter.

If the molecules of a substance can exist separately – water or benzene for example – the substance is said to be **molecular**. However, diamond and sodium chloride are examples of **non-molecular substances**. Their individual molecules cannot exist separately. For example, carbon can exist in different forms, according to the arrangement of its atoms. Graphite and diamond are both made of carbon, but their properties (and their value!) are very different. There is no such thing as an individual molecule of diamond – or, to put it another way, you could consider an individual diamond to be one huge molecule! Another very common example of a non-molecular substance is ordinary salt (sodium chloride).

The three states of matter

The three states of matter – solids, liquids and gases – are closely related. How the atoms are packed together determines whether a substance is a solid, a liquid or a gas (Figure 12.3). We can change a substance from one state to another by either adding or taking away heat; for example, ice to water to steam by adding heat, and steam to water to ice by taking heat away.

> Atoms build up into fixed patterns to form crystals as a liquid solidifies.

There are therefore two types of substance: those with no fixed crystalline pattern, where the atoms are completely disordered, such as **liquids** (known as **amorphous substances**); and those with a fixed crystalline pattern, such as **solids** (known as **crystalline**).

Crystals consist of plane faces (or facets) arranged in a symmetrical pattern. The geometrical pattern in which the atoms build up within the crystal determines its geometrical shape, and this varies from one substance to another (Figure 12.4).

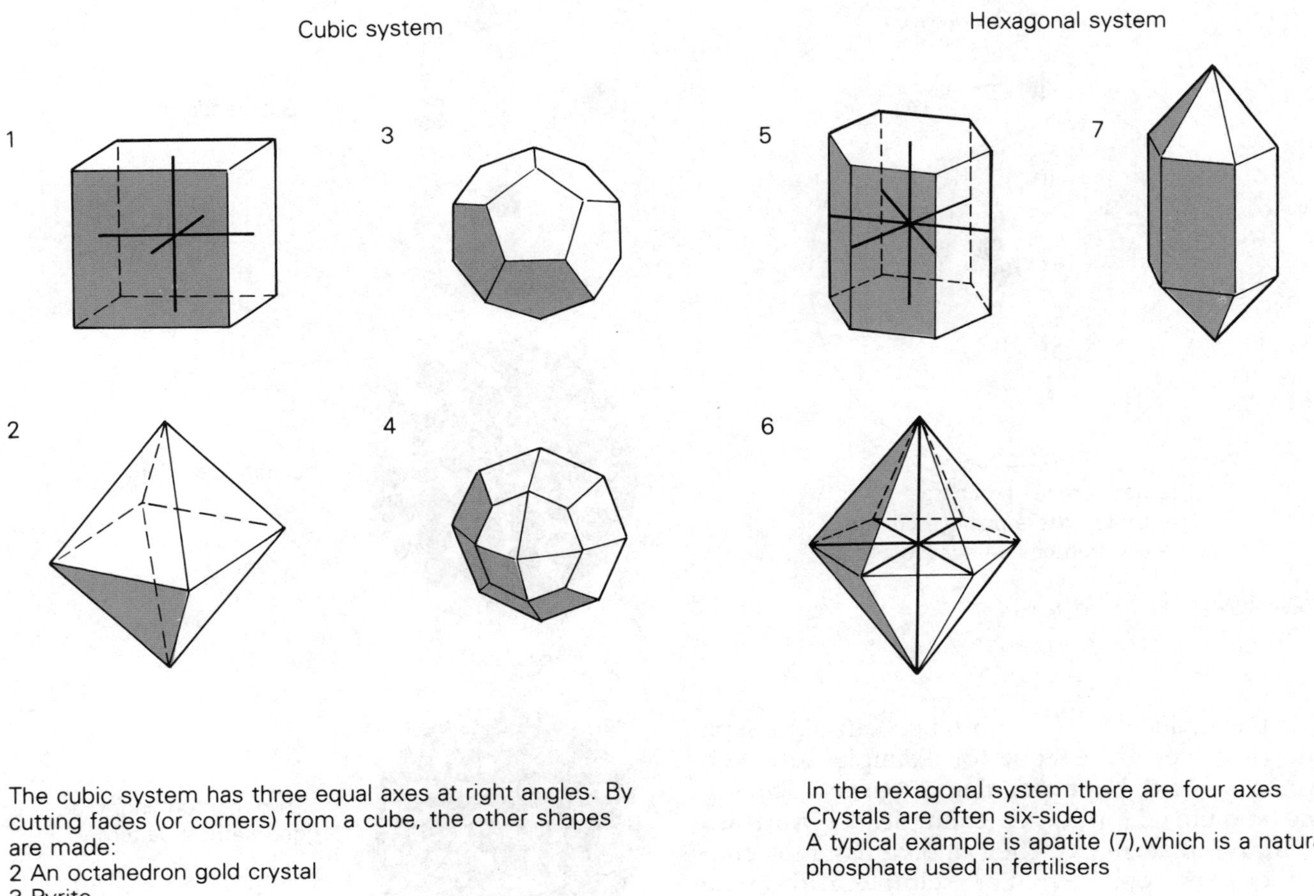

Figure 12.4 **The shapes of crystals are based on their axes of symmetry for the rows of atoms (called space lattices). The faces of the crystal are therefore always aligned with the axes of symmetry.**

Many crystalline formations, such as the ones produced by minerals, are large enough to be seen with the naked eye. The crystalline structures of metals are so small, however, that you can only see them if you view them under high magnification.

The close packing of atoms in a fixed geometrical pattern makes a solid rigid and difficult to distort. If a solid is stressed (below its elastic limit) it will distort, but any distortion will be temporary and the solid will return to its original shape once the stress has been removed.

Some substances that we think of as solids are in fact amorphous. Pitch is a very viscous liquid; if we place a ball of pitch into a container it will, over time, spread to cover the base of the container. New glass is another common example of an amorphous substance. Some metals have amorphous tendencies. For example, lead can creep or flow over time. Creep or flow in metals that have amorphous tendencies will take place faster with increased temperature.

> When a pure liquid starts to solidify, it does so at a set temperature known as the **freezing point**.

Figure 12.5 shows a typical cooling curve for a pure metal. The temperature drops steadily over a period of time, once the heat is taken away, until the freezing point is reached. At this point, the atoms begin to arrange themselves into set geometrical patterns. These atomic patterns are called

space lattices and they build up to form the crystals of the solid. This process of the atoms' building up to form the crystals gives off heat, and so the cooling curve will stay at the same temperature until the process is complete and freezing ends. The cooling curve will then begin to show a loss in temperature with time down to room temperature.

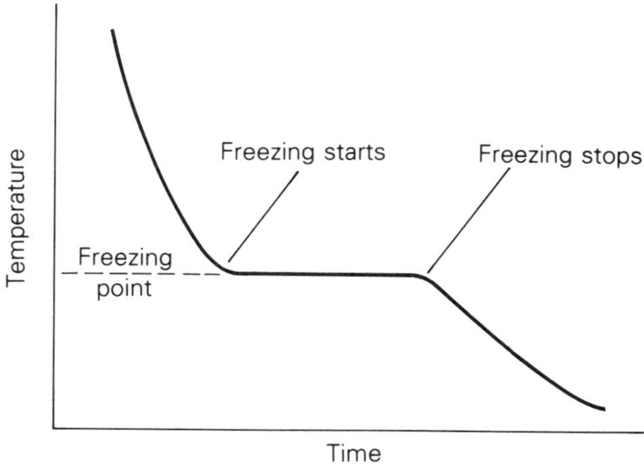

Figure 12.5 Typical cooling curve for a pure metal.

The oxyacetylene welding flame

Before we move on to look in more detail at the structure of metals, it is worth first looking at a chemical reaction that is extremely important in welding: the combustion of acetylene and oxygen in the oxyacetylene welding flame.

Acetylene is composed of carbon and hydrogen (C_2H_2). It normally burns in air with a black smoky flame. The smoke is caused by incomplete combustion of the carbon:

$$\text{acetylene} + \text{oxygen} \rightarrow \text{carbon} + \text{water}$$
$$2C_2H_2 + O_2 \rightarrow 4C + 2H_2O$$

However, if a special burner is used, almost complete combustion can be obtained. The acetylene will burn with a very brilliant flame, because of the glowing carbon.

When acetylene and oxygen are passed through a welding blowpipe, they mix before reaching the nozzle. When this mixture is made up of equal volumes of the two gases, then complete combustion can take place when the mixture is ignited with the addition of $1\frac{1}{2}$ volumes of oxygen from the surrounding atmosphere to form a neutral flame (Figure 12.6).

The process of combustion occurs in two stages:

1. The first stage takes place in the blue, luminous **inner cone**, which is well defined when the flame is correctly adjusted. In this region, the acetylene combines with the oxygen supplied, forming carbon monoxide and hydrogen:

   $$\text{acetylene} + \text{oxygen} \rightarrow \text{carbon monoxide} + \text{hydrogen}$$
   $$C_2H_2 + O_2 \rightarrow 2CO + H_2$$

   The temperature of this part of the flame, measured just in front of the inner cone, is approximately 3250°C.
2. The second stage of combustion is in the external zone, called the **outer envelope**. In this region, carbon monoxide burns and forms carbon dioxide, and the hydrogen that is formed from the first reaction combines with oxygen to form water:

   $$\text{carbon monoxide} + \text{hydrogen} + \text{oxygen} \rightarrow \text{carbon dioxide} + \text{water}$$
   $$CO + H_2 + O_2 \rightarrow CO_2 + H_2O$$

With this reaction, the combustion is complete. The chief products are carbon dioxide and water, which is turned to steam.

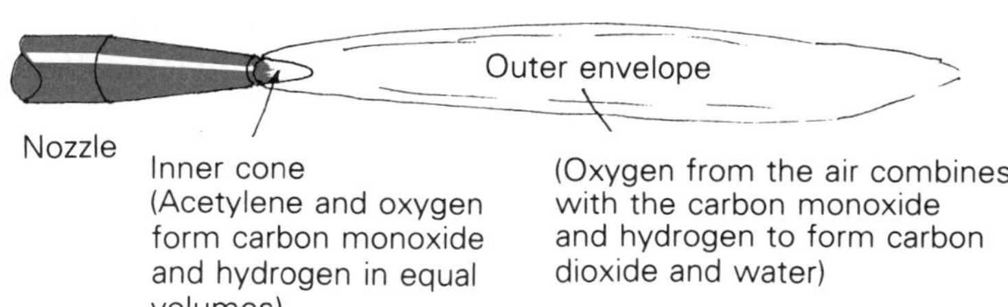

Figure 12.6 The oxyacetylene flame.

The complete reaction can be summarized as follows:

acetylene	+ oxygen (burner)	+ oxygen (air)
$2C_2H_2$	$+ 2O_2$	$+ 3O_2$
→	carbon dioxide	+ water
→	$4CO_2$	$+ 2H_2O$

Note that we have had to multiply both sides of the equation by 2 to make it balance, because we can't have $1\frac{1}{2}$ molecules of oxygen!

The oxyacetylene flame is a strong reducing agent (a reducing agent removes oxygen from a substance), as it absorbs oxygen from the air into the outer envelope. This is another benefit of using this flame for welding purposes, for as well as having the highest working temperature, it also greatly reduces the tendency to form oxides while welding.

For complete combustion, it is usual to have equal amounts of oxygen and acetylene being consumed. If there is more acetylene than oxygen, then combustion will be incomplete and the flame will give off free carbon. This type of flame is known as the carbonising or **carburising flame**.

If more oxygen is supplied than acetylene, then there is an excess of the amount required for complete combustion, and the flame is called an **oxidising flame**.

When welding low-carbon steel, the **neutral flame** is used, with equal amounts of oxygen and acetylene. For other applications, you may need to use either an oxidising or a carburising flame (see Chapter 4).

The temperature of the oxyacetylene flame is compared with the temperatures of other welding flames in Table 12.1. The metal arc has been measured at 6000°C and higher, depending on the type of arc.

Table 12.1 Approximate temperatures of various flames

Oxyacetylene	3250°C
Oxybutane (Calorgas)	2815°C
Oxypropane (liquefied petroleum gas, LPG)	2810°C
Oxymethane (natural gas)	2770°C
Oxyhydrogen	2820°C
Air–acetylene	2320°C
Air–methane	1850°C
Air–propane	1900°C
Air–butane	1800°C

CHECK YOUR UNDERSTANDING

- A substance that cannot be broken down into any simpler substances is called an element. A substance that can be decomposed into two or more elements is known as a compound.
- The basic structure of matter is described in terms of atoms and molecules.
- An atom is the smallest part of an element that can exist chemically.
- Matter can exist as either solid, liquid or gas.
- Atoms build up into a fixed pattern to form crystals as a liquid solidifies.
- Substances in which the atoms are completely disordered, such as liquids, are called amorphous. Those with a fixed crystalline pattern, such as solids, are called crystalline.
- The close packing of atoms in a fixed geometrical pattern makes a solid rigid and more difficult to distort.
- Some so-called solids can have amorphous tendencies. For example, lead can, over a period of time, creep or flow. Creep or flow in metals will take place faster with increased temperature.
- The oxyacetylene flame burns in two stages. The first stage takes place in the blue, luminous zone, known as the inner cone. The second state is in the external zone, called the outer envelope.

REVISION EXERCISES AND QUESTIONS

1. What is an element?
2. Name the three states in which matter can exist.
3. A substance with no fixed crystalline pattern is known as ________ .
4. Name one solid that can have amorphous tendencies.
5. How many stages of combustion are there in the oxyacetylene flame?

(Further practice questions can be found on page 202.)

13 The properties and structure of metals

Introduction

Having looked at the structure of materials in general, we now need to look more closely at the structure of metals, and at what happens when metals are welded. This will help you to appreciate the care that is needed when you are performing welding operations, and why you have to use different techniques and procedures with different metals.

However, first we need to look at the overall properties of metals, so that we can understand how these properties are affected by the details of the structure.

The properties of metals

Different metals have different mechanical properties. These properties determine how metals behave in use. The mechanical properties of interest to the engineer are described below.

Ductility

A ductile metal is one that can be easily drawn into a rod or a wire (Figure 13.1). A metal's ductility is determined by the amount it will stretch, lengthwise, before it becomes brittle and fails.

For a metal to be ductile, the molecules must have a great attraction for each other after the yield point (see definition later in this chapter) has been passed. As the molecules have a greater attraction for each other when cold, metals will be more ductile when cold. This is why wires and rods for the welding industry are drawn in the cold state.

Plasticity

This measures a metal's ability to be formed into a specified shape without fracturing, and to remain in that shape once the load has been removed. Plasticity usually increases with rise in temperature. Very few metals are plastic in the cold state, so heat is normally used when forming, to increase plasticity. For example, iron and steel are difficult to bend when cold, but bend easily when red hot. There are odd exceptions to this, when an increase in temperature can cause brittleness (see below) in some metals. Wrought iron, for example, is plastic, but can sometimes break (because of impurities) when red hot.

Brittleness

This is the opposite of plasticity. It refers to a metal's tendency to break suddenly when under load, without any appreciable deformation. Many metals in their cast state will fracture when subjected to a large enough impact. In some metals, an increase in temperature can reduce brittleness, while in others it can increase it. For example,

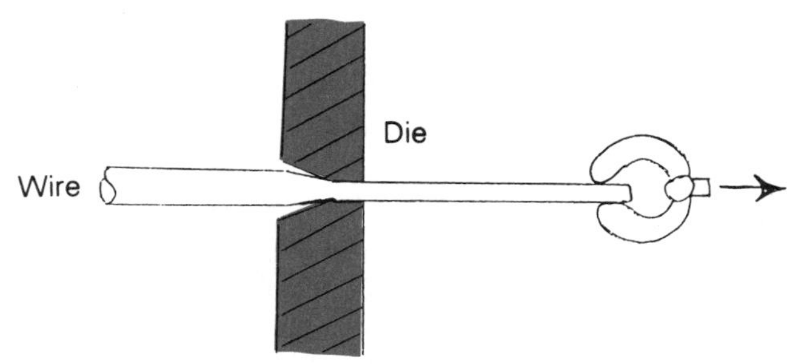

Figure 13.1 Wire needs to be ductile in order to be drawn through a die.

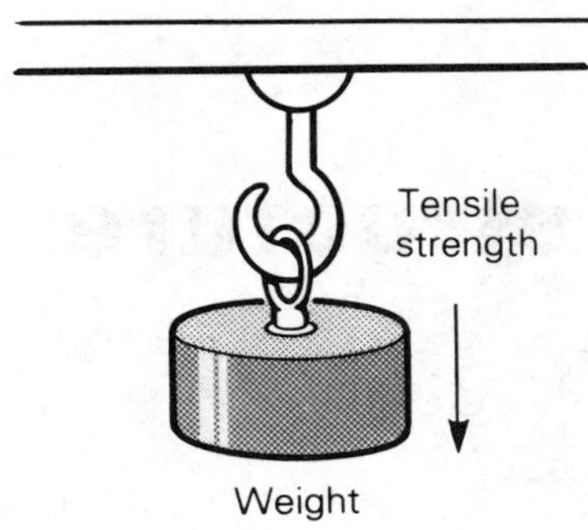

Figure 13.2 Tensile strength.

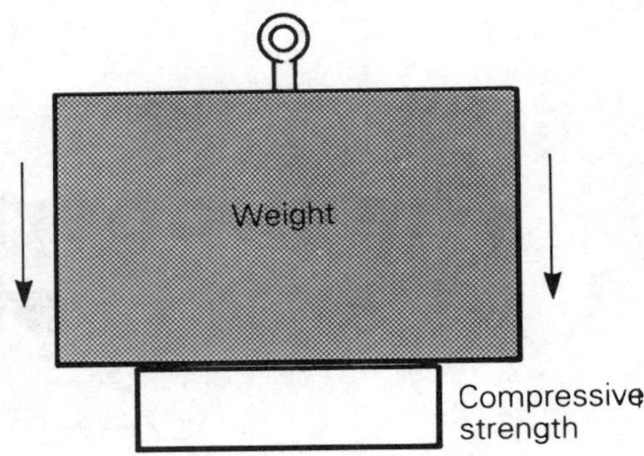

Figure 13.3 Compressive strength.

copper is a ductile metal, but it becomes brittle near its melting point. In general, most metals become less brittle when you apply heat to them. You should take special care when welding brittle metals, because of their lack of ductility.

Malleability

This property allows a metal to be compressed without failure. The metal can therefore be permanently flattened or stretched by hammering or rolling. The more malleable a metal is, the thinner the sheets into which it can be formed. Metals such as iron and steel become much more malleable with increased temperature. Copper is very malleable except near its melting point. Zinc is only malleable between 140°C and 160°C. Any impurities will reduce malleability. A rivet needs to be made of a malleable material in order to withstand the hammering.

Here is a list of some metals in order of decreasing malleability:

Gold	Au
Silver	Ag
Aluminium	Al
Copper	Cu
Tin	Sn
Lead	Pb
Zinc	Zn
Iron	Fe

Hardness

This is usually defined as a metal's ability to resist indentation or abrasion. The measurement of hardness is usually based on a metal's resistance to the indentation of either a hardened steel ball (the **Brinell hardness test**) or a diamond (the **Vickers** or **Rockwell hardness tests**). Abrasion tests are sometimes used, as in the shot- and sand-blasting industries, for example.

Hardness can be increased by deformation caused by cold working. This is known as **work-hardening**. In steels, carbon is the main hardening element, and in many ferrous alloys high levels of hardness can be obtained by heating the alloy to a high temperature followed by rapid cooling.

Tensile strength

This measures a metal's ability to withstand a stretching load without breaking (Figure 13.2). Another name for tensile strength is **tenacity**.

Toughness

This is a combination of ductility and tenacity. It is the property that enables a material to resist fracture by bending, twisting or shock.

Compressive strength

This is the property that enables a metal to withstand compressive loading without fracture (Figure 13.3).

Shear strength

This measures a metal's ability to withstand loads that are not in the same line of force (offset loads) (Figure 13.4).

Impact strength

This measures a metal's ability to withstand impact (Figure 13.5).

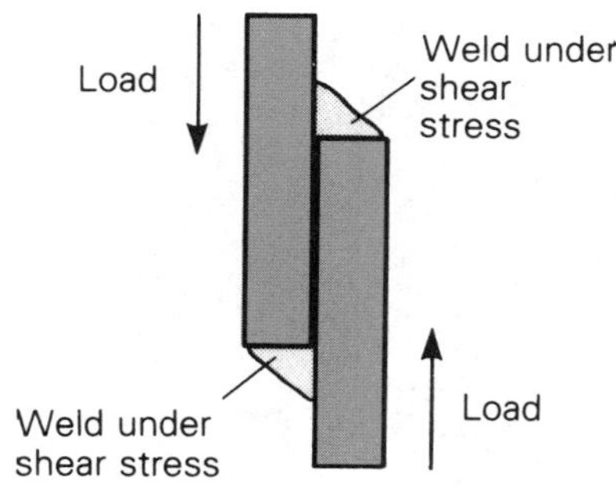

Figure 13.4 Shear strength.

Elasticity

This measures a metal's ability to deform under load and then return to its original shape once the load has been removed. A spring is a good example of elasticity.

Stress–strain and tensile strength

A tensile testing machine is specially designed to pull specimens of specified dimensions to breaking point in order to determine some of the metal's properties.

When the specimen is under tensile stress and the load is gradually increased until breaking point occurs, then the specimen will pass through certain phases. These phases can be shown by plotting a **stress–strain curve**. The curve is found by taking a number of load (stress) and extension (strain) readings and plotting stress against strain.

Figure 13.6 shows a typical stress–strain curve for a ductile material such as low-carbon steel. From A to B, the straight line indicates that the extension is proportional to the load. Between these points, the material still retains its elasticity, so that if the load is removed the specimen will return to its original length.

> If the extension (strain) is proportional to the applied load (stress), the metal is said to have obeyed **Hooke's law**.

For example, if the stress increases by 50 per cent, the strain will also increase by 50 per cent, producing a straight line, which will indicate the elastic range of the material.

$$\text{Stress} = \frac{\text{Load}}{\text{Cross - sectional area}}$$

$$\text{Strain} = \frac{\text{Extension of gauge length}}{\text{Original gauge length}}$$

$$\text{Hooke's law} = \frac{\text{Stress}}{\text{Strain}} = E$$

where E is a constant known as **Young's modulus**.

From B to C, the metal extends with no increase in load. The specimen is said to have taken **permanent set**; if the load is removed at this stage, the metal will not return to its original length. This is known as the **yield point**.

From C to D the extension is no longer proportional to the load. If the load is removed, little or

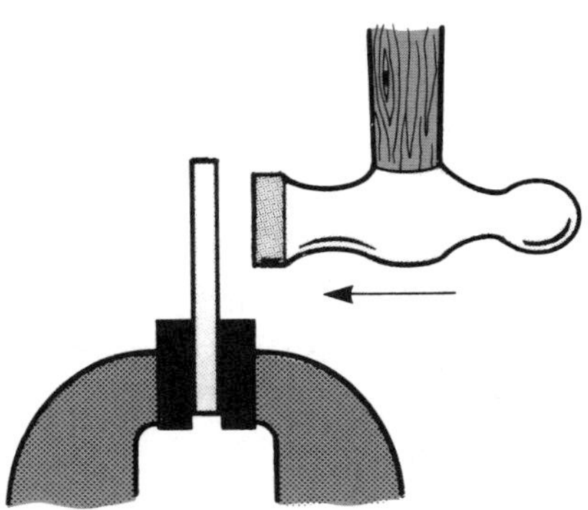

Figure 13.5 Impact strength.

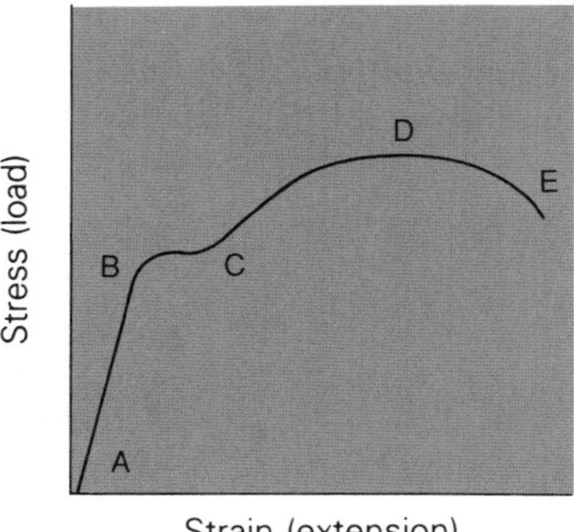

Figure 13.6 Stress–strain curve for a ductile material.

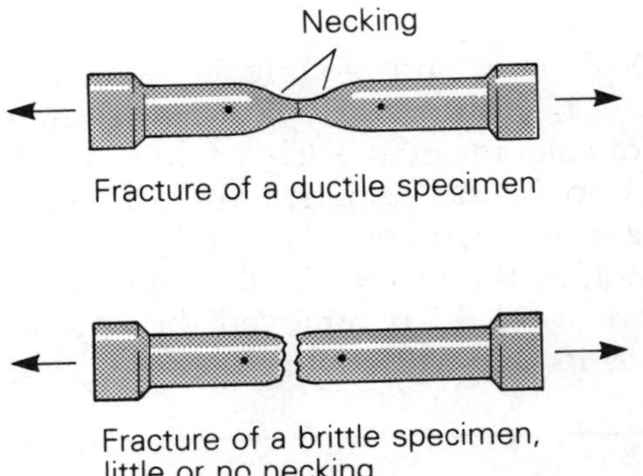

Figure 13.7 **Comparing the failure of a ductile specimen and a brittle specimen after loading.**

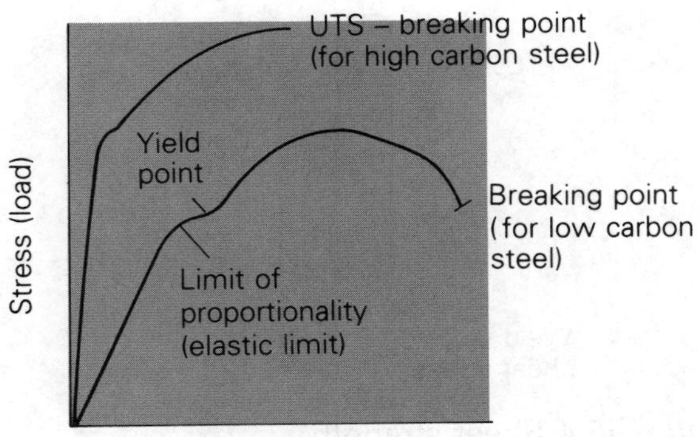

Figure 13.8 **Comparing the stress–strain curves of a high-carbon steel and a low-carbon steel.**

no spring-back will occur. In this stage the metal is said to be **plastic**.

Point D is the **ultimate tensile stress** of the material and point E represents the **breaking point** (or fracture point). From D to E the material appears to continue stretching under reduced load. In fact, the specimen, because it is a ductile material, is thinning out (necking), until it finally breaks at point E.

To calculate the **ultimate tensile strength** (UTS) of the metal, the maximum load indicated on the stress–strain curve (D) is divided by the original cross-sectional area. The UTS is mainly of use at the design stage.

The **yield stress** is calculated by taking the load at point B and dividing by the original cross-sectional area of the specimen. It is usual for designers to work at 50 per cent of this figure to give a 'safety factor'.

The **elongation percentage** is found by taking the increased length at fracture and dividing it by the original length. The resulting figure is expressed as a percentage and is an accurate indication of the material's ductility.

A brittle material will show little or no 'necking' and will fracture in a brittle manner, usually with a bang (Figure 13.7). Figure 13.8 compares the stress–strain curve for a high-carbon steel with that of a low-carbon steel. It shows that the carbon steel:

1. has a longer line of proportionality (elasticity);
2. indicates a higher yield point load;
3. has a higher ultimate tensile strength.
4. shows less elongation;
5. has its UTS and breaking point together.

This comparison shows that an increase in hardness will normally produce an increased tensile strength, but a reduction in ductility.

For certain welding tests, specimens can be machined entirely from weld metal. Figure 13.9 shows an example of an all-weld-metal specimen. In this specimen:

$$\begin{aligned}\text{Gauge length} &= 5.65\sqrt{\text{cross-sectional area}}\\ &= 5.65\sqrt{78.55}\\ &= 5.65 \times 8.862\\ &= 50\end{aligned}$$

Figure 13.10 shows an example of a tensile test specimen including plate material and weld. De-

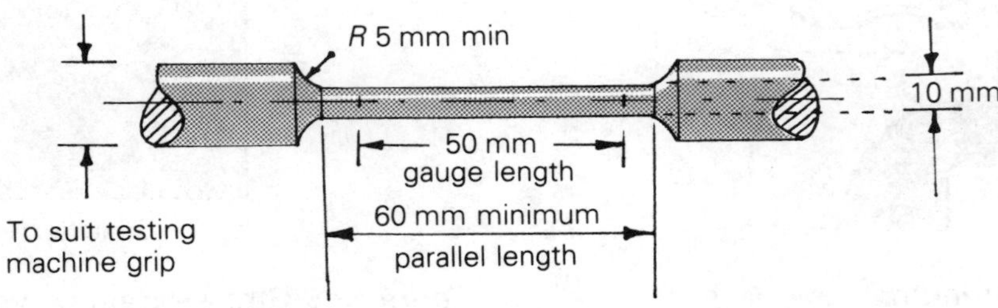

Figure 13.9 **An all-weld-metal test specimen.**

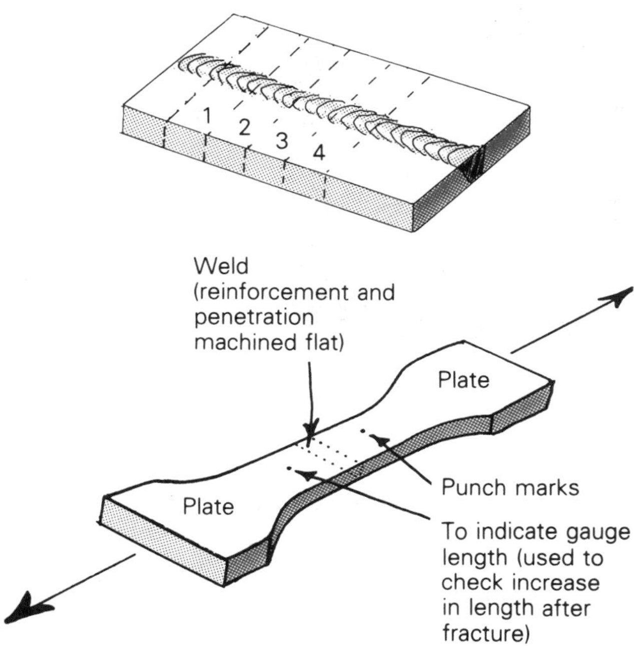

Figure 13.10 A tensile test specimen including plate material and weld.

pending on the code, sections 1 and 3 can be used for tensile specimens, and sections 2 and 4 can be used as bend test specimens.

Always check exact dimensions of tensile specimens against the requirements of the welding code or standard that you are working to.

The structure of metals

There are three main types of structure into which metallic elements (metals) crystallise. The three space lattice patterns in Figure 13.11 show graphical representations of the orderly geometric patterns into which the atoms arrange themselves on cooling from the liquid to the solid state.

The **body-centred cubic** structure has nine atoms, one at each corner of the cube and one at the centre. This crystal pattern is found in such metals as iron, molybdenum, chromium, tungsten and vanadium.

The **face-centred cubic** structure, as its name implies, has an atom in the centre of each face. Typical metals with this space lattice pattern are aluminium, copper, nickel, lead, platinum, gold and silver.

The **close-packed hexagonal** structure is more tightly packed than the first two. Cadmium, bismuth, magnesium, cobalt, titanium and zinc are among the metals that have this type of crystalline structure.

Generally, metals with the face-centred lattice structure are ductile, plastic and workable. Metals with the body-centred structure have higher strength with lower cold-working properties. Metals with the close-packed hexagonal lattice lack plasticity and cannot be cold worked.

In a pure metal, these individual crystals will start to form at many centres (or **nuclei**) throughout the cooling material. The process starts with one unit of the crystal lattice and rapidly builds up with the addition of atoms and lattice structures into a crystal framework called a **dendrite** (Figure 13.12).

From the dendrite, arms of space lattices start to grow in other directions, giving an appearance similar to a fir tree with the growth of its twigs and branches. The dendrite is sometimes called a fir-tree crystal because of this.

As the temperature continues to fall, the dendrite increases in size until its arms come into contact with other similar structures. At this point growth stops in that direction and solidification begins to take place between the arms of the dendrite. This solidification continues until the crystal is formed. Normally there is no trace of the original dendrite.

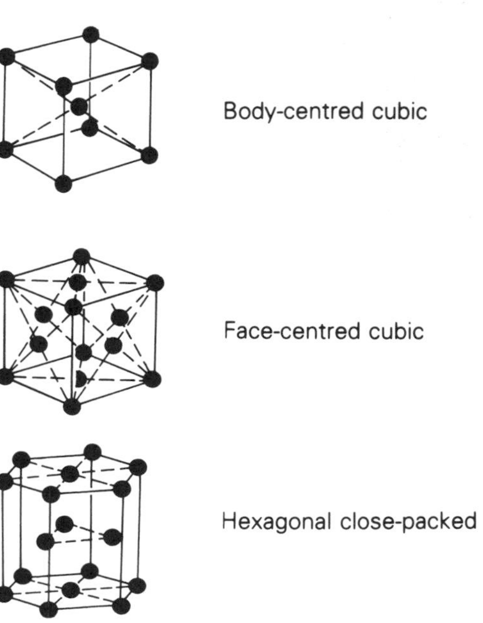

Figure 13.11 The three main types of lattice structure into which metallic materials arrange themselves.

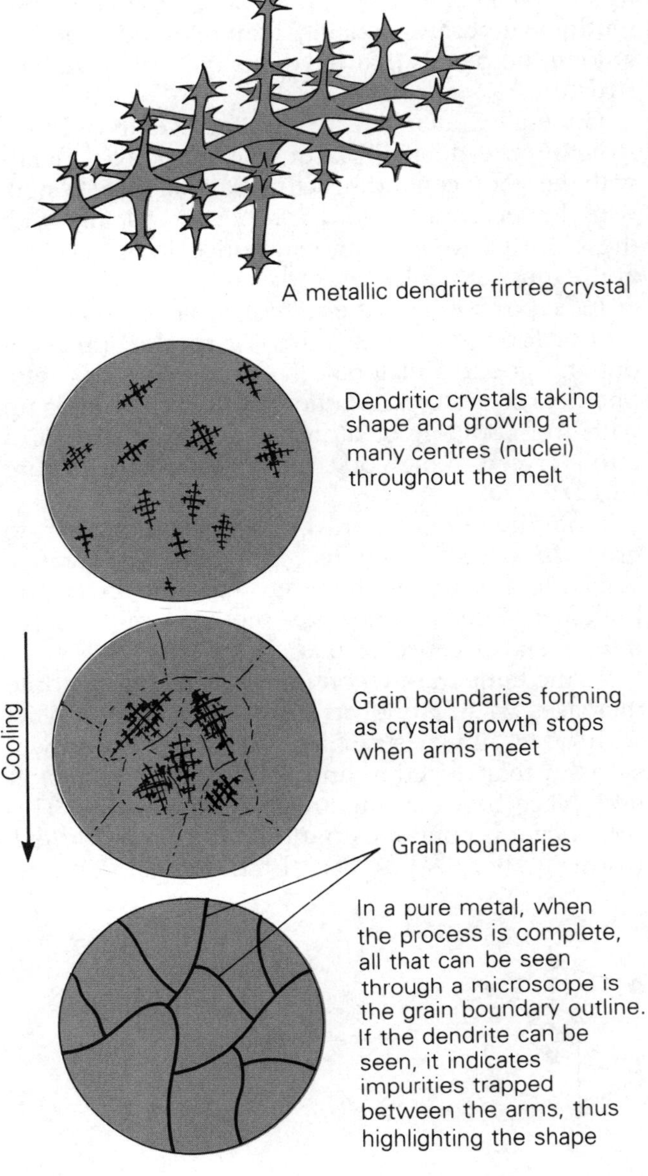

Figure 13.12 **The stages of crystallisation as a metal solidifies.**

However, if impurities have been trapped between the dendrite arms, or if the metal has cooled too rapidly, metal may not have fed completely into the spaces between dendrites. This will cause shrinkage cavities and allow the outline of the dendrite to be visible.

Effect of rate of cooling on grain growth

The rate at which a metal cools will affect the number of nuclei formed; slow cooling will promote the growth of fairly few nuclei. The result is that the crystals (or **grains**) will be large enough to be visible without the aid of a microscope. Fast cooling will promote many nuclei and a small fine-grain structure.

In a large ingot of cast metal or a large weld, the crystal sizes can vary considerably from the outer edges to the centre (Figure 13.13). This is due to variation in the temperature gradient, because as an ingot (or a large weld) solidifies, heat will be transferred from the metal to the mould (or the heavy parent material).

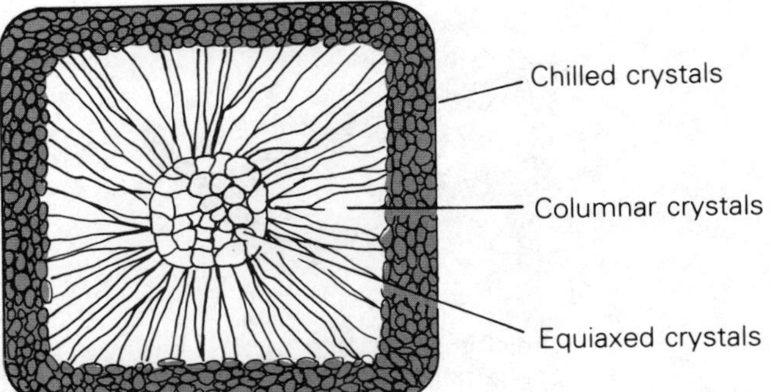

Figure 13.13 **An ingot of a pure metal showing the crystal structure.**

When the metal first makes contact with a cold mould there is a chilling effect and many small crystals form. As the mould warms up, the direction of cooling is mainly inwards and extremely elongated columnar crystals are formed. As heat is lost still further, the metal in the centre begins to form its own nuclei and a third type of crystal is formed, showing no preference for directional growth. These central crystals are much larger than the chilled crystals at the outer edges, because of their slower rate of cooling. These central crystals are known as **equiaxed**, because they have no preference for directional cooling.

Effect of grain structure on metal properties

The deformation of grains can have a big effect on the mechanical properties of a metal. Deformation can take place when a metal is being cold worked during operations such as hammering, pressing, rolling, drawing or bending. An example of how crystals can become greatly elongated and strain hardened is shown in Figure 13.14 where a plate is undergoing a cold-rolling operation.

This undesirable structure can be rectified by applying enough heat to produce the growth of new equiaxed crystal grains, which will return the

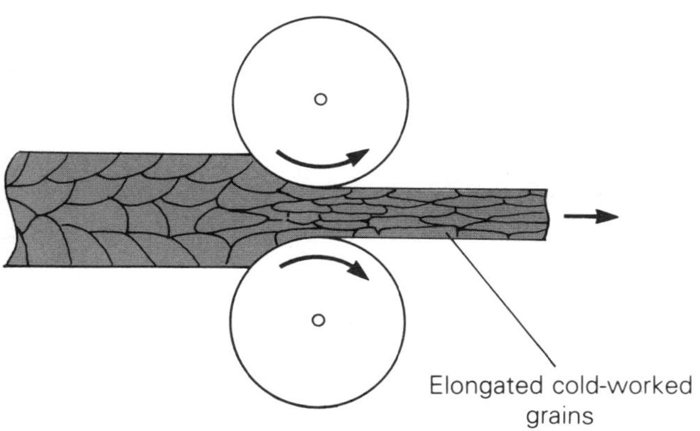

Figure 13.14 Cold rolling of a steel plate.

structure to an unstrained state with the same properties that it had before the cold working took place (Figure 13.15).

The temperature at which these new grains form is called the **recrystallisation temperature**. It is important to hold the metal at this temperature just long enough for the new grains to form, and then to control the cooling rate so that the structure will consist of the refined equiaxed crystals. If the metal is subjected to too much heating above its recrystallisation point, grain growth can occur. These weaker enlarged grains can also be formed if the cooling rate is too slow. Such enlarged grains can decrease ductility and tensile strength, but these properties could, of course, be restored by correct recrystallisation treatment.

CHECK YOUR UNDERSTANDING

- Different metals have different properties. The mechanical properties of interest to the engineer are: ductility, plasticity, brittleness, malleability, hardness, tensile strength (or tenacity), toughness (which is a combination of ductility and tenacity).
- In a pure metal, individual crystals will start to form at many centres (or nuclei) throughout the cooling material. The crystals continue to grow until they come into contact with other similar crystal growths. At this point growth in that direction stops and solidification begins to take place between the arms of the crystal or dendrite.
- Slow cooling promotes few nuclei, with the result that the crystals (or grains) will be larger than in a fast-cooling liquid, which will promote many nuclei.
- The deformation of grains can occur when a metal is being cold worked. This undesirable structure can be rectified by heating the material up to the recrystallisation temperature.
- Excessive heating above the recrystallisation temperature can cause a weaker grain growth structure.

REVISION EXERCISES AND QUESTIONS

1. Name three mechanical properties of metals.
2. Will slow cooling promote larger or smaller grains?
3. What type of structure is promoted by prolonged or excessive heating above the recrystallisation temperature?
4. What test is used to determine a metal's ability to withstand a stretching load?
5. How can the stress of a component be calculated?
6. Name the three main types of space lattice pattern.

(Further practice questions can be found on page 202.)

Figure 13.15 The stages of recrystallisation and grain growth.

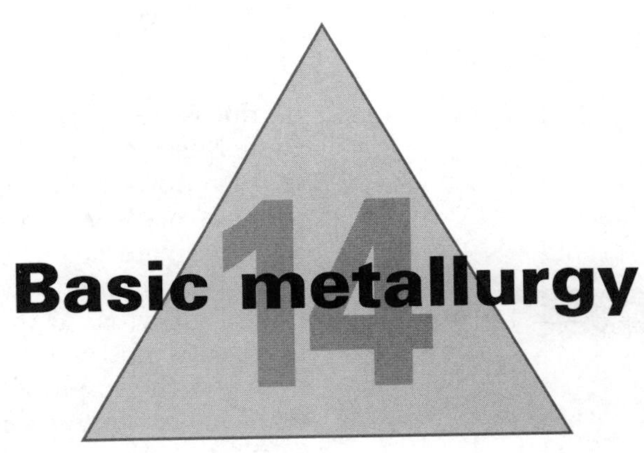

14 Basic metallurgy

Introduction

Metallurgy is the science and technology of metals and their alloys. It includes the methods used to extract metals from their ores (extraction metallurgy) and the way metals are used (engineering metallurgy). However, in this chapter we are concerned with basic metallurgy, which looks at the structure and composition of metals at the microscopic level.

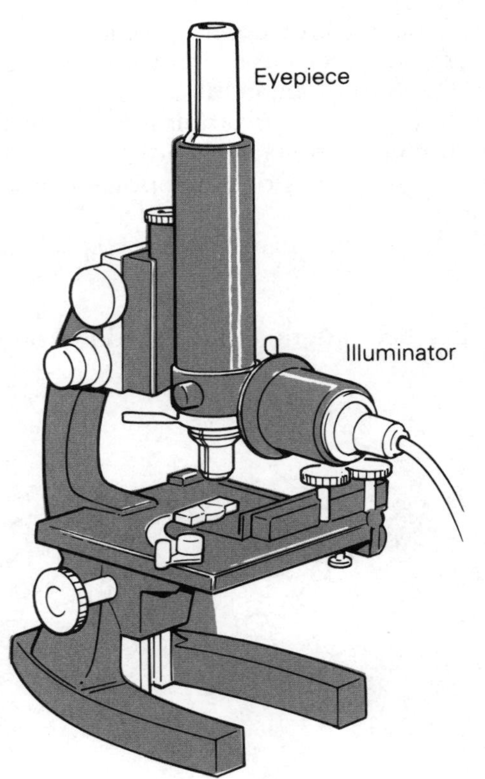

Figure 14.1 A typical metallurgical microscope.

A knowledge of metallurgy is not essential to carry out simple welding repairs, but it can help you to decide how to tackle different types of job, as you will understand what actually happens in the welding process, and the properties that metals possess before, during and after welding. An understanding of these points can make the difference between a welder and a good welder.

As we have already seen, a metal's properties can be changed by heating and cooling. Because heating and cooling occur when materials are welded by most processes, we need to know if such changes will be detrimental to the joint and, if they are, how they can be avoided or controlled.

The metallurgical microscope

The main instrument for examining metals is the metallurgical microscope (Figure 14.1). If a piece of metal is broken, the fracture surfaces will have a granular appearance. The grains may be large enough to see with the naked eye, or they may be so small that a magnifying glass is needed.

If we place this rough fractured surface under a microscope, we shall see very little, as we shall not be able to bring the rough surface into focus. A specimen for examination under a metallurgical microscope has to be ground flat and then polished with grades of increasingly fine abrasives until a mirror-like surface is obtained. Such a polishing process will spread a thin film of metal over the surface of the specimen. In order to see the grain structure and examine the metal in detail, an etching agent is used to remove this film. A typical agent for carbon steels is a 5 per cent solution of nitric acid in alcohol, which is called **nital**. You

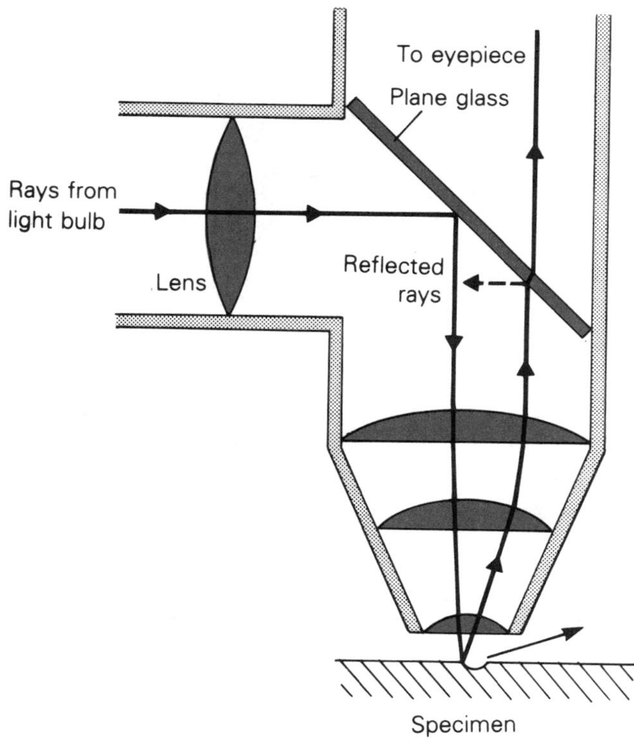

Figure 14.2 Showing how the illuminator works in a metallurgical microscope.

should always wear goggles when carrying out this process.

A metallurgical microscope is different from a biological microscope. A biological specimen is sliced very thinly and placed on a glass slide under the microscope. Light is then shone through the specimen by adjusting a small mirror from beneath or by electrical illumination from underneath. Light will, of course, not shine through a metal specimen, and so metal samples are viewed by reflected light from the polished surface. This is achieved by having an illuminator built into the metallurgical microscope (Figure 14.2).

A magnification of 100 times is usually enough to show the grains or crystals of a pure metal. (The words crystal and grain are both used to mean the same thing.)

Figures 14.3–14.5 show some typical modern metallurgical microscopes.

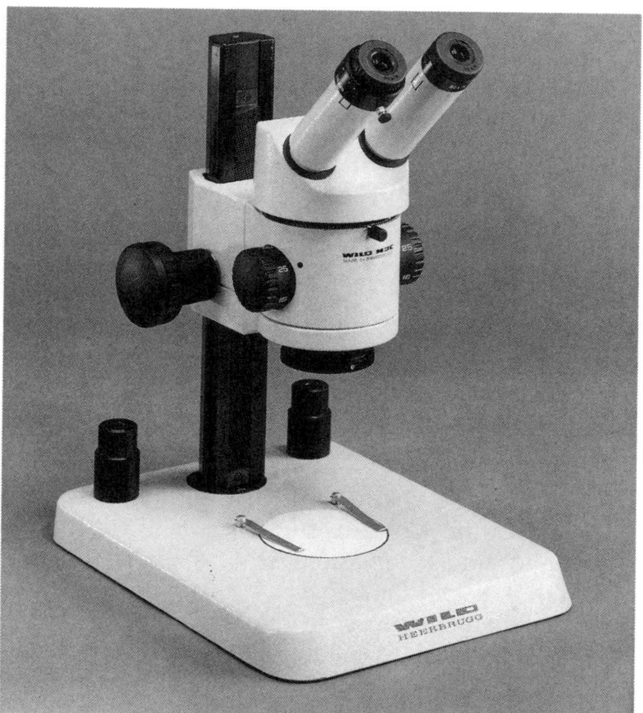

Figure 14.3 'Wild' stereo metallurgical microscope. (Courtesy of Leica, UK and Africa)

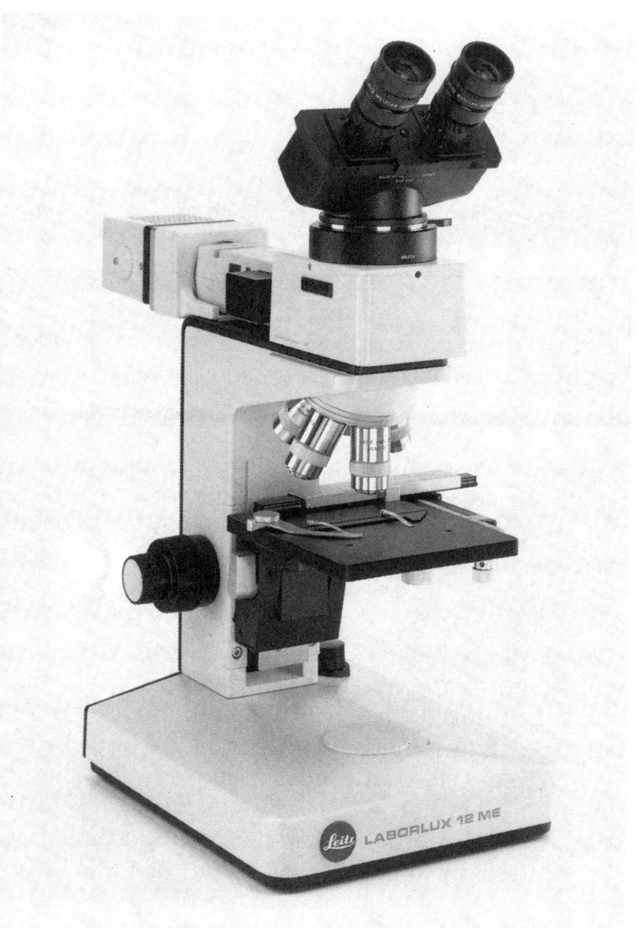

Figure 14.4 Leitz compound microscope for metallurgical use. (Courtesy of Leica, UK and Africa)

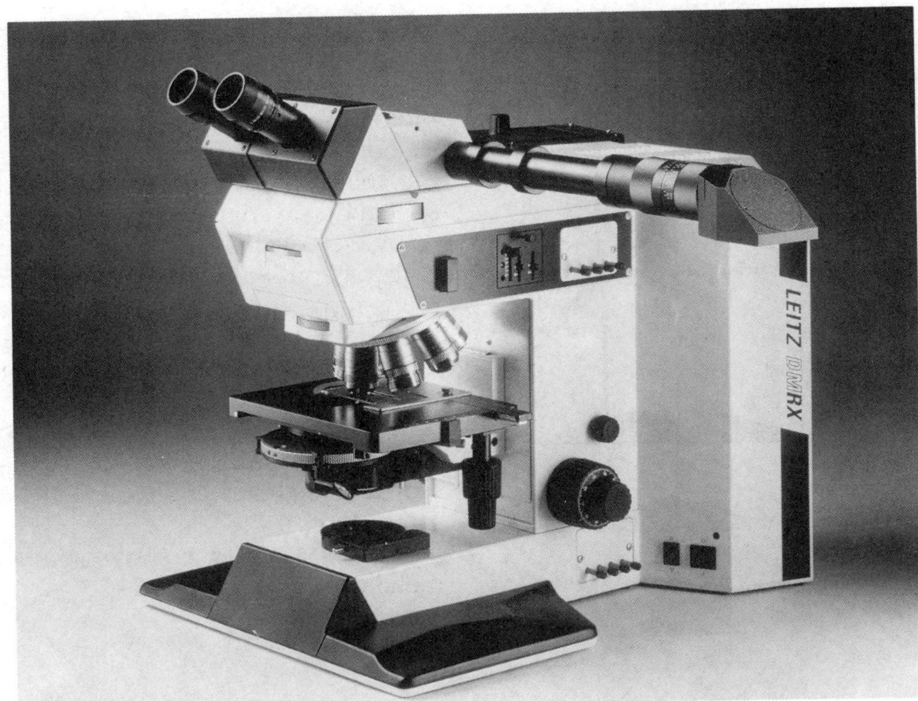

Figure 14.5 Leica research microscope. (Courtesy of Leica, UK and Africa)

Metallurgy of a weld in iron

Iron is a very interesting metal because it is **allotropic**: it can exist in more than one physical form.

At various specific temperatures the atomic space lattice structure changes from one type to another. We can best follow the various changes that take place in the weld and parent material by considering a simple fusion weld between two pieces of iron (Figure 14.6).

At around 1530°C the molten iron weld pool will begin to freeze. The temperature will remain constant until all the iron has solidified. The temperature again begins to drop steadily until 1400°C is reached. Here the temperature lags slightly; this indicates that a change is taking place in the solid iron, but this particular change has been determined by metallurgists to be of little importance.

The temperature falls steadily again until it reaches 910°C, where it again remains constant for a short time, indicating that a change is taking place in the solid iron. This change *is* important. The constant temperature at this point is due to heat being given off as the atoms rearrange themselves from a face-centred cubic lattice crystal to a body-centred cubic formation. Above 910°C the structure is known as **gamma iron**, and below 910°C it is known as **alpha iron**. The temperature at which such a change in crystalline structure takes place is known as the **transformation temperature**.

On cooling still further to 769°C, there is another change; the iron regains its magnetic properties. This point is called the **Curie point**.

We can see from Figure 14.6 that the single-pass weld builds up grains growing inwards and slightly upwards. The last of the columnar grains forms as the last portion of liquid iron freezes at the surface of the weld. The parent material that has been heated above 910°C will have undergone the crystalline structure change and the grains closest to the weld in the heat affected zone will be slightly weaker, owing to an increase in size. The parent material that did not reach 910°C will not have been subjected to any atomic change, but if the parent material had been cold worked prior to welding, then recrystallisation would have taken place in areas reaching above 450°C. Any iron not heated to over 450°C at a further distance from the weld is still in the cold-rolled state.

> When carbon is added to iron, the iron becomes known as **steel**.

The first change that an addition of carbon will have is to cause the material to freeze over a temperature range, instead of freezing at a definite temperature. The more carbon in solution with the iron, the lower the freezing temperature range.

With the body-centred atomic structure, iron can only hold a very small amount of carbon in solution: so little, in fact, that it is generally ignored. However, in the face-centred cubic structure, iron is capable of holding large amounts of carbon in solid solution. This solid solution of carbon in iron, if viewed through a microscope at 1000 magnifications, would appear as a pure metal rather than an alloy, with just the grain boundaries being visible.

It is easy to imagine liquid solutions, such as salt dissolved in water to form brine, but it is more difficult to imagine that iron can hold dissolved carbon in a **solid solution**. The fact that it does, though, is extremely important, as it means that iron–carbon alloys can be heat-treated to give a wide range of properties.

Iron with a very small amount of carbon added (up to 0.006 per cent) and pure iron are known as ferrite (Figure 14.7). If more than 0.006 per cent of carbon is added, changes to the microstructure

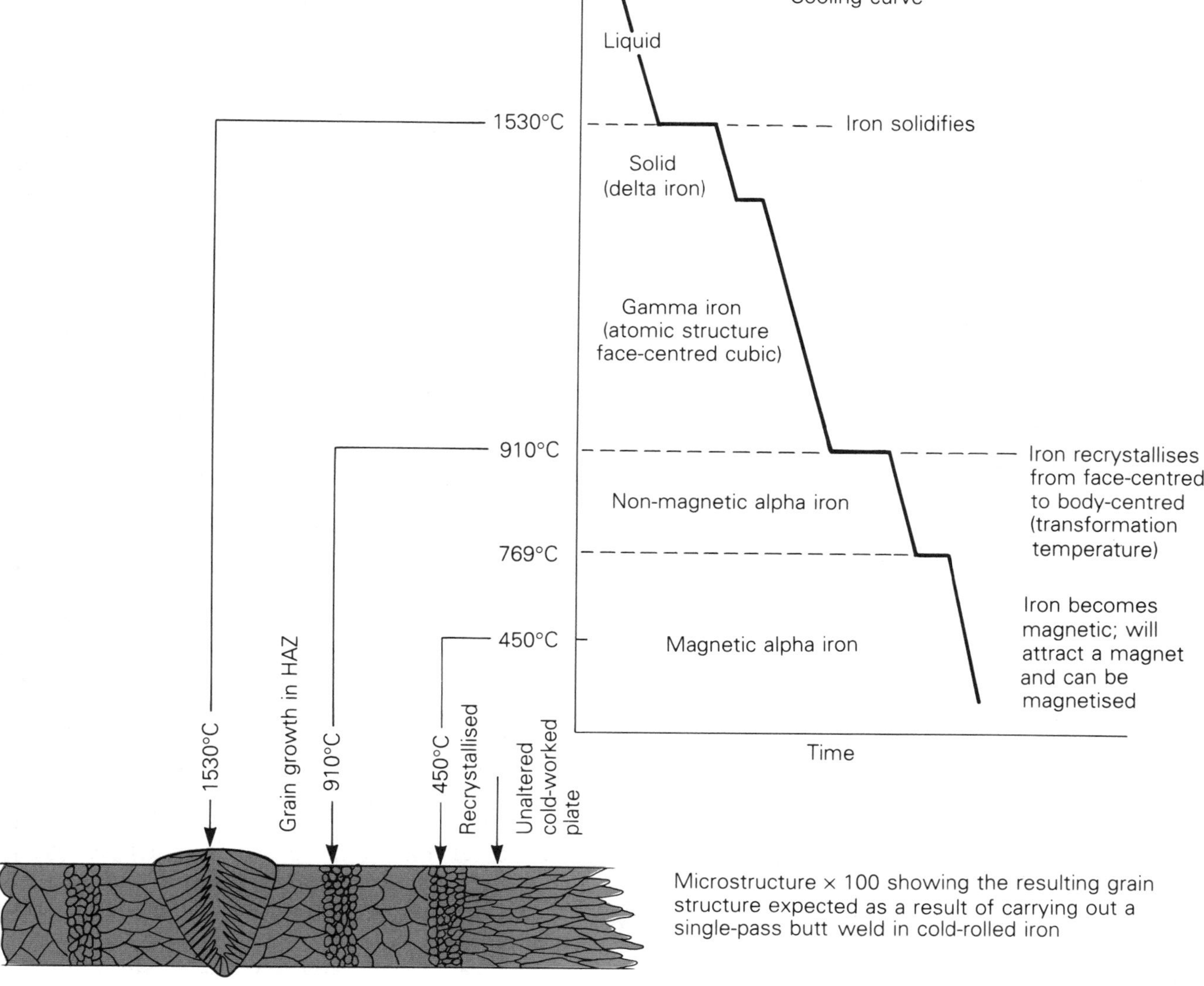

Figure 14.6 Single-pass butt weld in iron, related to the cooling curve.

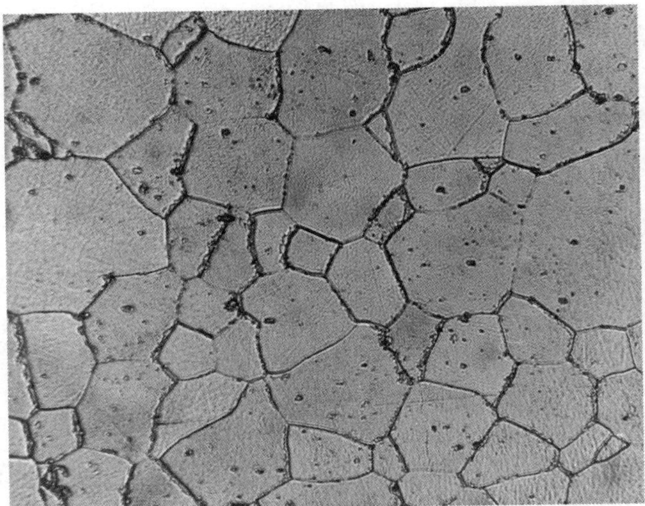

Figure 14.7 Ferrite through a microscope.

occur and the temperature of the alpha–gamma transition (body-to face-centred atomic structure) is gradually lowered from 910°C to 723°C, when the carbon content reaches 0.83%.

The changes that occur with various carbon contents and the resulting microstructures can best be understood by looking at Figure 14.8, the **iron–carbon equilibrium diagram**. This diagram has been constructed by plotting a series of curves and noting when the internal structural change takes place for each carbon percentage. These change points are then joined up to give the equilibrium diagram. Heating curves have been used to produce this diagram. There is approximately a 30°C lowering of results when cooling curves are used.

These microstructures will occur when cooling takes place slowly. Rapid cooling, such as quenching, will not allow the steel time to carry out the internal changes, and will give a different structure.

At 0–0.006 per cent the carbon will not be visible through a microscope and the structure will appear as a pure metal, with just the grain boundaries visible. As the level of carbon is increased, iron carbide (**cementite**) is formed by three atoms of iron combining with one atom of carbon (Fe_3C): the more cementite present, the greater the hardness and tensile strength of the steel.

Steels containing up to 0.25 per cent carbon are known as **low-carbon** or **mild steels**. Figure 14.8(b) shows the microstructure of a typical mild steel containing 0.25 per cent carbon. Here, in addition to the grains of ferrite, there are grains that contain alternate layers of black and white, giving an appearance similar to the edge of a piece of plywood. These grains are called **pearlite**; they are made up of alternate layers of ferrite and cementite. The amount of carbon in pearlite is always 0.83%. The pearlite will be distributed evenly through the microstructure. It increases the tensile strength and hardness of the steel but reduces the ductility.

Mild steel is generally easily welded by most welding processes. All the welding data and general notes in this book refer to the welding of mild steel unless they specifically refer to the welding of other metals.

At 0.6 per cent carbon (Figure 14.8(c)), more pearlite is present, giving a further increase in tensile strength and hardness with a further decrease in ductility. The opposite of a ductile material is a brittle material; as a steel becomes less ductile it will become more brittle. The more brittle it becomes, the greater the risk of cracking when welding takes place. Steels within the range of 0.25–0.45 per cent carbon are classed as **medium-carbon steels**. Above 0.6 per cent carbon they are classed as **high-carbon steels**, with those above 0.8 per cent carbon being known as **tool steels**.

A steel containing 0.83 per cent carbon is known as a **eutectoid steel** (Figure 14.8(d)), as it is formed at the **eutectic point** on the equilibrium diagram. This is the point where the lines for the upper transformation point, known as the upper critical point, and the lower transformation point, known as the lower critical point, meet. The transformation from austenite to pearlite takes place at the one temperature and the whole microstructure will be pearlite, composed of alternate ferrite and cementite layers.

Increasing the carbon content to 1.2 per cent (Figure 14.8(e)) distributes excess cementite around the pearlite grains, as only 0.83 per cent carbon is required to form the pearlite, the remainder being distributed at the grain boundaries.

Steels containing less than 0.83 per cent are called **hypoeutectoid**; the predominant ferrite will contribute to the metal's relative softness and ductility. Steels having more than 0.83 per cent carbon content are called **hypereutectoid**; the cementite produces the properties of hardness and brittleness.

Increasing the carbon content still further, to 1.7 per cent (Figure 14.8(f)), produces an even greater amount of cementite around the pearlite.

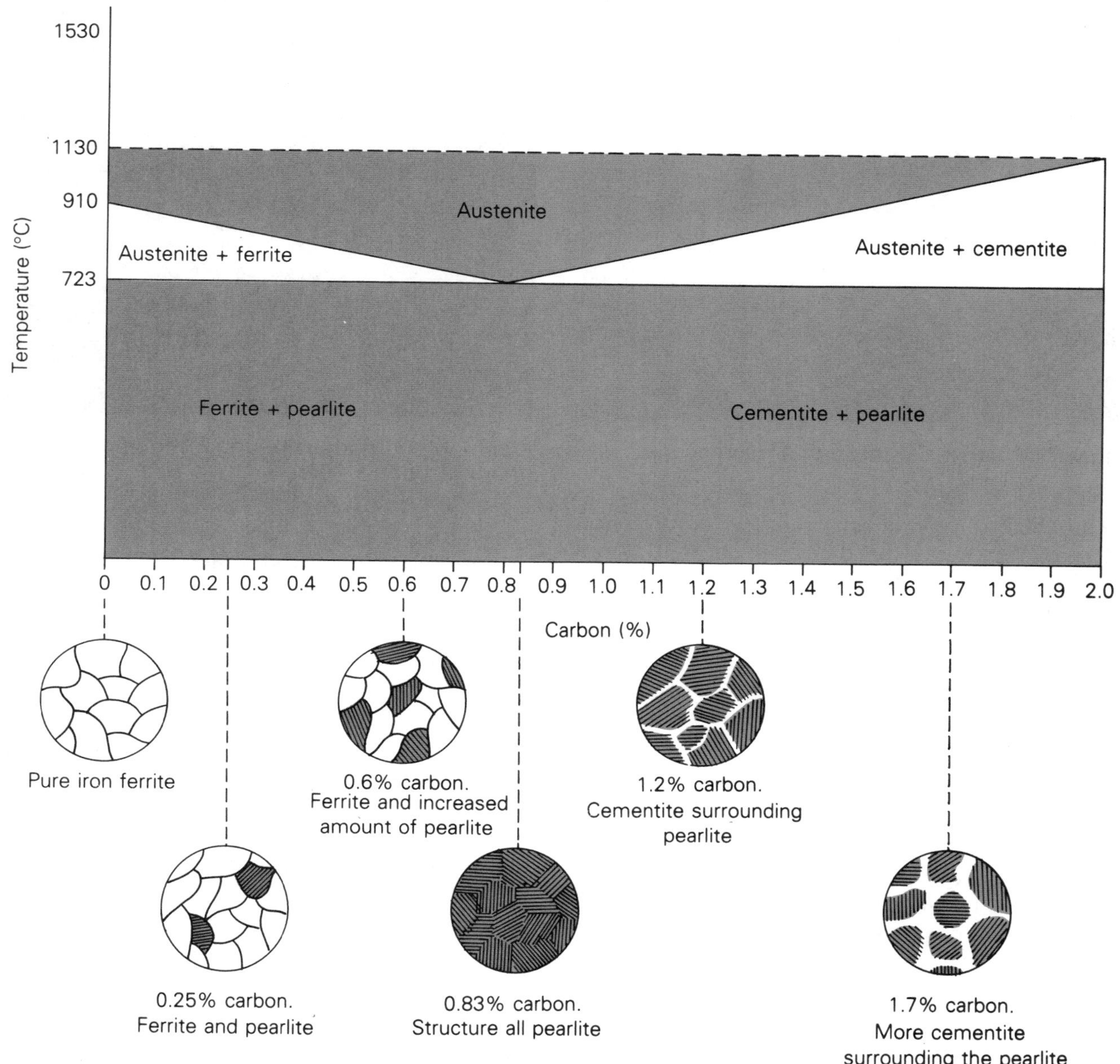

Figure 14.8 **The iron–carbon equilibrium diagram, showing the microstructures that result from increasing the carbon content.**

Effects of heat treatment and alloying on the structure of steel

As we have discussed, iron has a body-centred structure below 910°C, but undergoes an allotropic change when heated above this temperature. The rearrangement of atoms for a face-centred cubic lattice structure, which allows the iron to take a much greater amount of carbon into solution, gives a condition at high temperature where all the carbon present in the steel has gone into solution with the iron to produce a new structure called **austenite**, named after an English metallurgist, Sir W. R. Austen (Figure 14.9).

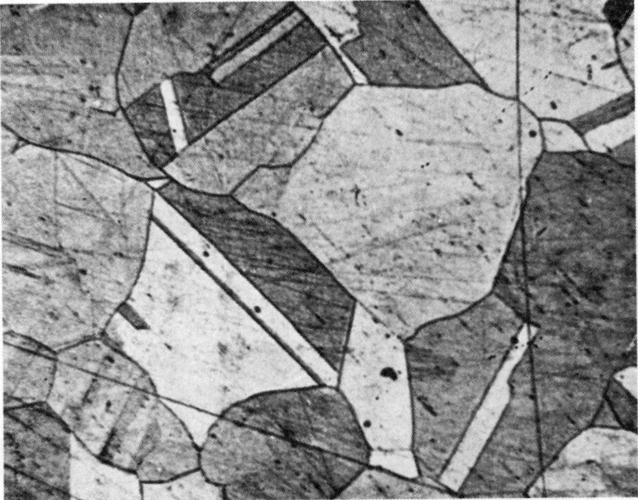

Figure 14.9 Austenite through a microscope.

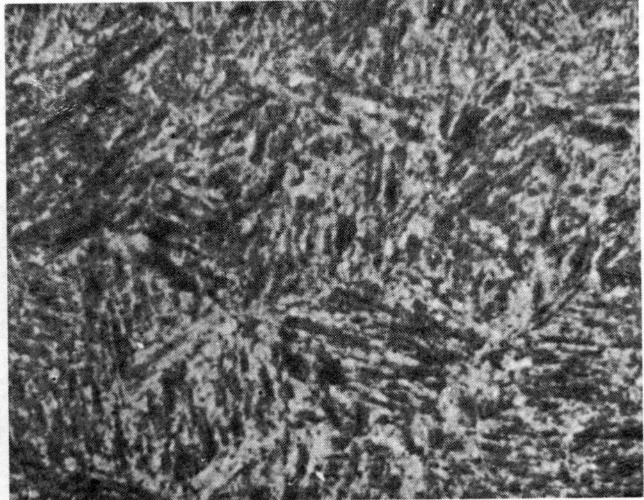

Figure 14.11 Martensite under the microscope (magnification × 700).

This solid solution of carbon in face-centred iron will not be retained as the steel cools to room temperature. As the iron–carbon equilibrium diagram shows, depending on the carbon content, the resultant structures on cooling will be either ferrite and pearlite or cementite and pearlite. However, by adding high percentages of manganese or nickel, the alloy steel formed will remain austenitic when cooled to room temperature.

Rapid cooling of a steel from above the transformation range, while it is in the austenitic state, can be performed in a tank of water or oil. Such a treatment is known as **quenching**. It can give a structure, on cooling, that is entirely different from that of a steel that has been cooled slowly. The steel does not have time to perform the internal changes that would normally take place in the transformation range. This distorts the lattice structure. The carbon atoms are trapped, causing a further distortion of the lattice arrangement.

With a very rapid quench, the lattice structures can be diamond-shaped instead of cubic. This prevents the rows of atoms from sliding when a metal is stretched, forming a very hard but brittle structure. For very fast quenches, brine (salt water) can be used, as the particles of salt explode, bursting the steam envelope that may form in an ordinary water quench around the component, preventing further cooling. With brine, the bursting of the steam envelope as fast as it forms enables the water to be in constant contact. If the quench is fast enough, the hardest structure obtainable in steel can be formed. This is known as **martensite** (Figures 14.10, 14.11).

It is for this reason that you usually have to let a weld cool down slowly in its own time.

> If you quench a weld as soon as you have completed it, the chances are that it will be hard and brittle and, if not already cracked, will easily crack in service.

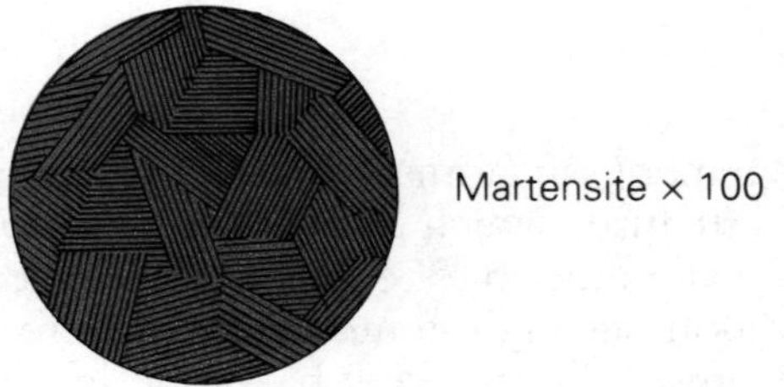

Figure 14.10 The needle-like structure characteristic of etched sections of hardened steel (steel that has been subjected to a rapid quench).

CHECK YOUR UNDERSTANDING

- A metallurgical microscope has an illuminator built into it to light up the specimen.
- In order to see the grain structure and examine a metal in detail, specimens are polished until a mirror-like surface is obtained. This surface is then etched with an acid solution. A typical etching

agent for carbon steels is a 5 per cent solution of nitric acid in alcohol, called nital.

- A magnification of 100 times is usually enough to show the grains (or crystals) of a pure metal.
- The atomic space lattice structure of iron changes from one type to another at various set temperatures. At around 1530°C, molten iron in a weld pool will begin to freeze. The next important temperature is 910°C. At this point the atoms change from a face-centred cubic lattice structure to a body-centred cubic formation. (Above 1400°C, iron will revert to body-centred cubic form, but this change has been determined by metallurgists to be of little importance.)
- At 769°C iron regains its magnetic properties.
- If a cold-worked piece of iron is heated to over 450°C, then recrystallisation will take place.
- Iron with a very small amount of carbon added and pure iron are known as ferrite.
- When the carbon added to iron reaches 0.83 per cent, the temperature at which the atomic structure changes from body- to face-centred is lowered from 910°C to 723°C.
- Mild steel contains carbon – generally around 0.25 per cent – and is easily welded by most welding processes. The more carbon that is added, the harder and less ductile the steel will become, and therefore greater precautions have to be taken to avoid cracking during welding.
- Steels within the range of 0.25–0.45 per cent carbon are classed as medium-carbon steels, with those above 0.6 per cent being classed as high-carbon steels. Above 0.8 per cent carbon is usually used for tool steel.
- Quenching a steel rapidly from a high temperature can give a structure on cooling that is entirely different from that of a steel cooled slowly. Fast quenches can produced extremely hard structures. In welding terms, this can cause cracking, and so methods are generally used to bring welds down to room temperature gradually. These include post-heating and slow cooling in sand.

REVISION EXERCISES AND QUESTIONS

1 How does a metallurgical microscope differ from a biological microscope?

2 State a typical etching agent for carbon steels.

3 Name the two types of atomic structure for iron at different temperatures.

4 What percentage of carbon would a mild steel usually contain?

5 Why might you need to take greater precautions, such as pre-and post-heating, when welding a steel with a higher carbon content than mild steel?

(Further practice questions can be found on page 202.)

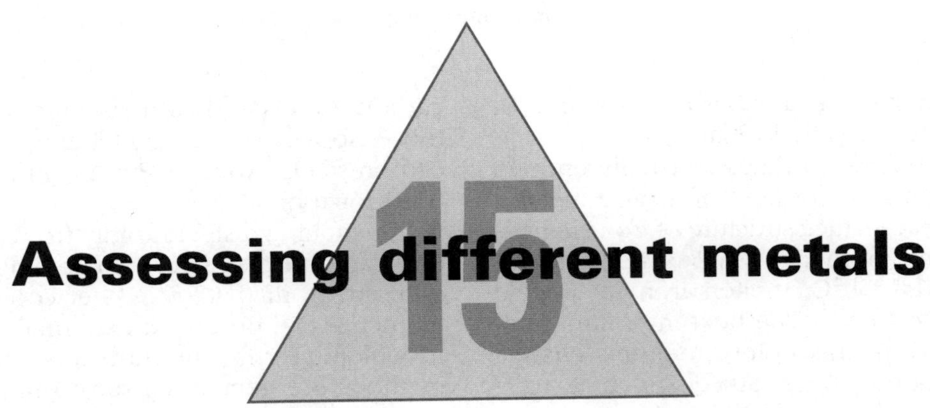

15 Assessing different metals

Introduction

Most welders learn to weld on mild or low-carbon steel, and a lot of fabrication work is undertaken in this material. However, sooner or later you will come across other materials that require welding, particularly if you work in a repair shop. Repair or salvage welding, as it is sometimes called, is a major industry. Often a component that is worth a great deal of money can be repaired by just one weld. There is a double benefit; if a component can be repaired it very often saves the time of ordering and waiting to receive the new component, and therefore saves the time that a particular machine may be out of use.

As we have seen in Chapter 13, different metals behave in different ways. Some can be stretched or bent easily while it is impossible to stretch or bend others. Some metals can be scratched with a finger-nail or dented with a hammer; others will dig into solid rock for hours without being marked. This chapter includes some workshop methods for identifying metals, and some methods for determining their properties.

This chapter is therefore very important. Until you know what the metal is that you are going to weld, you cannot plan how you are going to weld it.

Identifying metals

Being able to recognise different metals and alloys is obviously important, particularly in repair work, where it is often up to the welder to decide the welding process and procedures.

If the component can be readily identified, the welder with a good mechanical background will be aware that certain machine parts are always made from specific metals. The use to which the component is put is therefore a good starting point in the identification process.

Some metals can be readily recognised by their colour and weight: copper, aluminium and brass, for example.

For the various types of steel and iron, **spark-testing** the metal on a grinding wheel or with a hand grinder (Figure 15.1) is a good method of identification. Figure 15.2 shows some of the spark patterns. Many welding repair shops have labelled samples of known steels, so that the spark patterns can be compared with the sample being identified.

Figure 15.1 Sparks given off when using a hand grinder.

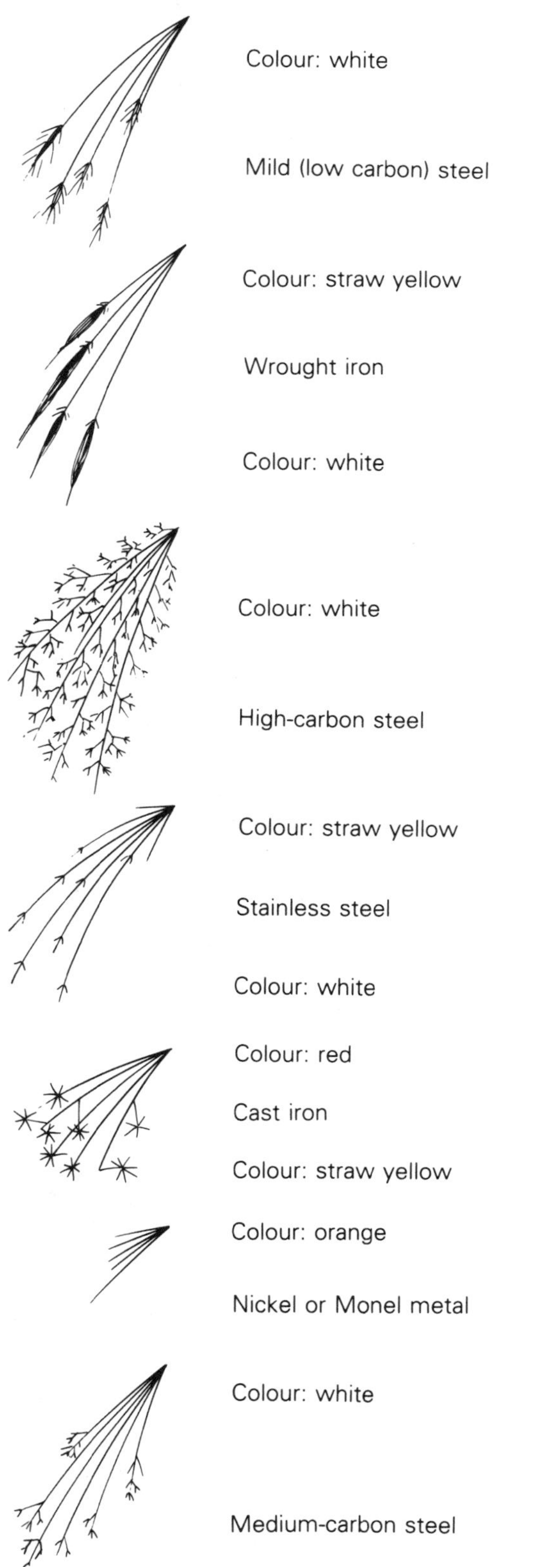

Figure 15.2 **Using the spark test to identify metals.**

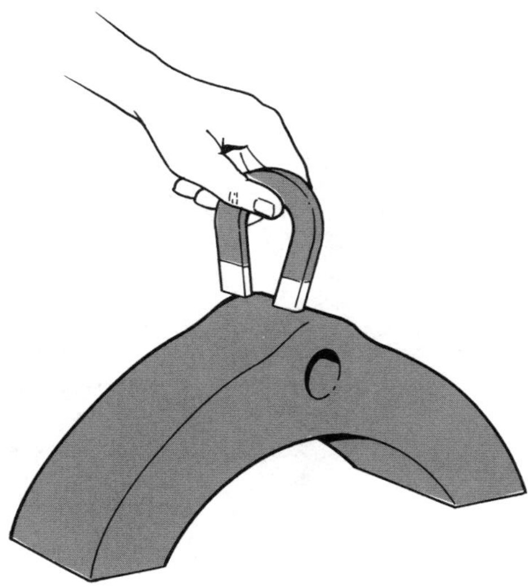

Figure 15.3 **Checking the material with a magnet.**

Testing with a magnet

It is useful to have a magnet or a piece of magnetised metal in the workshop, as you will then be able to test if the material that requires welding is magnetic or not (Figure 15.3). Most steels and cast irons are very magnetic; only manganese steel and austenitic stainless steel are non-magnetic.

Most of the non-ferrous metals are non-magnetic. The exceptions are nickel, which is very magnetic, and Monel, which can be slightly magnetic. Some nickel alloys, such as Inconel, and certain types of Monel are non-magnetic.

Sometimes components are coated or **clad** with nickel or stainless steel. In such cases, it will be necessary to clean back the surface coating on either side of the joint to be welded and to use two welding techniques/procedures, one for the base material and one for the coating. By welding in such a way, the original properties of the repaired component should be restored.

Acoustic or sound test

With experience, metals can be identified by the sound they give off when struck by a hammer (Figure 15.4). For example, steel will give off a higher-pitched tone than cast iron. The sound test can also be used to indicate if a component has a flaw or crack inside it. This method is still employed to check railway wheels. If the wheel is

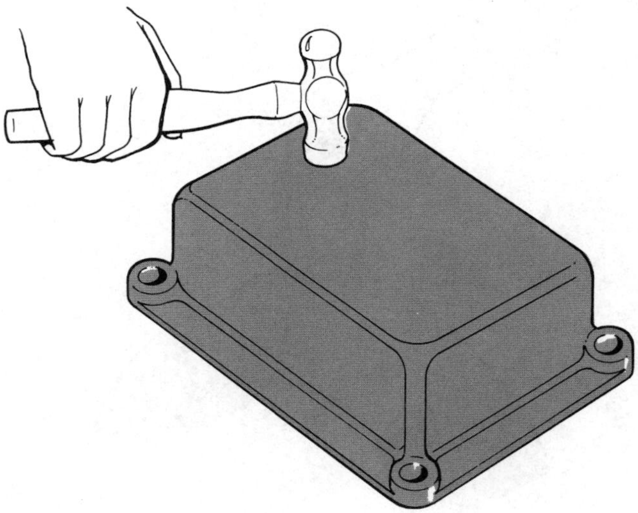

Figure 15.4 Acoustic test (sound test).

Figure 15.5 Acid test on a sample plate. Always wear gloves and goggles.

free from defects, when it is struck by a hammer it will give out a high-pitched ringing sound. However, if there is a crack or defect inside, the sound will be a dull 'thud', with no ringing.

Acid test to determine stainless steel and Monel

 Always wear protective gloves and goggles when carrying out this test.

Drop one or two drops of concentrated nitric acid on a clean surface of the metal to be tested (Figure 15.5). If there is no reaction, this indicates stainless steel or an alloy high in nickel–chromium content. If there appears to be a reaction, add three or four drops of water, one at a time. If the area turns greenish-blue, this is an indication of Monel.

Measuring the properties of metals

There is a close relationship between a metal's various properties. If one property is changed, it will cause a change in the others. For example, if a piece of steel is treated so that its hardness is increased, the tensile strength will also be increased, but the ductility will be reduced. Likewise, if a metal is heated and it becomes soft, with an increase in ductility, its tensile strength will be lowered.

Properties are therefore very important to welders. Generally, we can take it that the harder a material is, the more brittle it is likely to be, and special precautions such as preheating and post-heating may well have to be used in order to carry out a satisfactory weld without cracking.

If a piece of scrap material, the same as the metal to be welded, is available, you can perform a bend test to measure the ductility. The file hardness test provides a workshop method of estimating hardness and tensile strength.

Table 15.1 The file hardness test

Approximate Brinell hardness number	Ease with which the steel surface can be filed with a new file
100	File cuts into surface very easily and metal is very soft.
200	File still removes metal but a bit more pressure is required. Metal still quite soft.
300	Metal begins to exhibit resistance to file.
400	File will still remove metal but with difficulty; metal is quite hard.
500	File barely removes metal, showing the metal is only slightly softer than file.
600	File will slide over surface without removing metal. The file teeth are dulled.

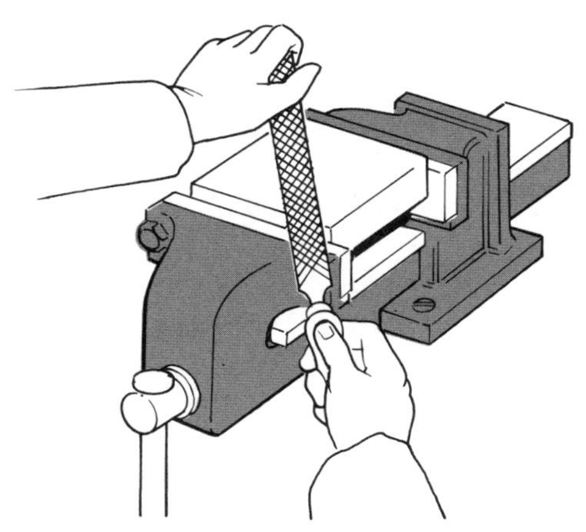

Figure 15.6 The file hardness test.

File hardness test

This test can give a rough estimate of a material's Brinell hardness number, by determining the material's resistance to the cutting action of the file (Figure 15.6). The test is best performed with a new file if possible. Table 15.1 explains how the method works.

Bouncing ball test

This is another workshop hardness test that can be developed into quite an accurate method. For this method you need a steel ball bearing and a glass tube. The ball bearing is allowed to fall down the glass tube on to the surface being tested (Figure 15.7), and the height of bounce is measured. A steel ball bearing is manufactured with great accuracy as to its hardness, so that it provides a cheap tool that will give reasonably accurate results. The glass tube will guide the fall and the bounce of the steel ball. If the glass has no markings on it, you can make these carefully with a file at regular intervals in order to measure the bounce.

The test can be made quite accurate by calibrating the glass tube after comparative tests of known hardness. The heights of the bounces can be marked on the glass, one low and one high. The spaces between these two marks can then be divided and marked evenly. To obtain a very hard specimen and a very soft specimen the file hardness test can be used.

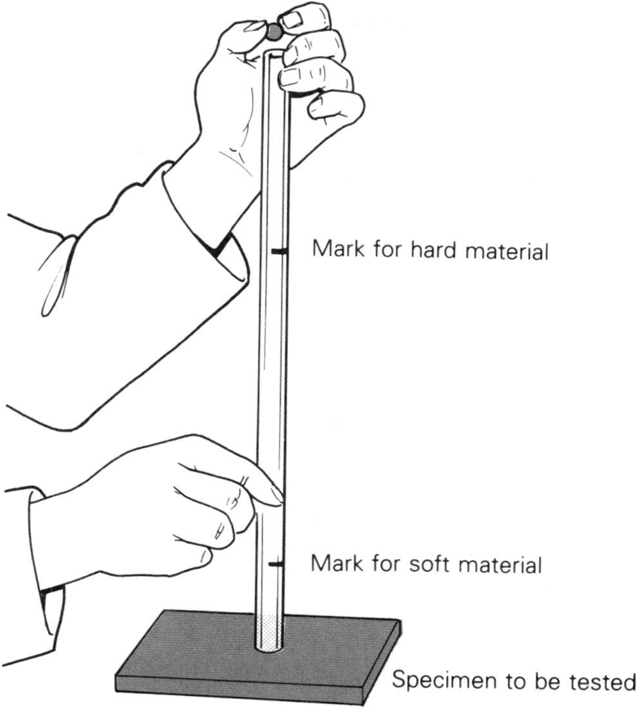

Figure 15.7 The bouncing ball test. The ball should run freely in the glass tube. The higher it bounces off the surface, the harder the material.

CHECK YOUR UNDERSTANDING

- Identifying metals is important. Until you know what the metal is that you are going to weld, you cannot plan how you are going to weld it.
- Some metals can be readily recognised by their colour and weight: copper, aluminium and brass, for example.
- For various types of steel and iron, spark-testing the metal on a grinding wheel or with a hand grinder is a good method of identification. Spark patterns can be compared with a previously identified sample.
- A magnet can be used to distinguish between most ferrous and non-ferrous materials. Only manganese steel and austenitic stainless steel are non-magnetic.
- Some metals can be identified with an acoustic or sound test, by the noise given off when they are struck by a hammer. Sometimes it is also possible to detect internal flaws with this method.
- The hardness of a material can be estimated by the file hardness test or the bouncing ball test.

REVISION EXERCISES AND QUESTIONS

1 Why is it important to be able to identify metals?
2 How can metals such as copper, aluminium and brass be readily identified?
3 Why is it important to use a new file when performing the file hardness test?
4 In what way can a magnet be used to distinguish between different metals?
5 If a component has an internal flaw is it likely to give out a ringing sound or a dull thud when struck with a hammer?

(Further practice questions can be found on page 202.)

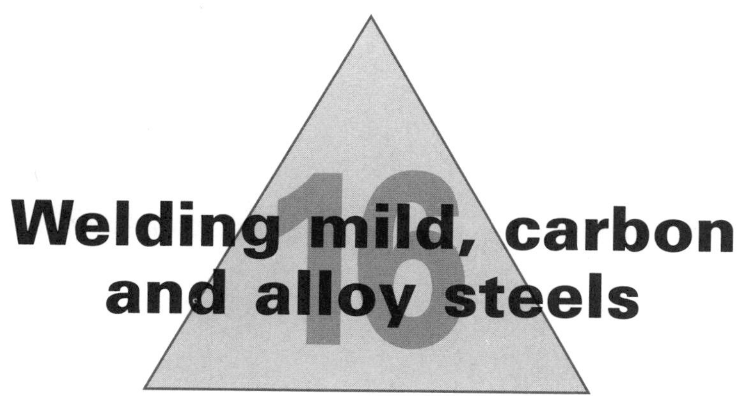

16 Welding mild, carbon and alloy steels

Introduction

We saw in Chapter 14 that slow cooling of steels with a low carbon content produces a structure of ferrite dispersed in pearlite. Steels of a higher carbon content produce structures of cementite dispersed in pearlite. The amount of ferrite and pearlite in a steel at room temperature is therefore controlled directly by the carbon content.

As the carbon content increases above 0.25 per cent we need to take increasing precautions when performing welding operations. Although the carbon will increase the tensile strength and hardness, this will be at the expense of ductility, because of the amount and dispersion of the carbide (cementite), which is extremely hard and brittle.

> The main precaution when welding steels of higher carbon content is to **preheat**, and to cool slowly after welding. This is essential.

If the work is cooled too quickly, the brittle effects of a rapid quench will result, causing cracking or the possibility of cracking. Preheating can be as simple as using the oxyacetylene torch before welding, or it may involve large specially built furnaces. Slow cooling is sometimes obtained by a **post-heat** treatment: letting the component or fabrication cool down slowly in the furnace by gradually reducing the furnace temperature. It may be sufficient for small components to let them cool down in sand. Special electrical induction or resistance pads can be used for large vessels (Figure 16.1).

Stress relieving is another type of post-heating operation that removes internal stresses in the work caused by the prevention of full contraction when a welded fabrication cools.

Mild steel

Although mild steel is generally easily weldable by all the major welding processes, consideration should be given to process selection and methods of welding for particular applications.

Figure 16.1 Fixing electrical resistance elements for internal heating of a vessel seam, before welding. (Courtesy of Cooperheat (UK) Ltd)

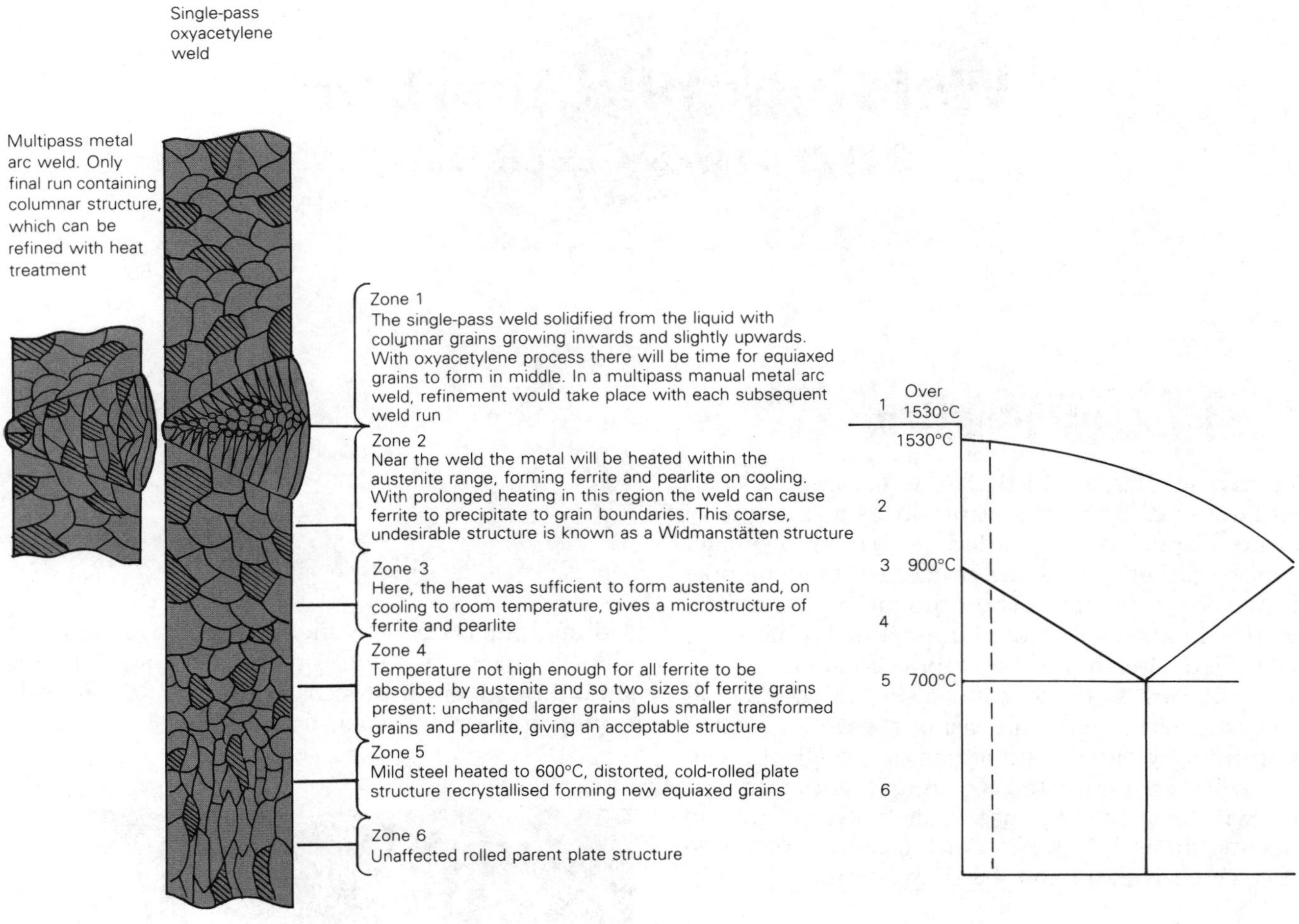

Single-pass oxyacetylene weld

Multipass metal arc weld. Only final run containing columnar structure, which can be refined with heat treatment

Zone 1
The single-pass weld solidified from the liquid with columnar grains growing inwards and slightly upwards. With oxyacetylene process there will be time for equiaxed grains to form in middle. In a multipass manual metal arc weld, refinement would take place with each subsequent weld run

Zone 2
Near the weld the metal will be heated within the austenite range, forming ferrite and pearlite on cooling. With prolonged heating in this region the weld can cause ferrite to precipitate to grain boundaries. This coarse, undesirable structure is known as a Widmanstätten structure

Zone 3
Here, the heat was sufficient to form austenite and, on cooling to room temperature, gives a microstructure of ferrite and pearlite

Zone 4
Temperature not high enough for all ferrite to be absorbed by austenite and so two sizes of ferrite grains present: unchanged larger grains plus smaller transformed grains and pearlite, giving an acceptable structure

Zone 5
Mild steel heated to 600°C, distorted, cold-rolled plate structure recrystallised forming new equiaxed grains

Zone 6
Unaffected rolled parent plate structure

1 Over 1530°C
1530°C
2
3 900°C
4
5 700°C
6

Figure 16.2 **The various microstructures for a butt weld in mild steel linked to the iron–carbon equilibrium diagram.**

Figure 16.2 shows the various microstructures for a butt weld in mild steel plate under slow cooling conditions. With a single-pass run, the grain size can be quite large. Grain size is dependent on prolonged heat input and would therefore be larger for an oxyacetylene weld than an electric arc weld with a faster heat input. However, multipass welds with both processes will have the effect of refining the lower deposits, because of reheating, leaving only the final capping run with the larger, weaker structure. Refinement of this last deposit would require a further post-weld heat treatment.

Boiler steels and ship plate steels are specially developed mild steels. Boiler-quality steel limits the phosphorus and sulphur content to 0.05 per cent, while ship quality allows up to 0.06 per cent. The carbon content in both types must be kept down to 0.26 per cent to allow welding to take place.

Most steels used for welding fall into the low or mild steel category with less than 0.3 per cent carbon. When any carbon steel is welded, a zone on each side of the weld will be heated to above the upper critical temperature and can, therefore, harden when cooling. The degree of hardness will increase with increased carbon content and the rate of cooling. For medium-carbon steels (above 0.3 per cent carbon) and high carbon steels (more than 0.6 per cent carbon), the risks will obviously be greater.

As the tendency of the metal to crack is related to the hardness, every attempt must be made to reduce the hazard. The first precaution should be to use a steel with the minimum carbon content necessary to obtain the properties required in the job. The cooling rate should also be controlled with pre- and post-heating, as well as by employing a large-diameter electrode to give a higher heat input.

Preheating

In most cases, it will not be necessary to preheat steels with a carbon content up to 0.3 per cent. Above this percentage, up to 0.5 per cent carbon, preheating to 100–350°C is recommended; the temperature is increased as the carbon content increases if mild steel electrodes are being used. Above 0.6 per cent carbon, steels are known as **tool steels** and are not often welded by the arc process. If welding *is* required on this type of material, you are advised to use the buttering technique.

The use of buttering to prevent carbon pick-up

Cracking in a weld can sometimes be caused by **carbon pick-up**. This occurs when carbon from the parent material diffuses into the weld metal. It makes the weld brittle and prone to cracking, usually along the centre of the weld.

The **buttering** technique can help to overcome this problem by depositing a layer of weld metal on the faces before joining them together (Figure 16.3). Some carbon will be picked up by this layer, but because the components are not joined together, the weld metal will not be highly stressed and therefore should not crack. The carbon content of the buttering runs will be considerably lower than that of the parent material, so that when the joining weld is made, the carbon pick-up will be much less than if directly made with the parent material. The joining weld or welds should be made while the work is still warmed up from the buttering process. Buttering can also be used in joining certain combinations of dissimilar materials and in cast iron repair welding.

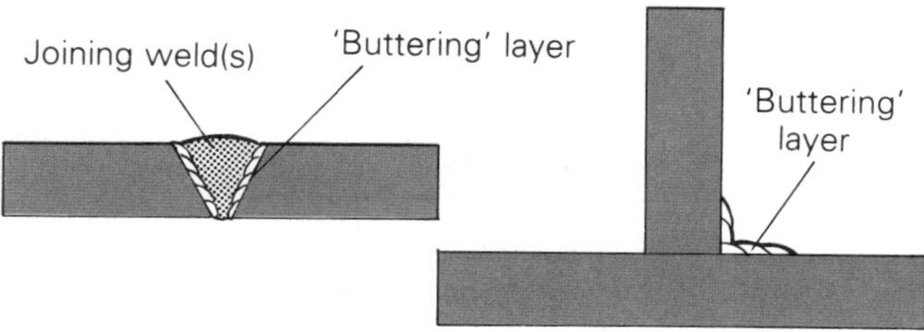

Figure 16.3 The use of 'buttering' on butt and fillet welds.

Low-alloy, medium and high-tensile steels

These steels contain small additions of alloying elements to improve their mechanical properties such as tensile strength, ductility and toughness. Typical elements include manganese, silicon, nickel, chromium, molybdenum and vanadium. Such steels have similar welding properties to carbon steels and care must be taken to avoid hardening. Medium and high-tensile steels are low-alloy steels possessing even higher physical properties. Such steels generally have welding instructions issued by the supplier and these must be closely followed.

In general, the effect of the various alloying elements can be calculated as a **carbon equivalent**, and any pre- and post-heating requirements can be determined from this figure (see Chapter 22).

Because the zones of parent metal each side of the weld will be heated above the critical tempera-

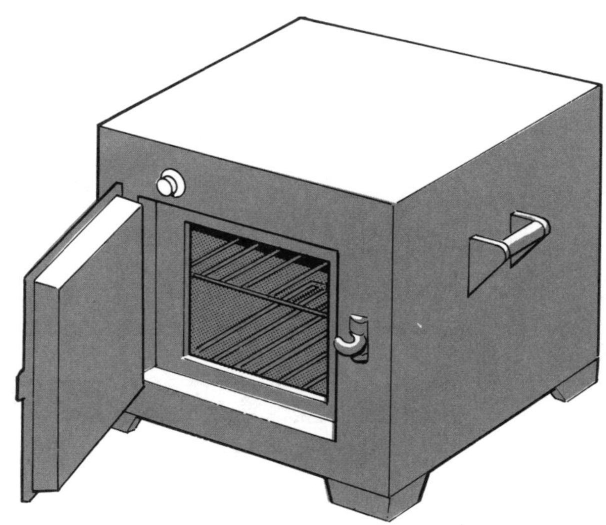

Figure 16.4 An electrode-drying oven.

ture and will therefore be subject to hardening on cooling, the cooling rate should always be controlled, particularly in the range from 400°C to 100°C. Use a low-hydrogen process (such as MAGS) or low-hydrogen electrodes. It is essential to ensure that there is no moisture in electrode coatings, as moisture will cause hydrogen. Electrodes should be baked for at least 30 minutes at 150–200°C in an electrode-drying oven (Figure 16.4) if available; if not, an ordinary oven with temperature control will do.

Avoid stray arcing (catching the electrode on the work in an area that is not being welded): stray arcing on these materials can create a 'stress raiser', causing cracking. The same is true if small tacks are used. Always make strong tack welds and use a planned sequence of welding to reduce the chance of distortion and restraint on joints. On these materials never use small electrodes or low current, or deposit welds with a shallow cross-section, as such actions can increase the risk of cracking.

Armour plate

This is a nickel–chromium–molybdenum steel that can contain between 0.25 and 0.35 per cent carbon. Such steels must be welded with austenitic electrodes that have been designed for the purpose. All the previous precautions, including preheating, should be employed. The welding of these materials usually has to be carried out to a set government welding procedure.

Manganese steels

These fall into two groups: steels containing up to 2 per cent manganese and high-manganese steels containing 12 per cent or more. The first type can be classed as **low-alloy**, and if the carbon content is below 0.25 per cent, normal procedures as for steel are generally satisfactory. Above 0.25 per cent carbon, preheating and the other special precautions for low-alloy steels will be necessary. With high manganese, as heating and slow cooling will

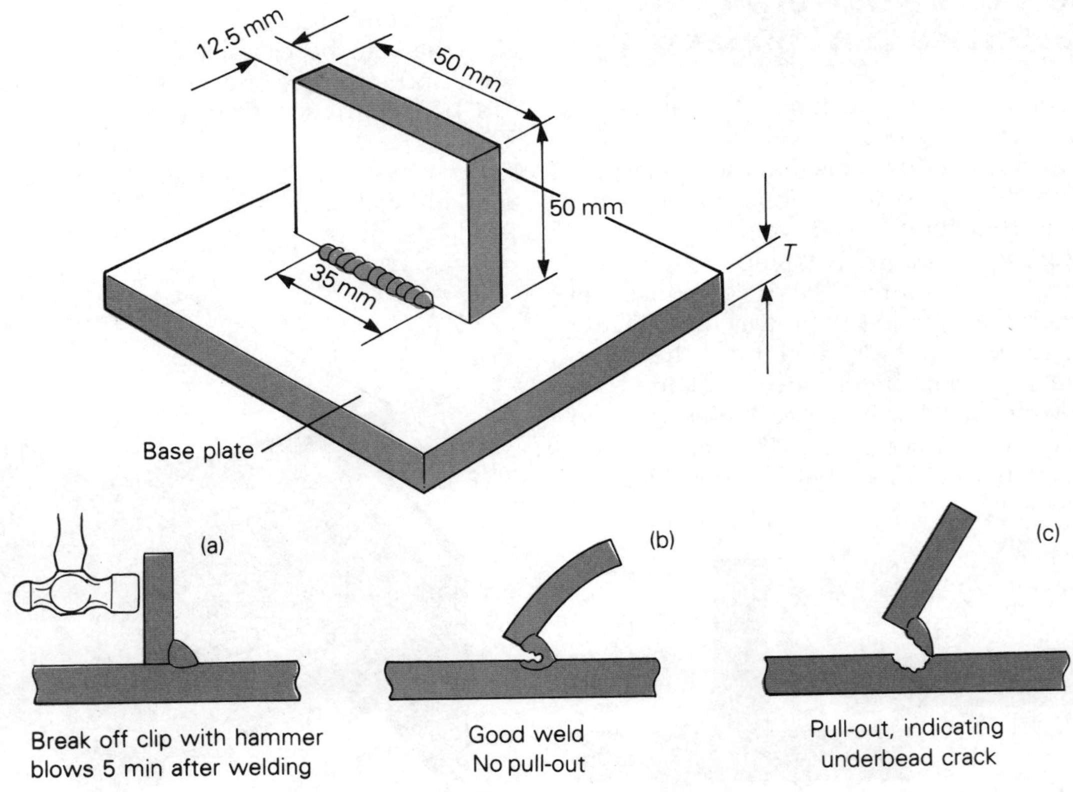

Figure 16.5 The clip test.

cause brittleness, use the lowest current capable of making a satisfactory weld, in order to keep the heat input to an absolute minimum.

The clip test

There are many tests to determine the preheat temperature that may be needed for an unknown steel, but the clip test provides a quick method on site or in the workshop. It is only suitable for sections down to $\frac{3}{8}$ inch (1 cm) thick. It was developed by Sheeham of the Portsmouth Naval Ship Yard.

To perform this test, a clip or lug of low-carbon steel 2 or 3 inches square (50 or 75 mm) and $\frac{1}{2}$ inch thick (12.5 mm) is fillet welded to the unknown steel using the same type of electrode and method that will be employed on the welding job. With a large electrode and a slow speed, clips up to 1 inch (25 mm) thick can be used (Figure 16.5). On completion, allow the weld to cool for five minutes, then break off the lug by hitting it with a hammer. If the lug bends and then finally fails through the weld, the test indicates that the analysis of the steel, the temperature of the steel before welding and the welding procedure are such as to prevent serious underbead cracking (Figure 16.5(b)).

A steel that requires preheating will fail the clip test by the weld pulling out of the parent metal (Figure 16.5(c)). The pulled-out metal is usually bright, indicating that the crack did not extend to the surface or that the crack formation had occurred after the metal had cooled below the temperature at which temper colours occur.

If pull-out takes place, the clip test should be repeated using preheat, starting with 200°C, until satisfactory results are obtained. When the correct parameters are found, these should then be employed on the job.

If the preheat is too high for use on the job, then try the test using a low-hydrogen electrode and reduced preheat. The 18/8 stainless steel electrodes will also make crack-free welds at much lower preheat temperatures than ordinary low carbon steel electrodes.

CHECK YOUR UNDERSTANDING

- Although mild steel is generally weldable by all the major welding processes, you need to consider carefully the appropriate method of welding for a particular application.
- Multipass welds refine the grain structure in the lower deposits.
- Preheating is recommended for steels at increased temperatures as the carbon content exceeds 0.3 per cent.
- Buttering can be used to prevent carbon pick-up. It can also be used for welding certain combinations of dissimilar materials and in cast iron repair.
- For alloy steels, the effect of the various elements can be calculated as a carbon equivalent. Any preheating and post-heating requirements can be determined from this figure.
- When low-hydrogen electrodes are used, it is important to bake them for at least 30 minutes before welding.

REVISION EXERCISES AND QUESTIONS

1. Why should the quality of a multipass weld be better than that of a single-pass weld?
2. State one method of determining the preheat and post-heat requirements of an alloy steel that is to be welded.
3. Name a simple workshop test that can be used to determine how an unknown steel should be welded.
4. What is meant by carbon pick-up?
5. Name a technique that can be used to overcome the problem of carbon pick-up.

(Further practice questions can be found on page 202.)

17 Joining dissimilar metals and coated or clad metals

Introduction

Difficulty is often encountered when dissimilar metals are required to be joined, for a number of reasons, including dilution of one metal, different melting points, and removal of oxide films. Conventional welding processes may not be able to join certain combinations of metals. In such cases, it may be necessary to use a non-fusion technique such as brazing or bronze welding. For example, brass may be joined to steel by depositing bronze on to the steel and then joining the two surfaces with a bronze filler rod or electrode of the same composition.

Brazing and bronze welding

Brazing was developed for applications when soldering was not strong enough. It uses a filler material with a melting point above 430°C, but below that of the metals being joined. Brazing has many valuable applications, but is limited by the fact that preheating must be general. A flux is used to help clean the oxide from the work surfaces and help the filler metal to flow more easily. This flux is usually applied by dipping the heated end of the rod into the tin of flux, although rods can be obtained with a flux core.

Typical examples of the use of brazing are the manufacture of motorcycle and cycle frames. It is also frequently used for the joining of tungsten carbide tips to machine tools. For motorcycle and cycle frames, one tube usually fits inside the one it is to be joined to. The tube surfaces are precleaned by wire brushing or the use of emery paper. The smaller tube is dipped into a flux paste made by mixing the flux with water, before inserting into the larger-diameter tube. The joint area is brought up to red heat using an oxyacetylene flame, and the flux-coated brass rod is melted into the joint.

When brazing steel, the brass (copper and zinc) filler material melts at around 950°C, which is much lower than the melting point of steel. As heat is applied to the joint area, the brass will flow around the joint between the tube surfaces by **capillary attraction**. (Capillary attraction describes the way a liquid travels in a narrow gap. It does not occur if the gap is wide, so joints for brazing are made a fairly close fit.)

For brazing, any suitable heat source can be used, such as a blowpipe, resistance heating or a furnance. For bronze welding, a brass filler rod or electrode is employed, and the heat is therefore obtained by an oxyacetylene flame or an electric arc. The technique of oxyacetylene bronze welding is explained in more detail later in this chapter in the section on joining galvanised steel and in Chapter 18 on joining cast iron.

In both brazing and bronze welding, the filler material melts at a lower temperature than the base material and so they are classed as non-fusion processes.

Transition pieces

Awkward combinations of materials can sometimes be joined together by using what is known as a **transition piece**. This is a piece of metal to which both materials can be readily welded. A novel method of manufacturing a transition piece is by the use of **friction welding**. This is capable of joining dissimilar metals together as it is a solid-state welding process; melting does not take place. It is therefore possible to weld materials such as aluminium to steel with this method.

To make a transition plate that can be used within a fabrication, an aluminium tube can be welded to, say, a stainless steel tube of the same diameter by friction welding. The tube can then be cut and flattened into a plate and the respective sides welded by conventional welding processes, aluminium to aluminium and stainless steel to stainless steel.

Buttering

Buttering is often used when joining dissimilar metals, again to reduce the amount of carbon pick-up by the weld. A typical example is the joining of mild steel to manganese steel. It is best to deposit a layer of manganese on to the mild steel before making the joining weld. Preheat may also be necessary. Another method is to butter the manganese steel surface with a layer of 18/8 stainless steel, and then join the latter to the low-carbon steel by either a stainless steel electrode of similar composition or a mild steel electrode.

When joining cast iron to steel, one method is to deposit either a couple of layers of steel on the cast iron, or a layer of nickel–iron, and then join using either a steel electrode or a nickel–iron electrode. For really difficult material, the cast iron can be bronze welded to the steel, and this can sometimes be made easier by first coating the cast iron with a layer of bronze.

Welding clad materials

A typical clad material is low-carbon steel with a layer of stainless steel to allow the material to be used in a corrosive situation at less expense than if the whole thickness was stainless steel. Such materials can be welded by stainless steel electrodes throughout, or by using mild steel electrodes to just below the cladding and then completing with stainless electrodes. Another way is to treat the clad side as the root and place the bulk of the preparation within the mild steel plate. The mild steel is then welded normally with mild steel electrodes; the root is chipped out to clean metal and welded from the clad side using a stainless steel electrode.

Welding galvanised steel plate

Galvanised plate is just steel plate with a coating of zinc, again to give protection from corrosion. The welding of this material gives off zinc fumes, which can cause 'galvo', or **zinc fume fever**. This is a condition that can last a couple of days, causing sickness and dizziness. Galvanised plate should only be welded out of doors or with the use of a fume extractor. For prolonged welding, a respirator should be worn. After welding using a mild steel electrode or oxyacetylene process, the weld area should either be regalvanised or at least painted to restore protection.

Bronze (braze) welding mild steel (including galvanised steel)

Before bronze welding, ensure that the work surfaces are free from oil, grease and dirt. Remove oxides by grinding, filing or wire brushing. When welding galvanised steel, you can protect the zinc coating near the weld area to some extent by applying copper welding flux in paste form.

If you are not using prefluxed rods, then apply flux by heating the end of the rod and dipping it into powder, or by applying it in paste form. You can use a square-edge preparation with a gap of

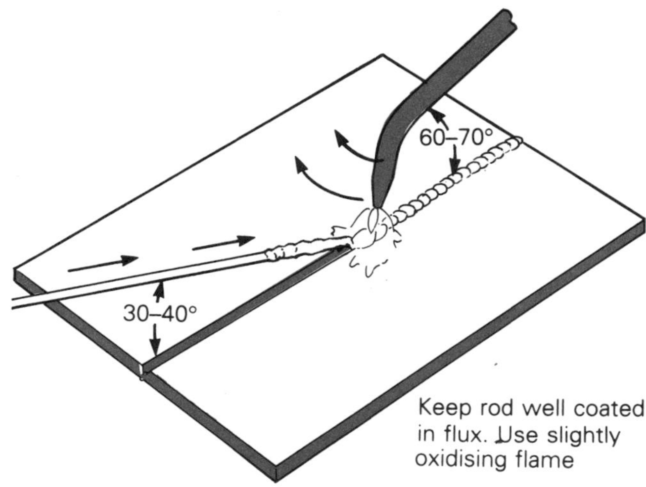

Figure 17.1 Bronze welding of mild galvanised steel sheet.

half the plate thickness up to 3.5 mm plate; above this thickness change to 60–90° 'V' preparation with a gap of around a quarter of the plate thickness. Set the plates with a slight tapered gap (wider at the end you are welding towards), and use a slightly oxidising flame. The blowpipe and filler rod should be held as in Figure 17.1. To prevent overheating or oxidation make sure that you direct the flame only on to the melting filler and weld deposit.

When the pool is established, withdrawing the flame slightly allows partial freezing of the molten pool. Then introduce the filler rod and the flame again. This careful procedure, when repeated, allows for heat control and the controlled progression of the molten pool. The weld area only needs to be heated to bright red for the brass to run freely, and so care must be taken not to overheat. The finished weld surface should be bright in appearance and free from any porosity. Clean flux residue from the completed weld. You can complete fillet joints in a similar manner.

CHECK YOUR UNDERSTANDING

- Brazing is one method of joining dissimilar materials if a colour match is not required and a non-fusion method is acceptable.
- Bronze welding can also be used for welding coated or galvanised steel.
- Full fume extraction, or welding out of doors, is required with galvanised material.

REVISION EXERCISES AND QUESTIONS

1. Why must galvanised steel be welded out of doors, or full fume extraction be used if welding indoors?
2. Explain the term 'capillary attraction'.
3. What is a transition piece?
4. When a low-carbon steel is coated with a layer of stainless steel, what is it then known as?

(Further practice questions can be found on p. 202.)

18 Welding cast iron

Introduction

Cast iron is a general term used to cover a wide range of alloys of carbon and iron with carbon content between 2 and $4\frac{1}{2}$ per cent. Increased carbon content improves hardness with a decrease in ductility. From a welding point of view, we must always consider cast iron as being extremely hard and brittle. Always take great care in planning and carrying out welding operations on these materials.

Types of cast iron

The bronze welding technique can be used satisfactorily on many types of cast iron repair. It is generally used when a colour match is not important (if the component is to be painted afterwards), or if a lower-temperature process is necessary. The oxyacetylene method is shown in Figure 18.1. Tacks are made and then the surfaces to be joined are coated with a layer of filler metal for a distance of about 20 mm ($\frac{3}{4}$ inch). The weld is then commenced and continued to conclusion with repeated 'tinning' and welding.

Very broadly, the composition of cast iron will be 2–4 per cent carbon, 0.4–1 per cent manganese, 0.04–0.15 per cent sulphur, 0.4–1 per cent phosphorus and 1–3 per cent silicon. From the welding point of view, after the high carbon content, the sulphur is the most undesirable element because it will reduce the ductility of the material at red heat and increase the amount of shrinkage

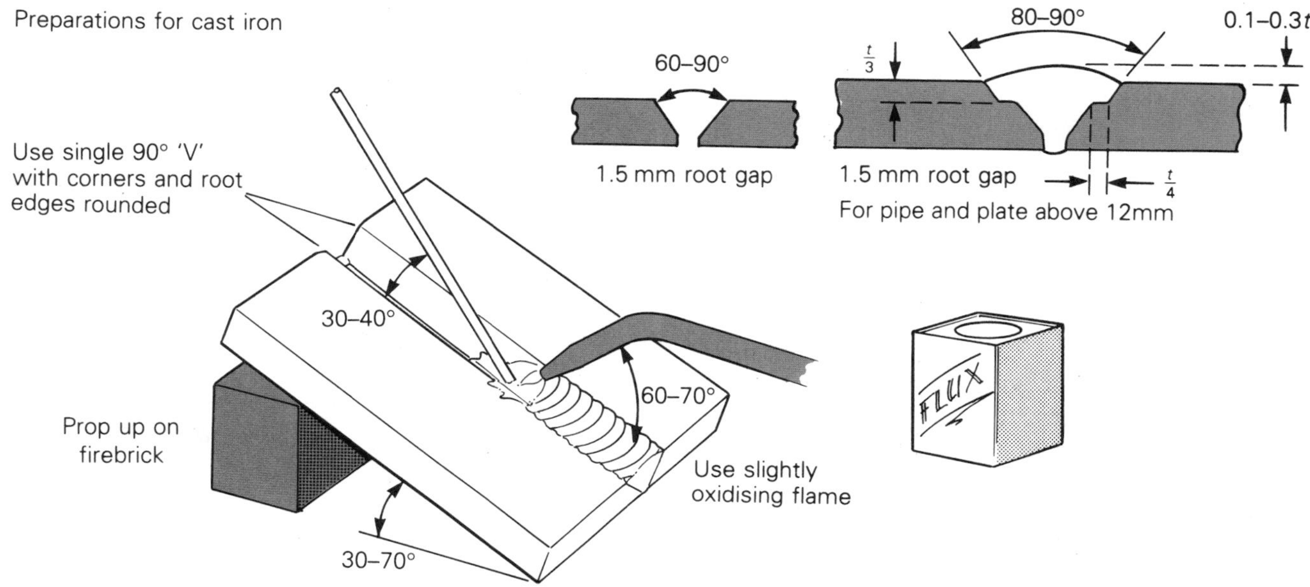

Figure 18.1 Bronze welding of cast iron.

on cooling. In manufacture, therefore, attempts are made to keep the sulphur content as low as possible.

Cast iron welding will be used mostly in the salvage or repair welding of cast iron components. Each welding job will therefore present its own problems and require a planned procedure. Before we can weld this material, we need to consider the different types of cast iron and the various welding methods available.

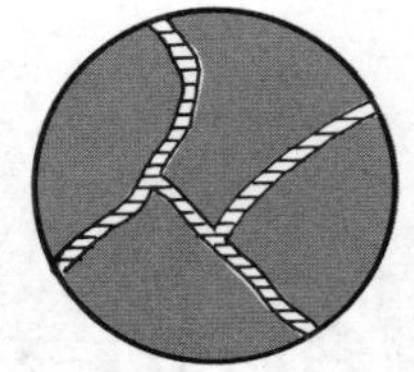

Low-strength sulphide films on grain boundaries will cause metal to tear apart under contraction, as they remain liquid until a low temperature is reached

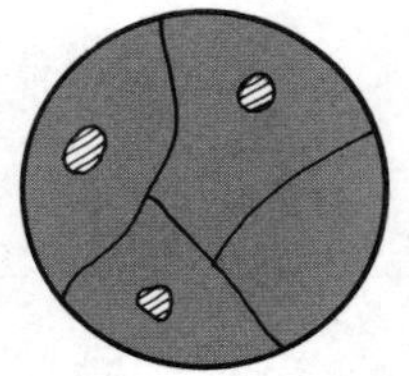

Manganese sulphide globules. Sulphur is removed from grain boundaries

Figure 18.2 Showing how addition of manganese prevents grain boundary films.

White cast iron

This is an extremely hard and brittle material. The carbon is combined as either cementite or martensite. A fracture in this material will have a white appearance, which gives the metal its name. White cast iron is produced either by rapid cooling, which will prevent the carbon from separating out, or by adding alloying elements that prevent the carbon from forming graphite.

White cast iron is classed as very difficult to weld, and is therefore only welded when low-quality welds will be satisfactory, as when building up chilled iron rolls, for example. Using coated manual metal arc electrodes, the first couple of layers will be cracked and porous, but the result will improve with a third and fourth layer. The coating will probably serve its purpose, but will be only moderately fused to the white iron. Oxyacetylene welding of this material is also limited.

In all welding operations, care must be taken to avoid producing white cast iron, unless it is required for providing a hard surface. When welding, fast cooling will produce white cast iron from grey cast iron, and the only way to restore it to grey cast iron would be to remelt the whole casting!

Grey cast iron

This is the most widely used type of cast iron. It is used for components where strength and wear resistance requirements are not too high and there is no shock loading in service. It can be found in use as flywheels, gear wheels, bedplates, machine frames, crankcases, cylinder blocks, brackets and pump bodies. Grey iron is so called because of the grey colour of a fracture surface in this material.

Grey cast iron is much softer than white cast iron, and is readily machinable. This is because not all the carbon is in the combined state cementite form, as in white cast iron; a certain amount is in the form of free graphite. The precipitation of the carbon in graphite form can be aided by the addition of silicon to the cast iron. However, slow cooling is essential for the cementite to break down into free graphite and iron. This takes place between around 750°C and 650°C when the casting is cooling down, and a definite expansion of the casting occurs between these temperatures. Too rapid a cooling rate, even when a casting contains silicon, will prevent the carbon from leaving the combination with iron, which will result in the formation of white cast iron.

Manganese is added to cast iron to prevent the formation of sulphide films (Figure 18.2). Both sulphur and manganese, as separate elements, will tend to prevent the breakdown from cementite to graphite, but when they are combined as manganese sulphide the effect is removed, as the sulphur is not able to form boundary films.

The small amount of phosphorus present in cast iron will have no adverse effect on the carbon in grey cast iron. It will, however, improve the fluidity of the cast iron.

Grey cast iron can be welded by the electric arc or oxyacetylene processes. Large castings can also be welded, after preheating, by either the carbon arc process using cast iron filler rods or the Thermit process (see Chapter 27).

Malleable cast iron

This type of cast iron is made by the prolonged heating of white cast iron in the presence of iron oxide. This has the effect of decarburising the surface to a depth of about 3 mm (depending on the length of time heated). This makes the surface soft and ductile, and the general strength and ductility of the whole casting are considerably increased. Malleable cast iron can be distinguished from ordinary cast iron by removing a chip by means of a hammer and chisel. A chip from a malleable iron casting will curl off in a similar manner to mild steel, instead of breaking in a brittle manner like a brittle cast iron chip.

As fusion welding of malleable iron would destroy its malleability and ductility, non-fusion welding is recommended. Oxyacetylene welding using bronze filler rods will give the best results, as this will minimise reduction in the malleability of the metal and yet will provide a joint as strong as the casting.

Painting the completed job after welding can conceal the difference in colour match.

Spheroidal cast iron

This is a special type of cast iron to which magnesium has been added in order to change the flake-graphite structure into spheroidal or nodular form. This has the effect of approximately doubling the strength and also increasing the ductility and shock resistance. It is readily welded by the normal methods. A typical example is the use of a 55% nickel and 45% iron electrode for electric arc welding.

Choice of welding method

In general, if a full preheat of 650°C (or 700°C for a casting of complicated shape) can be given, then the oxyacetylene method using the leftward technique and a cast iron filler rod and flux will provide a very sound fusion weld, as will the use of a cast iron filler rod and the carbon arc process. The Thermit process can be employed for large fractures. All of these methods are actually 'casting' similar material into the fracture and provide the nearest match to the parent material.

Preheating furnaces can be either permanent gas-fired or 'temporary' charcoal (Figure 18.3). The charcoal type can provide more equal heating for complicated shapes. If possible, the casting should be welded in the furnace, the furnace lid replaced and the casting left to cool down with the furnace.

With the arc welding procedure, using stick electrodes, only complicated castings should require preheating, unless the weather is very cold, in which case they should be preheated to around 300°C to minimise the risk of cracking.

As with other materials, the prepared edges for cast iron welding must be clean. For thick sections vee out both sides if possible, leaving a central portion of original fracture for alignment. Chipping or melting out is preferable to grinding, as grinding can smear graphite over the surfaces.

For gas welding, use cast iron rods of the high-silicon type and a cast iron flux, as the surface oxide has a higher melting point than the cast iron. The flux helps to break this down, as does stirring the molten pool with the filler rod and skimming any oxide out of the weld with the end of the rod. When adding filler metal, always keep the end of the rod in the molten pool. Always use a strictly neutral flame.

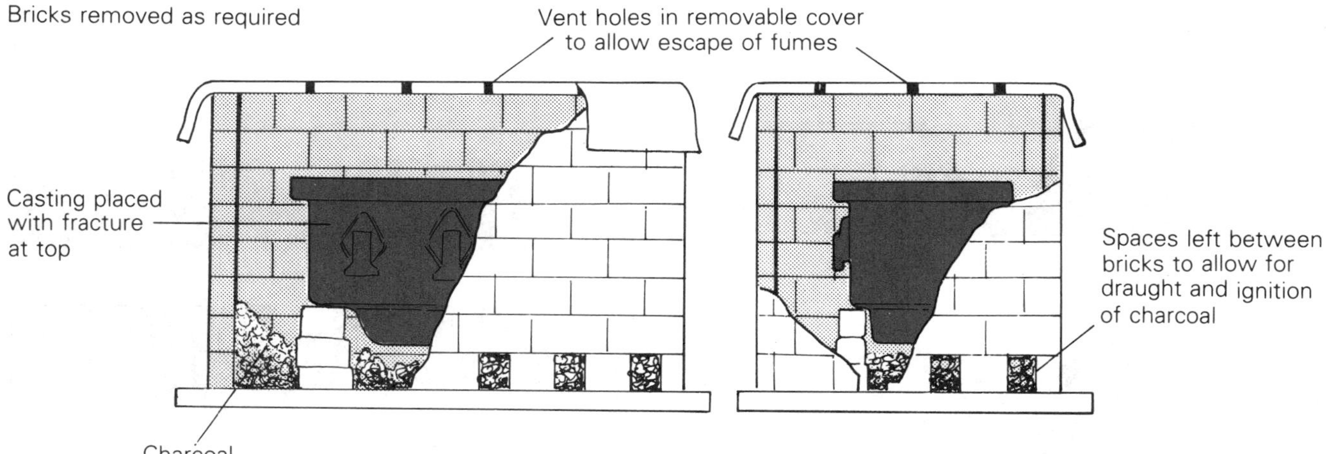

Figure 18.3 A temporary charcoal preheating furnace; bricks partially removed to show inside.

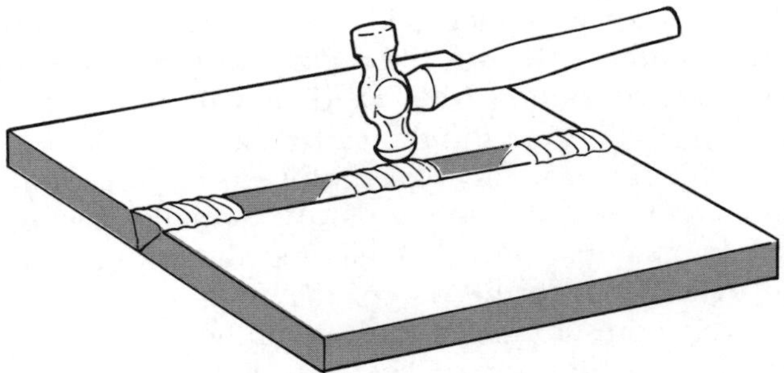

Figure 18.4 Peening and skip welding method.

For manual metal arc welding there are four main categories of electrode:

1. Those with a core wire of Monel metal.
2. Electrodes with a core wire of 55% nickel 45% iron. Both these types will deposit a machinable weld metal and can be used for the repair of castings with or without preheating.
3. Electrodes with a core wire of low-carbon mild steel. This type is sometimes used for the welding of thick section repairs and will require full preheating if machining is required.
4. Electrodes with a bronze core wire. These can be used for the repair of thin section castings and malleable iron where the colour of the deposit does not matter too much. Preheating is not required.

If castings are arc welded without preheat, the main problem will be to keep the contraction stresses to a minimum and avoid hard zones. This can be largely achieved by keeping the casting as cool as possible and employing a filler material giving a deposit that is capable of absorbing contraction stresses.

Skip welding should be employed, depositing short runs (40 mm length) and immediately lightly peening the deposit with a ball peen hammer, in order to expand the shrinking weld deposit and, in so doing, reduce the contraction stresses (Figure 18.4). Depositing short weld beads helps to reduce the heat input, minimising the chance of hard zones forming. As a test, you should be able to place your hand on the casting about 80 mm away from any welding area before recommencing welding; if you cannot do this, the casting is too hot and you should not recommence welding until it has cooled.

For full-thickness welds (Figure 18.5) a buttering layer can be deposited on each face, using nickel-alloy electrodes. This will ensure that the fusion zone will be soft and ductile and free from hard carbides. The bulk of the weld can then be completed by using less expensive low-carbon steel electrodes which, because of the buttering layer, will no longer be affected by the carbon in the casting.

When access to the repair is limited to one side, a grooved preparation can be employed (Figure 18.6), although preparation from both sides is preferable. As the deposited metal is stronger than the grey cast iron, the weld need not be made through the full section thickness and, as stated earlier, retaining an area of fracture face can assist in aligning the components.

Mild steel studs can be screwed into the fracture surfaces to give basic reinforcement for welded repairs (Figure 18.7). On fracture surfaces, the studs should be staggered and should project from the fracture face for a distance of 3 mm ($\frac{1}{8}$ inch) less than the amount of build-up required.

When welding preheated castings with buttered faces, deposit up to half the electrode in one run, as long runs can cause transverse cracking. Allow the welding area to cool down to the preheat

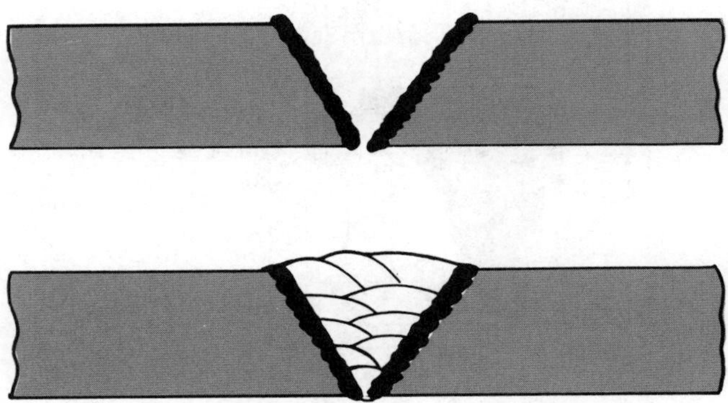

Figure 18.5 The buttering technique for welding cast iron.

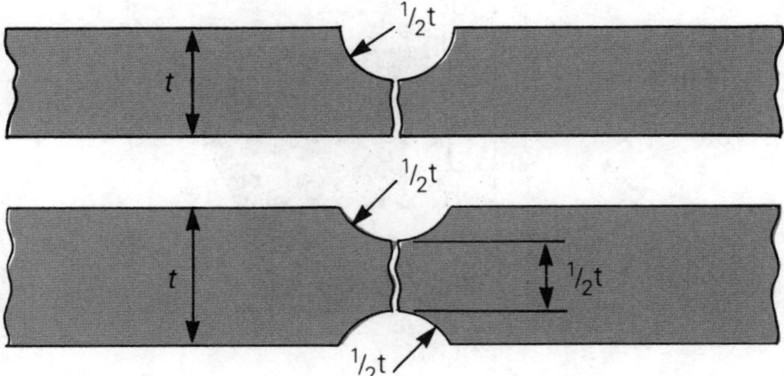

Figure 18.6 Examples of single-sided and double-sided preparations for welding cast iron fractures.

Figure 18.7 **Studding as preparation for the welded repair of a cast iron gear tooth.**

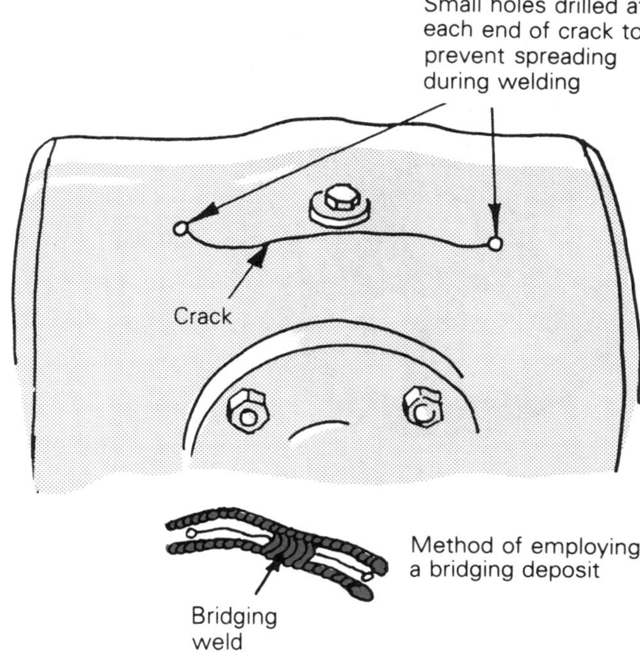

Figure 18.8 **Methods to prevent a crack from spreading.**

temperature before depositing the next run. Use the skip welding technique to balance out the heat input. Deposit on one side of the joint and then the other, joining together the metal deposited on both sides with the final runs.

When welding cold castings with prepared or buttered faces, if preheat is not possible, allow the heat to disperse down to hand heat after depositing each run. Restrict the length of each run to a maximum of 75 mm (3 inches). Do not weave the electrode.

A tip when welding a crack in a casting is to drill a small hole at each end of the crack to prevent it from spreading during welding (Figure 18.8).

A grey cast iron that has been subjected to repeated high temperatures will become unweldable because of internal oxidation. Items such as fire grates that have been subjected to high temperatures are therefore unweldable. If an oxyacetylene flame is applied to such a material it will refuse to melt, and will give off a dazzling light similar to that produced when a flame is directed on to a fire brick.

Figures 18.9 and 18.10 show the welding sequence and local preheat required for two types of repair on a cast iron wheel.

Figures 18.11–18.18 show various types of cast iron repair welds. Such repairs can save a lot of money, for they not only save the cost of the original component and the cost of a new component, but much time in waiting for a new component to arrive (if one is available).

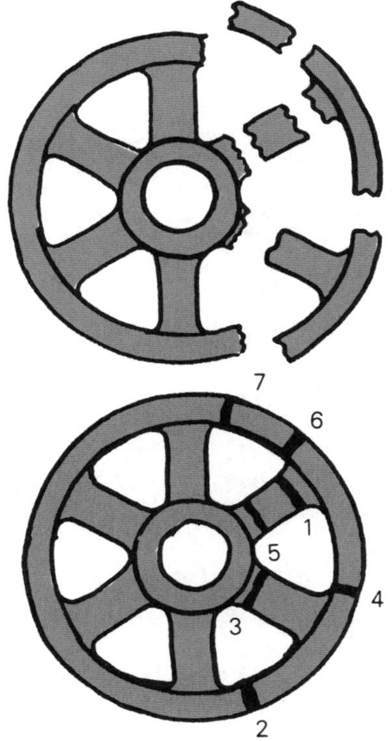

Figure 18.9 **Welding sequence for repairing a badly broken cast iron gear wheel (see also Figures 18.12 and 18.13).**

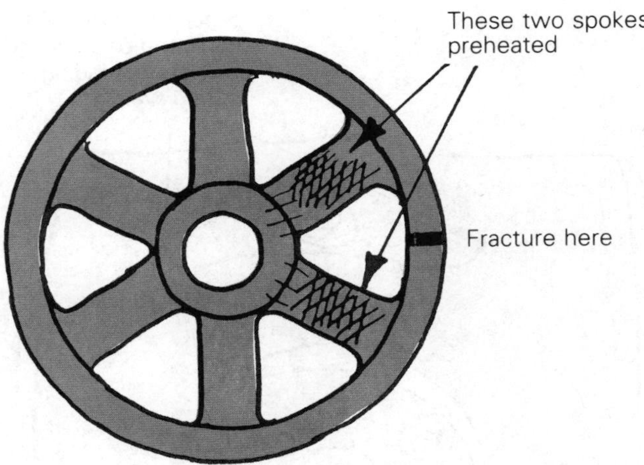

Figure 18.10 Showing local preheat to spokes in order to weld fracture in rim.

Figure 18.11 Broken gear wheel teeth repaired by welding without preheat using nickel–iron electrodes. (Courtesy of UTP, UK and UTC, Nigeria and Ghana)

Figure 18.12 Mortar mixer drive gear in need of welding repair. (Courtesy of UTP, UK and UTC, Nigeria and Ghana)

Figure 18.13 The same mortar mixer drive gear, ready for putting back into service after repair by manual metal arc welding. (Courtesy of UTP, UK and UTC, Nigeria and Ghana)

Figure 18.14 Cracked diesel engine block. (Courtesy of UTP, UK and UTC, Nigeria and Ghana)

Figure 18.15 Cracked block welded with pure nickel deposit and engine ready for putting back into service. (Courtesy of UTP, UK and UTC, Nigeria and Ghana)

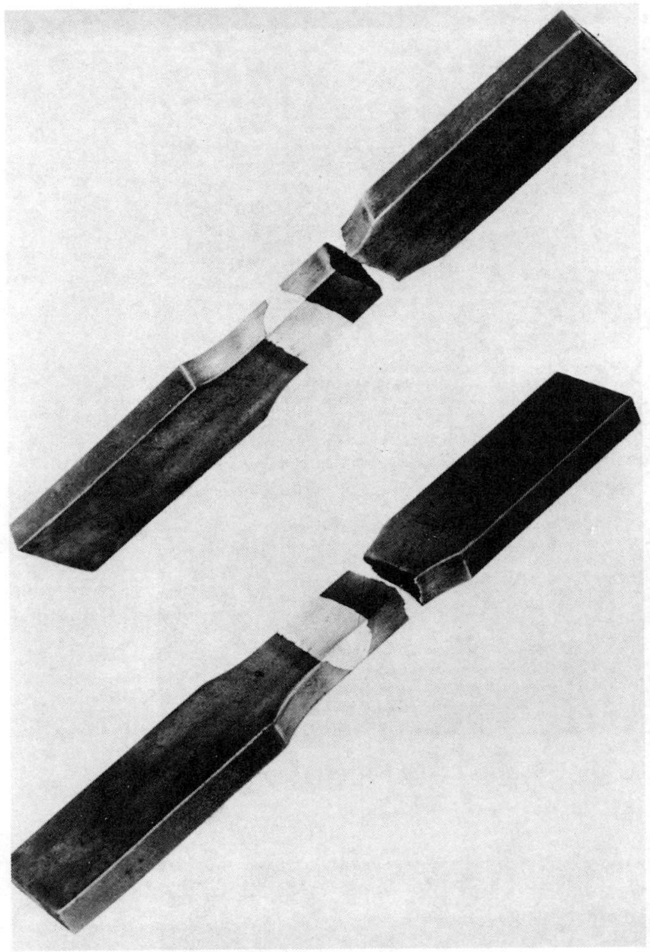

Figure 18.16 Showing the strength of a nickel–iron manual metal arc weld between two cast iron plates. In a tensile test, the plate fails, not the weld. (Courtesy of UTP, UK and UTC, Nigeria and Ghana)

Figure 18.17 Cracked cast iron compressor cylinder. (Courtesy of UTP, UK and UTC, Nigeria and Ghana)

Figure 18.18 Cylinder put back into service after repair by manual metal arc welding using nickel electrode. (Courtesy of UTP, UK and UTC, Nigeria and Ghana)

CHECK YOUR UNDERSTANDING

- Bronze welding is one method of carrying out cast iron repairs.
- Grey cast iron is the most widely used type. For full fusion oxyacetylene welding, a preheat of around 650°C will be required; for manual metal arc welding, only complicated castings should require preheating.
- Studs screwed into the preparation faces can give extra strength to a repair.

REVISION EXERCISES AND QUESTIONS

1 Name the most widely used type of cast iron.
2 What preheat temperature will be required for oxyacetylene fusion welding of cast iron?
3 How does white cast iron get its name?
4 Why is white cast iron difficult or impossible to weld?
5 When oxyacetylene welding cast iron, what type of flame should you use?

(Further practice questions can be found on page 202.)

19 Welding stainless steel

Introduction

The term **stainless steel** covers a group of corrosion- and heat-resisting steels containing larger percentages of chromium and nickel than in the high tensile steels.

Types of stainless steel

There are many different compositions, but all the stainless steels fall into three main groups (see also Appendix 8, Duplex stainless steels, on page 238), as follows.

Martensitic stainless steel

This group contains from 11.5 to 14 per cent chromium and from 0.2 to 0.4 per cent carbon. Such steels are difficult to weld because they can form the very hard martensitic structure regardless of the cooling rate. They are known as **air-hardening steels**. They can be welded by preheating to around 350°C and using a 25 per cent chromium and 20 per cent nickel flux coated electrode. A post-heat of 750°C usually ensures acceptable ductility.

Ferritic stainless steel

This group contains between 16 and 30 per cent chromium, with a maximum of 0.1 per cent carbon. These materials can be welded with a preheat of 150°C and the use of the 25 per cent chromium and 20 per cent nickel core wire electrode. Sometimes combination welds are made, with the final layers being completed with electrodes of even higher chromium content (up to 30 per cent), in order to give the surface an extremely high resistance to corrosion. A postheat at 730°C should be performed immediately after welding to prevent brittleness.

Austenitic stainless steel

This third group contains chromium and nickel in amounts that give a predominantly austenitic structure. The composition of austenitic stainless steels can be varied to suit the application, with chromium content from 7 to 30 per cent and a range of nickel content from 6 to 36 per cent, with carbon content below 0.25 per cent.

One of the most important steels in this group contains approximately 18 per cent chromium and 8 per cent nickel, with a carbon content less than 0.12 per cent. This steel is readily welded by many processes if small amounts of titanium or niobium are added in the manufacturing process (see the section below on weld decay).

For special use at high temperatures, steels with 25 per cent chromium and 20 per cent nickel can be used.

Practical welding considerations

In general, austenitic stainless steels are much more easily welded than martensitic and ferritic stainless steels. Although they work-harden more easily than mild steel, they can be readily formed by the usual fabrication processes. Oxyacetylene cutting will not work on stainless steel, as it cannot form

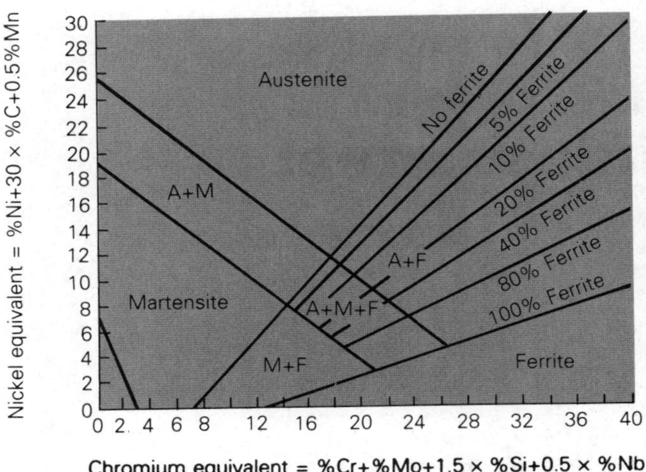

Figure 19.1 The Schaeffler diagram.

oxides, but powder injection cutting and the plasma arc will cut through it easily. The best results are obtained with plasma.

Stainless steels have a higher coefficient of expansion and a much lower heat conductivity than mild steel. This means that distortion can be more of a problem. Because of the lower conductivity, shorter electrodes are made to avoid overheating.

Hot cracking (see Chapter 22) can be a problem in fully austenitic welds, because impurities in the form of low-melting-point compounds can form at the grain boundaries, weakening them. This problem can be overcome when welding most austenitic materials by adjusting the filler rod/electrode material to produce 4–5 per cent ferrite in the weld deposit. It is considered that harmful impurities are more soluble in ferrite than austenite.

The guide to choosing the correct filler material is given by the **Schaeffler diagram** (Figure 19.1), in which the chromium equivalent and the nickel equivalent can be worked out to give a position for filler material within the diagram. (See also Appendix 9, page 239). However, **dilution** (see Figure 19.2) must also be taken into account.

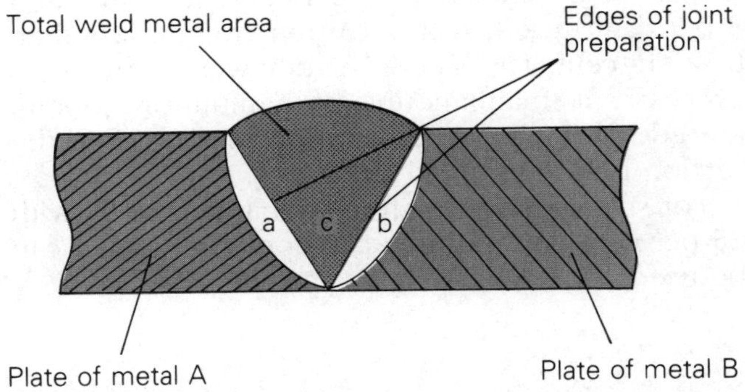

$$\text{Dilution} = \frac{\text{Area } a + \text{Area } b}{\text{Area } c} \times 100\%$$

where a = melted area (or volume) of plate A
b = melted area (or volume) of plate B
c = Total area (or volume) of weld

Figure 19.2 Explanation of 'dilution'.

Weld decay

An unstabilised stainless steel – one without additions of titanium or niobium – is likely to suffer from what is known as intercrystalline corrosion or **weld decay** if welding takes place. This condition is caused by precipitation of chromium carbides at the grain boundaries in those areas where the steel has reached temperatures within the range of 450–850°C because of the heat of welding. Weld decay can occur at a slight distance from the actual weld, on either side in the plate material (Figure 19.3). The removal of chromium from the edges of the grains makes the material much less resistant to corrosion, and can cause failure of the material.

Weld decay can be prevented by heating the work to 1100°C and then cooling very rapidly or by using material with a very low carbon content (less than 0.04 per cent). The best solution, and the one most widely employed, is to use materials containing added elements that have a greater affinity for carbon than chromium has. These elements are called stabilising elements and include titanium, niobium and tantalum (Niobium is also known as columbium.) It is fairly common practice for titanium to be added to the plate material and niobium to be added to the electrodes.

There are a wide range of stainless steels and matching electrodes and filler rods available, designed to give a deposit that will match the different parent metals as closely as possible.

Welding stabilised stainless steels

These materials can be welded by all the main processes. Oxyacetylene, manual metal arc, tungsten arc gas-shielded and metal arc gas-shielded welding will all produce sound welds when the following considerations are taken into account (Figure 19.4).

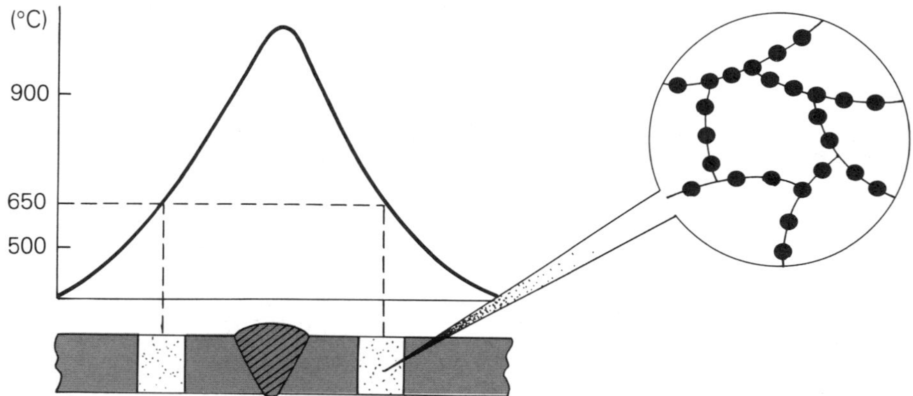

Figure 19.3 Weld decay. Precipitation of chromium carbides at the grain boundaries leaves areas of chrome depletion open to corrosive attack.

Because of the higher coefficient of expansion, great care must be taken to prevent distortion. For example, tacks must be made closer than for mild steel and they should be ground out before completing the joint. To minimise the likelihood of distortion, careful consideration should be given to the sequence in which welds are deposited. Weaving should be kept to a minimum or not used at all, and a short arc should be maintained.

Figure 19.4 Stainless steel vessel fabricated using the manual metal arc process and an all-positional niobium-stabilised stainless steel electrode. (Courtesy of UTP, UK and UTC, Nigeria and Ghana)

Weld preparations are usually the same as those used for mild steel, although when welding thin sheet by the manual metal arc process (up to and including 3 mm), it is good practice to deposit a run of weld on both sides to ensure that there is sound metal on both faces (Figure 19.5). When using a backing bar, this will not be necessary, as good penetration will be possible by welding from one side, using a larger-gauge electrode.

For oxyacetylene welding, clean the joint area on both sides. Remove any oil or dirt using a solvent, and then wire-brush using a stainless steel brush or stainless wire wool. Brush stainless steel flux paste on the underside of the joint; fluxing of the filler rod is not normally necessary. Use a strictly neutral flame and the leftward technique. On fabrications, plan the deposition of runs to spread out heat input and to avoid an end crater. Withdraw the flame slowly to allow the weld metal to solidify under its protection.

The tungsten arc gas-shielded and metal arc gas-shielded processes are well suited to welding this material. TAGS welding is capable of producing welds of high quality, although it is of course much slower than manual metal arc or MAGS welding. Backing bars with the facility for back purging (Figure 19.6) can be employed with both TAGS and MAGS in order to control and protect the penetration bead.

For TAGS welding, the plates should be cleaned as for gas welding, although of course no flux will be required. A direct current supply is used with the tungsten electrode negative. It is best to use a thoriated tungsten if possible, as it will produce a

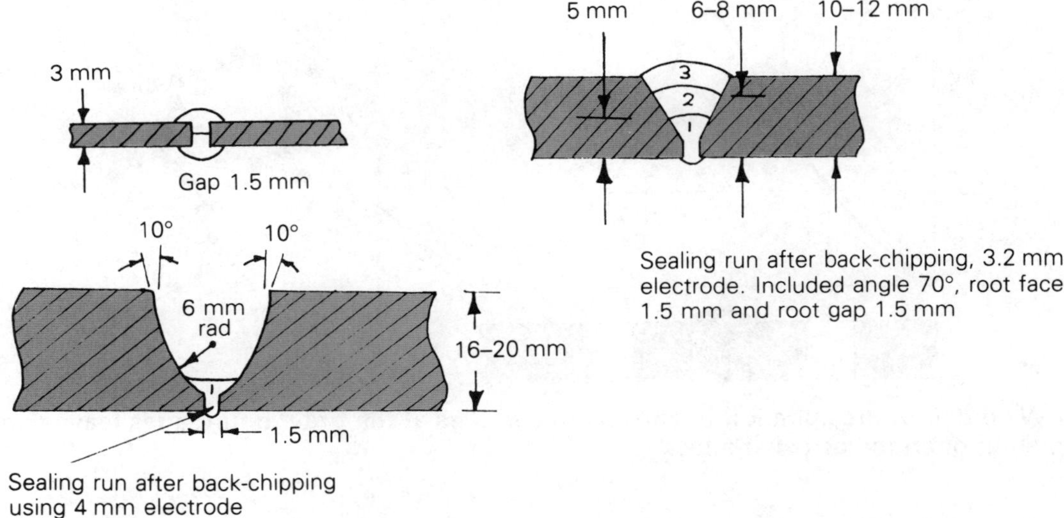

Figure 19.5 **Example procedures for butt welding of austenitic stainless steels by the manual metal arc process in the flat position.**

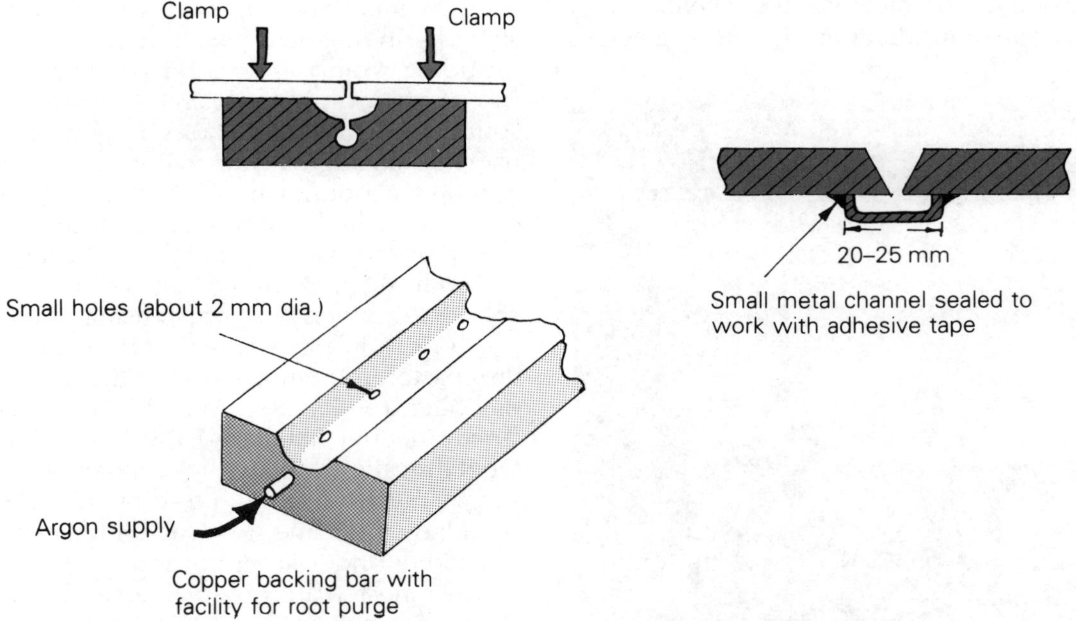

Figure 19.6 **Methods of back purging (protecting root with shielding gas) applicable to TAGS and MAGS welding.**

more stable arc and can be used with higher currents than a pure tungsten electrode. The shielding gas is usually argon, but mixtures of argon and helium or argon and hydrogen (up to 5 per cent) can be employed on thicker plate. These mixtures can help to give a more fluid weld pool and faster deposition rates because of the higher temperature of the arc.

Avoid all draughts with gas-shielded methods, and place tents over welding points when welding outside, in order that the protective shield is not blown away. Hold the TAGS welding torch almost vertical to the line of travel, feeding the filler rod into the leading edge of the molten pool and never removing the heated end of the rod from the protection of the gas shield while welding. To prevent excessive dilution keep weaving to a minimum. The electrode extension (beyond the nozzle) should be as little as possible: 3–5 mm for butt welds and 6–12 mm (maximum) for fillet welds.

Keep the arc length at around 2 mm when welding without filler and between 3 mm and 4 mm when filler rod is employed. Gas shielding should be plentiful, using a gas lens (see Figure 7.9) if required, to prevent turbulence.

For MAGS welding, as with the other processes, clean the material around the joint area, and choose a filler material whose wire composition matches the material being welded and the properties required from the welded joint. Generally, all austenitic wires will fall into the following designations: 18/8 stainless steel, 18/8 stabilised stainless steel, 25/12 heat-resisting steel, 25/20 heat-resisting steel and 18/8/3 Mo stainless steel.

The shielding gas most used for austenitic steels is argon with 2 per cent oxygen at flow rates of 1.15 m^3/hr for spray transfer and 0.80 m^3/hr for pulsed transfer.

For welding stainless steel to mild steel it is best to use a stainless steel electrode (or wire). This is even more necessary when making welds between stainless steel and low-alloy or high-carbon steels to prevent weld embrittlement and cracking. Dilution must also be considered.

CHECK YOUR UNDERSTANDING

- The term 'stainless steel' covers a group of corrosion- and heat-resisting steels containing large percentages of chromium and nickel. The three main groups of stainless steel are: martensitic, ferritic and austenitic.
- In general, austenitic stainless steels are much more easily welded than martensitic or ferritic.
- Stainless steels have a higher coefficient of expansion and much lower heat conductivity than mild steel. This means that distortion can be more of a problem.
- Hot cracking can be overcome when welding most austenitic materials by adjusting the filler rod/electrode material to produce 4–5 per cent ferrite in the weld deposit, as harmful impurities are more soluble in ferrite than in austenite.
- The guide to choosing the correct filler material is given by the Schaeffler diagram.
- Weld decay can be eliminated by adding stabilising elements such as niobium both to the plate material and to the electrodes/filler wires.
- MAGS and TAGS welding are widely used on stainless steels.

REVISION EXERCISES AND QUESTIONS

1. What are the main alloying elements in stainless steel?
2. Which is the easiest type of stainless steel to weld?
3. Why might distortion be more of a problem with a stainless steel fabrication than a mild steel structure?
4. How can hot cracking be overcome when welding austenitic materials?
5. How is weld decay eliminated?

(Further practice questions can be found on page 202.)

Welding aluminium

Introduction

Aluminium and aluminium alloys are the lightest commercial metals in use in large quantities. Correct alloying gives the alloys good tensile strength.

The manual metal arc and oxyacetylene processes require corrosive fluxes made from chlorides and fluorides in order to dissolve the layer of aluminium oxide (alumina) from the metal's surface and also to prevent further oxidation during welding. These fluxes require the joint to be designed so that flux does not become trapped and allowed to 'eat' away at the joint during service. These fluxes and flux residues must also be thoroughly removed after welding. This is done by washing and brushing with hot water after the component has cooled, or by immersion in a 5 per cent solution of nitric acid in water, followed by washing and rinsing with hot water.

If manual metal arc and oxyacetylene processes are the only ones available, then avoid lap and fillet joints, as they will tend to trap residues of this corrosive flux in areas that cannot be reached by post-weld cleaning.

If TAGS or MAGS welding is available, these types of joints can be readily welded, as no flux is required with these two processes. The oxide film is removed by the electrical cathodic cleaning action, and further contamination during welding is prevented by the inert gas shield.

For all processes, take care that the area to be welded is free from contaminants such as paint, oxides and oil. Clean it immediately before welding. (See Chapter 3; if solvents are used they must be completely evaporated from the area before welding.)

Aluminium has a low melting point (around 660°C) and a high thermal conductivity. These properties, combined with the fact that there is virtually no colour change before melting takes place, require practice to get used to. If a welder has never welded aluminium before, some time should be spent in practice on scrap materials to fully master the technique, before attempting a real job.

Oxyacetylene welding

For oxyacetylene welding, a good flux having a melting point of around 570°C will be necessary to dissolve the oxide film, which has a higher melting point than the aluminium. Dip the filler rod in the flux and then make the flux wash down the rod using the torch flame. On thin plate, the upturned edge preparation can be used, as for mild steel, without the use of a filler rod. For thicker sections (over 3 mm) the edges should have a 90° 'V'. For plates over 6 mm in thickness, a double 90° 'V' may be used. Adjust the flame to neutral and use the leftward technique. Clean the weld after welding.

Manual metal arc welding

For manual metal arc welding, connect the electrode to the positive terminal of a direct current welding supply. You will find that a layer of flux can form on the end of the electrode in use, and that you therefore have to strike it very hard in order to reignite the arc.

Keep the electrode at right angles to the weld. Use a short arc with no weaving (Figure 20.1). Too long an arc length can allow oxidation and the formation of a brittle weld. Preheat castings to 200°C before welding; this reduces the tendency to

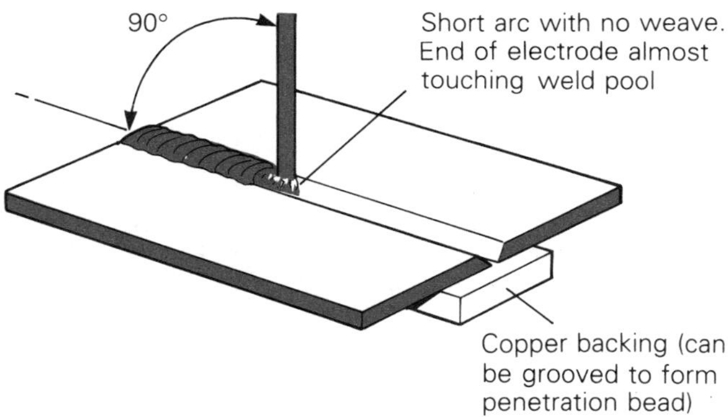

Figure 20.1 Manual metal arc welding of aluminium.

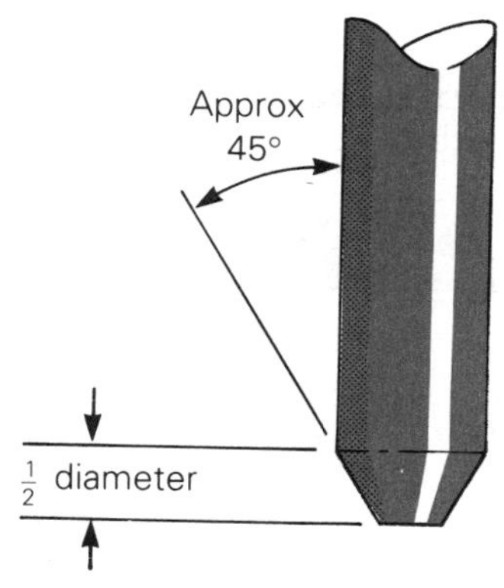

Figure 20.2 Electrode shape for a.c. TAGS welding. It will round up once the arc is struck.

cracking and speeds up welding. For pure aluminium and non-heat-treatable alloys, the preheat temperature should be 350°C.

TAGS welding

Tungsten arc gas shielded welding is usually employed on aluminium using an alternating current supply, as the oxide film is removed when the tungsten is positive on one half-cycle, allowing the tungsten to cool when it is negative on the next half-cycle. However, direct current pulsed arc welding can be employed on very thin sheet of high purity.

Argon or helium is employed as the shielding gas and electrodes for use on a.c. should be of 0.8 per cent zirconiated tungsten. The electrode tip should be ground as shown in Figure 20.2.

For best results, use filler rods as soon as they are removed from the packet.

MAGS welding

When metal arc gas shielded welding is used, the recommended shielding gas is argon. Helium can be used for welding very heavy sections, as it tends to provide deeper-penetration welds, but the arc is more erratic in helium and the resulting weld bead appearance is usually not as good as for a weld produced with argon shielding. Mixtures of argon and helium can be used to give advantages not obtained with either gas on its own.

Some aluminium wires, such as the pure aluminiums (99.8 or 99 per cent aluminium), are too soft to feed through a long conduit from a spool based on the welding machine. A **spool-on-gun** arrangement (Figure 20.3) can be used in such cases. The addition of magnesium and other alloying elements can help to stiffen the wire, allowing the use of large machine-mounted reels.

Again, you will need to clean the joint area, and you should avoid over-handling the electrode wire. Wear clean cotton gloves when loading the spool and replace the plastic cover over the spool electrode wire as soon as possible to prevent possible contamination. The gun should point in the direction of welding at an angle of 15° to the vertical. Ensure that the welding area is free from draughts and that fume extraction equipment is not overpowerful, as this can disturb the protective gas shield. As with the other processes, temporary or permanent backing can be employed. Pipes can be filled with argon from a separate supply, using inserted dams to prevent wastage, in order to give a protective back purge.

Welding problems

> Welding heat has an adverse affect on the mechanical properties of all aluminium alloys, and the strength of the weld area will be less than that of the unaffected parent material.

Satisfactory results can be obtained by upgrading the filler metal with suitable alloys, increasing

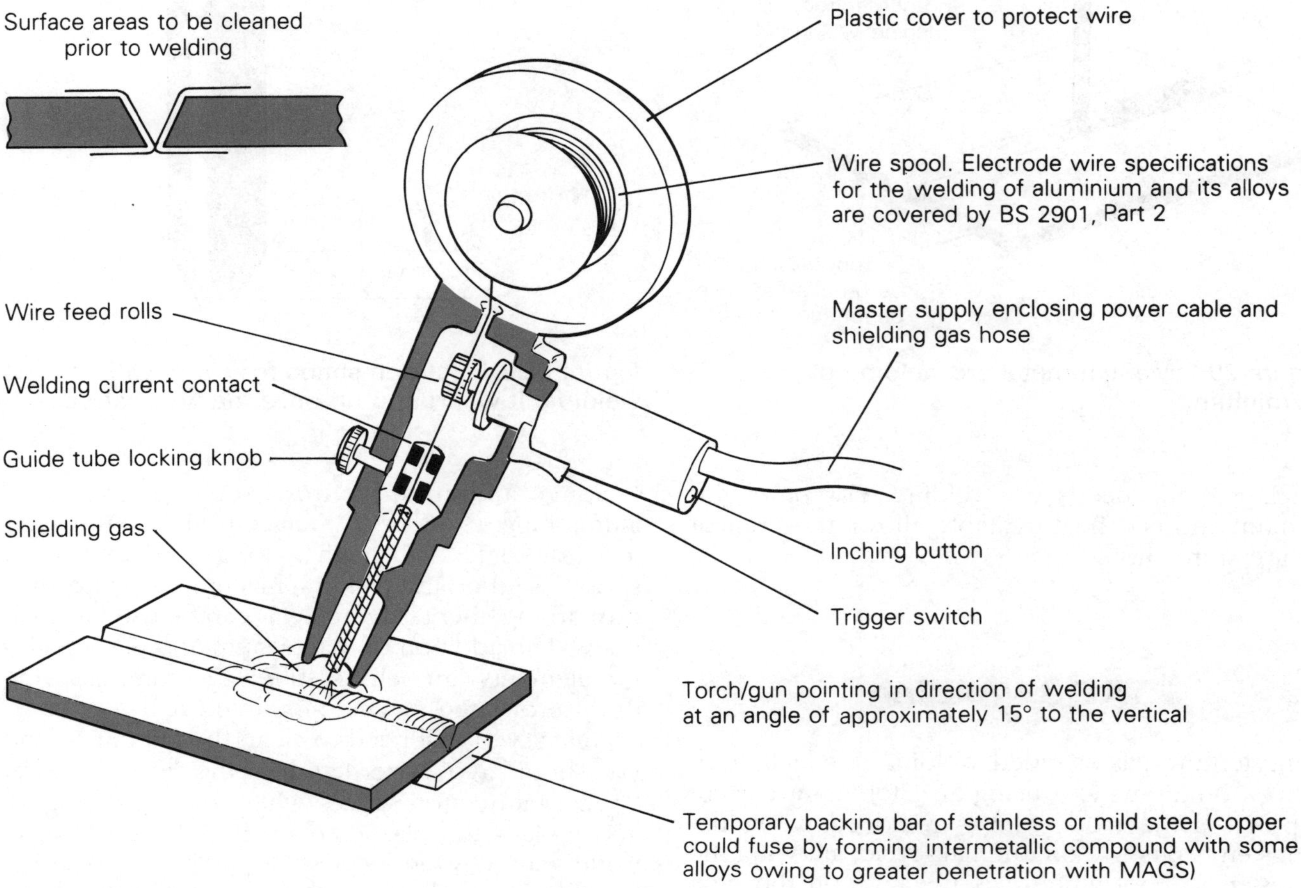

Surface areas to be cleaned prior to welding

Plastic cover to protect wire

Wire spool. Electrode wire specifications for the welding of aluminium and its alloys are covered by BS 2901, Part 2

Wire feed rolls

Master supply enclosing power cable and shielding gas hose

Welding current contact

Guide tube locking knob

Shielding gas

Inching button

Trigger switch

Torch/gun pointing in direction of welding at an angle of approximately 15° to the vertical

Temporary backing bar of stainless or mild steel (copper could fuse by forming intermetallic compound with some alloys owing to greater penetration with MAGS)

Figure 20.3 **Spool-on-gun arrangement for MAGS welding using 'soft' aluminium wire electrodes.**

the welding speed and ensuring adequate reinforcement.

The problem of **hot cracking** (Figure 20.4) can be caused by contraction stresses as the weld cools. Hot cracks usually form in the weld, although they can sometimes occur in the heat-affected zone adjacent to the weld. Certain types of alloys are **hot short**. This means that they are weak at high temperatures and can crack. Pure aluminium is not usually prone to hot cracking, but cracking is likely to occur if the alloy content of the weld is within the following composition ranges:

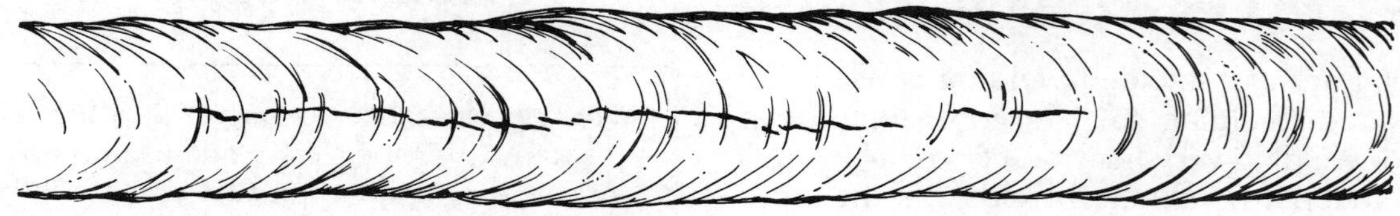

Figure 20.4 A typical hot short crack in an aluminium weld.

Silicon	0.5–1.2 per cent
Copper	2.0–4.0 per cent
Magnesium	2.0–5.0 per cent
Manganese	1.5–2.5 per cent
Zinc	4.0–5.0 per cent

The composition of the filler material therefore has to be considered with great care because, when dilution is taken into account, the resulting weld deposit must have a composition of individual alloy content either above or below the hot-short ranges.

Fast welding speeds help to prevent hot shortness, as the weld metal will be in the hot-short range for less time, and the faster cooling rates will produce a finer grain structure that is less prone to cracking. The use of preheat and an unrestrained joint design will also reduce stresses. Joint designs in aluminium fabrications are often best designed by an evaluation of sample weld tests if no previous information is available.

Duralumin

Duralumin is an alloy of aluminium that contains approximately 4 per cent copper. When added to the aluminium, the copper first forms a solution and then an intermetallic compound ($CuAl_2$). In the correct composition, this alloy possesses the strength and hardness of mild steel, but is much lighter.

The fast welding speeds of the MAGS process reduce the heat affected zone with this material, and will reduce the risk of fracture caused by contractional stresses. To restore the strength of this material after welding, the whole job must be reheated to 500°C and then quenched.

The copper–aluminium compound will then precipitate out of solution over a period of about six days if the alloy is kept at room temperature. Thus the mechanical properties will be restored.

CHECK YOUR UNDERSTANDING

- Aluminium and aluminium alloys are the lightest commercial metals in use in large quantities. Correct alloying also produces good tensile strength.
- A corrosive flux is necessary to remove the oxide film when welding aluminium with the oxy-acetylene or manual metal arc processes. This is not required with the TAGS and MAGS processes; the electrical action of the arc removes the oxide, and the inert gas shield prevents further contamination.
- 'Soft' wires can be fed using a spool-on-gun arrangement. The addition of magnesium and other elements can help to stiffen electrode wires for MAGS welding, allowing the use of large machine-mounted reels.
- Argon is generally the recommended shielding gas. Helium is used on very heavy sections.
- Duralumin is an alloy of aluminium that contains about 4 per cent copper. In the correct composition and with the correct heat treatment, duralumin has the strength and hardness of mild steel, but is much lighter.

REVISION EXERCISES AND QUESTIONS

1 Why is a flux not necessary for welding aluminium by the TAGS and MAGS processes?

2 How can 'soft' aluminium wires be fed in the MAGS process?

3 What makes duralumin a very useful engineering material?

(Further practice questions can be found on page 202.)

21 Welding copper

Introduction

▲ Good ventilation (see Chapter 3) must always be used when welding copper and its alloys, including brasses.

For prolonged welding, either work out of doors or wear a respirator, as the fumes are dangerous.

Tough pitch copper – copper containing copper oxide – is very difficult to weld, and welds can crack. Copper purchased for welding should therefore be specified as the deoxidized type.

Because of the high heat conductivity of copper, it will be necessary to preheat material thicker than 4.5 mm between 500 and 600°C, to ensure the correct amount of fusion. Thin plates can be prepared with an upturned edge; plates of 1.5 mm will require a gap of half the sheet thickness. Over 1.5 mm a single 'V' with a 90° included angle is recommended. For even thicker plates, the double 'V' preparation can be employed, or for arc welding methods the single or double 'U' with a 6 mm radius at the bottom can be employed.

Oxyacetylene welding

For oxyacetylene welding of deoxidized copper, the plate surfaces and edges must be cleaned. Because of the high coefficient of expansion, you will need to set the plate edges with a widening gap, tapering at the rate of 3–4 mm for every 100 mm of weld run. Because copper is weak at high temperatures (hot short), support it by firebricks or other material, such as synthetic asbestos placed on a steel backing. Tacks are not recommended for welding long seams, because they can fail when they become hot; use clamps and/or jigs to maintain the taper spacing.

You will need to use a nozzle of a size larger than that required for mild steel welding and a neutral or very slightly carburizing flame. For a butt weld, it is a good procedure to clamp in the middle and then start welding one third from the end of the joint towards the far end of the seam. When you reach the far end, come back to the starting point and complete the weld to the other end in the opposite direction.

You can weld copper by the oxyacetylene process without a flux, or you can use borax. The technique can be either leftward or rightward; for very thick plates, copper can be welded from both sides at once in the vertical position using the **double operator technique**.

The only difference from the technique used on mild steel (apart from the larger nozzle) is that the blowpipe angle should be steeper, at 60–80° to the plate, in order to put in as much heat as possible. Maintain the rod in the molten pool for the duration of the weld. After welding, the strength of the weld can be improved by light peening, while the work is still hot. Annealing can be carried out, if required, by heating to 600–650°C.

Manual metal arc welding

Electrodes for manual metal arc welding are usually of the silicon–bronze or tin–bronze type, as copper electrodes tend to give a porous weld with this process. Therefore, if the weld has to have characteristics that match the parent material, for electrical conductivity or other reasons, you should use the TAGS or MAGS processes.

If you are using the manual metal arc process, connect the electrode to the positive terminal of a d.c. power source. After preheat, make the weld with a short arc and, holding the electrode almost vertical, perform a crescent-shaped weave, pausing slightly at each fusion face.

TAGS welding

For TAGS welding, use direct current with the electrode negative and a pure argon shielding gas. (You can use helium for very heavy sections.) You can use a mild or stainless steel backing, but these should be coated with antispatter spray to stop them fusing.

MAGS welding

With MAGS welding, there is a choice of shielding. The following gases can be employed: argon, nitrogen, helium, argon–nitrogen mixtures and argon–helium mixtures. Nitrogen and helium will give off large amounts of spatter but give a high heat input; they will reduce the preheat temperatures required. Argon–helium mixtures produce welds with the best appearance.

The preheating will oxidise the area around the joint to be welded. This can be reduced by mixing borax with alcohol and painting the joints prior to preheating. All flux residue must be removed after welding, to prevent corrosion.

CHECK YOUR UNDERSTANDING

- Always use good ventilation and fume extraction when welding copper and its alloys.
- Because copper has a very high heat conductivity, it will almost always be necessary to preheat material thicker than 4.5 mm, to ensure fusion.
- TAGS and MAGS welding are widely used in the welding of these materials. For TAGS, either argon or helium shielding can be used. For MAGS, there is a choice of shielding, using any from argon, nitrogen, argon–nitrogen mixtures or argon–helium mixtures, depending on the application.

REVISION EXERCISES AND QUESTIONS

1 Why is preheating almost always necessary when welding copper?

2 When might helium be used instead of argon for TAGS welding copper?

(Further practice questions can be found on page 202.)

22 Difficulties and defects in welding

Introduction

We have now completed our coverage of the methods used for welding the principal metals of engineering interest. Before we move on to look at some of the more specialised areas and applications of welding, this is a suitable point to review the problems that can occur in welds, including deformation and stresses, and cracking.

Arc and gas welding

Table 22.1

Difficulty/defect	*Possible causes*	*Possible correction*
Incomplete penetration	1. Joint design faulty. 2. Welding speed too rapid. 3. Insufficient welding current or nozzle size. 4. Too large an electrode/filler rod.	Check root gap, root face.
Poor appearance	1. Current too high or too low – flame too large or too small. 2. Incorrect use of electrode/ blowpipe or filler rod. 3. Faulty electrode. Incorrect flame setting.	Check procedure and slope and tilt angles. Dry or change electrode. Readjust flame, clean nozzle.
Undercutting	1. Current too high/nozzle too large. 2. Incorrect manipulation. 3. Arc length too long 4. Welding speed too rapid.	Check angles so that arc force is used to fill undercut.
Excessive spatter	1. Current too high 2. Arc length too long. 3. Arc blow. 4. Faulty electrode.	See Arc blow.

Table 22.1 (continued)

Difficulty/defect	*Possible causes*	*Possible correction*
Arc blow	Magnetic field created when welding with direct current.	Use a.c. machine. Rearrange or split return clamp. Use copper back-up bar or magnet to oppose field. Change direction of welding. Change angle of electrode when deflection begins. Use small-gauge electrode and more runs.
Pin holes	1. Contamination of joint. 2. Damp electrodes	Remove paint, rust, scale etc. from work. Check electrodes for dampness.
Slag in weld	1. Joint design contains too narrow an included angle. 2. High viscosity of molten metal. 3. Rapid chilling. 4. Too low a weld temperature.	Use preheat. Failure to remove a slag from previous weld in multirun welds.
Porous welds	1. Weld speed too rapid. 2. Current too low. 3. High sulphur or other impurities in metal. 4. Faulty electrodes.	Use low-hydrogen electrodes or process.
Cracked welds	1. Faulty electrodes. 2. Stressed welds. 3. Shape of weld bead incorrect. 4. Craters present. 5. Too fast a cooling rate.	1. Use low-hydrogen electrodes. 2. Redesign work or jig, or preheat. 3. Use slower travel speed. 4. Fill craters. 5. Post-heat as well as preheat.
Distortion and warping	1. Incorrect design of weld. 2. Overheating. 3. Incorrect welding sequence.	Preset work. Use skip or backup welding.
Brittle welds	1. Incorrect choice of electrode. 2. Incorrect heat treatment. 3. Air-hardening deposit. 4. Base metal pick-up.	

Distortion and stresses in welding

When metal is subjected to a source of heat, it will expand. However, if the heat is applied to one area only, the expansion can be local and therefore uneven.

The metal surrounding the heated area can remain comparatively cool and tend to prevent expansion of the heated area. Therefore, if the yield point of the metal is reached, permanent deformation will occur. On cooling, the metal does not return to its original form but remains distorted. The same effect can happen in cooling: the surrounding cooler metal can offer resistance, and

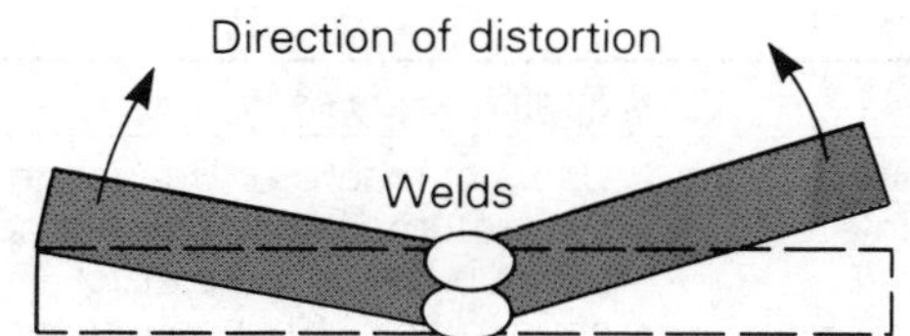

Figure 22.1 **Angular distortion in a butt weld.**

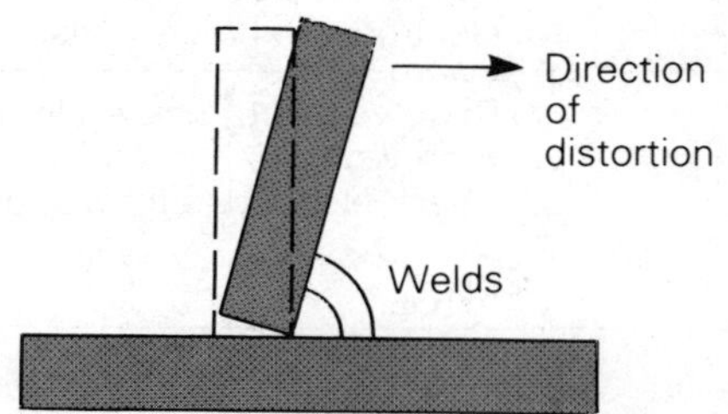

Figure 22.2 **Angular distortion in a fillet weld.**

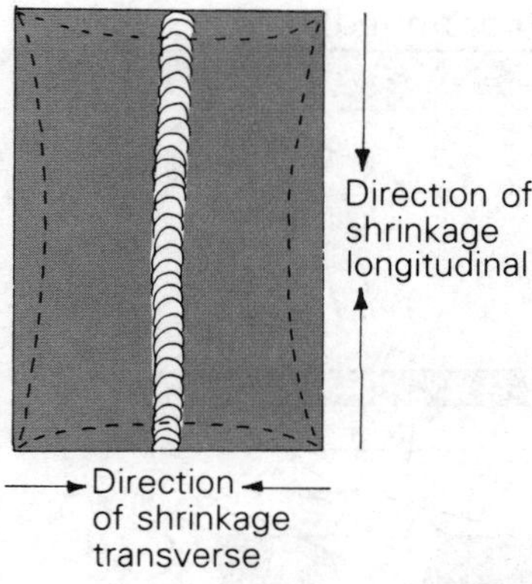

Figure 22.3 **Longitudinal and transverse distortion.**

contractional stresses can also add to the distortion. The amount of distortion that takes place has a large influence on the amount of structural strain that will stay in the metal after it has cooled.

As the amount of distortion increases, the amount of strain in the metal will be reduced, influenced by a reduction in plastic flow. However, if restraint is placed on the metal to prevent distortion, residual stresses will remain after the metal has cooled, and the final structure will be in a stressed condition. This situation can be remedied in most instances by a process known as **stress-relieving**, which involves controlled reheating of the component to a carefully predetermined temperature that is normally below the recrystallisation temperature. Stress can therefore be removed without too much disturbance of the metal's grain structure.

In welding, the amount of weld metal deposited is relatively small compared with the parent metal. The greatest amount of heat is therefore concentrated in this area. Also, as the strength of the weld metal will be greatly reduced at high temperatures, and since it is such a small mass when compared with the structure as a whole, the weld will be forced to take most of the plastic flow as the

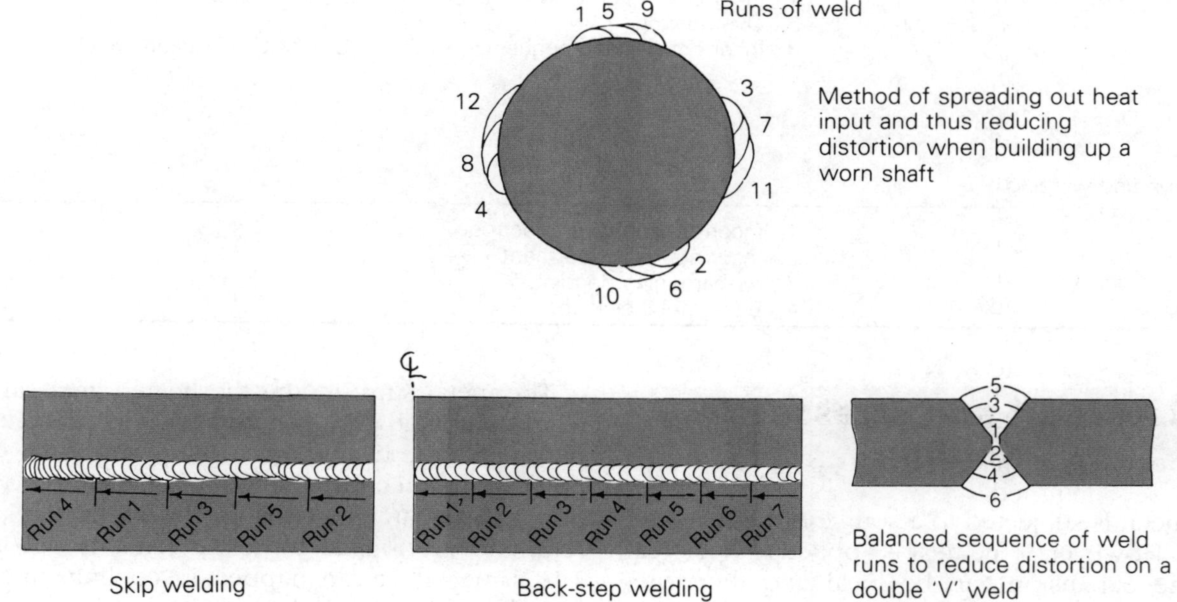

Figure 22.4 **Methods of balancing heat input.**

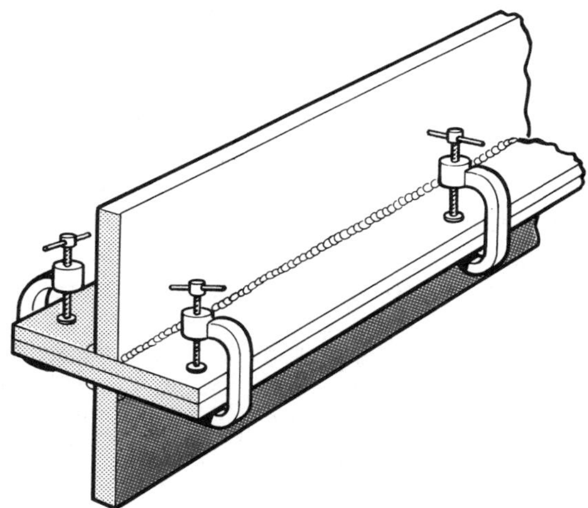

Figure 22.5 'Back to back' welding to reduce distortion.

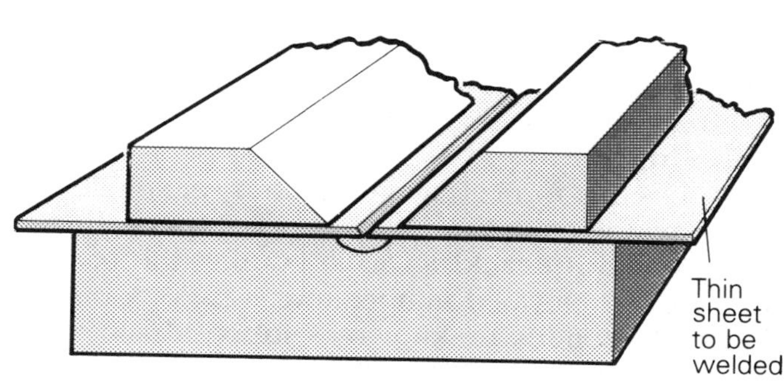

Figure 22.6 The use of large blocks to hold thin sheet in place for welding, and to act as 'chills'.

structure cools. If this plastic flow is greater than the metal's ultimate tensile strength, then a fracture can result.

Types of distortion

There are three main types of distortion that can be set up in welded structures if care and preventive measures are not taken: **angular distortion**, **longitudinal distortion** and **transverse distortion**. (Figures 22.1–22.3).

One method of overcoming angular distortion is to **preset** the plates to be welded. In other words, they are set in the opposite direction, so that when distortion takes place, the plates will pull into the required position. A test weld can be made and the amount of distortion measured with a protractor. The plates for the actual fabrication can then be preset to the required angle, thus compensating for angular distortion and minimising residual stresses.

Distortion can be minimised right from the design stage, by reducing the amount of welding to as low an amount as possible. This can involve using folds in the material or using welding processes with the lowest heat input available.

If it is possible to preheat the component and control the cooling after welding, then distortion can also be controlled, but of course this is not always practicable.

There are ways of reducing distortion without preheating or presetting, using weld sequences such as skip and backstepping, or using the shrinkage of one weld to counteract the shrinkage of another, as in the welding of a double 'V' joint or when building up a worn shaft. (Figure 22.4).

Figure 22.5 shows how, for components of the same dimensions, **back to back** welding can reduce distortion. Clamps or tack welds are only removed when the components have fully cooled down.

It is important to remember that stresses can be introduced into materials during manufacturing processes, such as forming and cold rolling. Then, when the metal is heated during welding operations, the stresses are relieved but distortion is introduced.

A **chill** in welding is a large block of metal placed next to the line of weld. It dissipates the welding heat during actual welding and minimises the area affected by the welding heat input (Figure 22.6). Copper in the form of a block or strip is sometimes used as a chill because it is a very good conductor of heat and will therefore conduct heat away from the weld area. Chills are therefore another method of distortion control.

The problems of cracking in welds

The contraction forces occuring as a weld cools will set up tensile stresses in the joint and may cause what is one of the most serious of weld defects: cracking.

Cracking can occur in the actual weld deposit, in the heat-affected zone, or in both regions. Cracks can either be large, visible to the naked eye and known as **gross** cracks or **macrocracking**, or they can be of the type visible only through a microscope, known as **microcracking** or **microfissuring**.

Cracks that form above the solidus (or solidification) temperature are known as **supersolidus** cracks or **hot cracking**, to show that the cracks occurred at elevated temperature. Cracks forming below the solidus are known as **subsolidus** cracks or **cold cracking**, a term that is often applied to cracking in low-alloy steel welds at room temperature.

From a metallurgical point of view, and therefore from a welding engineering point of view, the distinction between cracks that have occurred at high temperature and those that have occurred at low temperature is very important. We shall therefore look at weld cracking under these two headings.

Hot cracking

Two conditions must be present for cracking to occur during the weld thermal cycle:

1. the metal must lack ductility;
2. the tensile stress developed as a result of contraction must exceed the fracture stress.

The lack of ductility at high temperatures is usually due to the effects of low-melting-point films on the grain boundaries, such as sulphides in steels or a eutectic in certain crack-sensitive aluminium alloys.

> The main element causing hot cracking is **sulphur**.

Hot cracking is likely to occur when sulphur-bearing steels are welded, particularly under restraint. Another cause is the weld metal picking up impurities from a dirty or contaminated surface.

The stresses that aid hot cracking are usually the shrinkage stresses associated with the cooling weld metal, and these are of course greatest when the weld joint is restrained from moving. Restraint is therefore an important factor to consider when fusion welding and should be minimised or counteracted where possible.

A typical example is the welding of the centre disc into a heavy gear ring blank. It will be necessary to heat the ring in order to prevent cracking. This heating is required not because the material is necessarily difficult to weld but in order to counteract the contraction stresses that would tend to crack the weld. Careful and uniform pre- and post-heating are therefore sometimes necessary even when welding fabrications in mild steel merely to prevent expansion/contraction stresses, and not as a metallurgical requirement.

Hot cracking is usually longitudinal, occurring down the middle of the weld, but it sometimes takes place across the weld at roughly regular intervals, which may range between 12 and 150 mm (Figure 22.7). This type of cracking is generally associated with contraction stresses in the weld metal, especially if the contraction rate is high or if it is greater in the weld metal than in the parent metal.

Manganese will tend to globularise sulphur, and can help to prevent cracking caused by low-strength sulphide films. If the carbon content is less than 0.15 per cent and the Mn/S content is greater than 15 per cent in the weld metal, there is little danger of hot cracking (Figure 22.8).

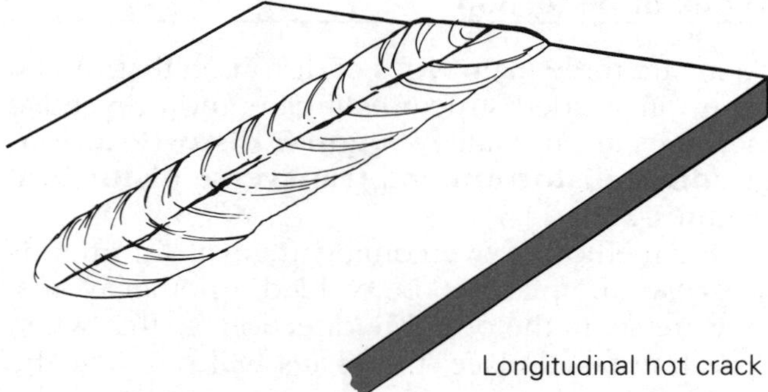

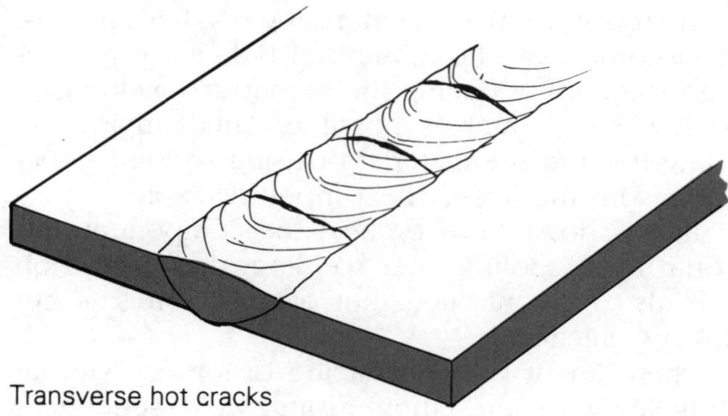

Figure 22.7 **Longitudinal and transverse hot cracking in welds.**

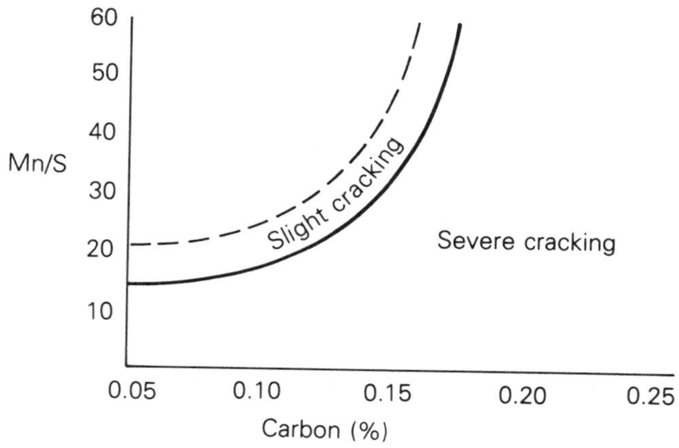

Figure 22.8 Effect of Mn/S ratio and carbon content on cracking possibilities. (Based on TWI and Russian work for manual metal arc welding)

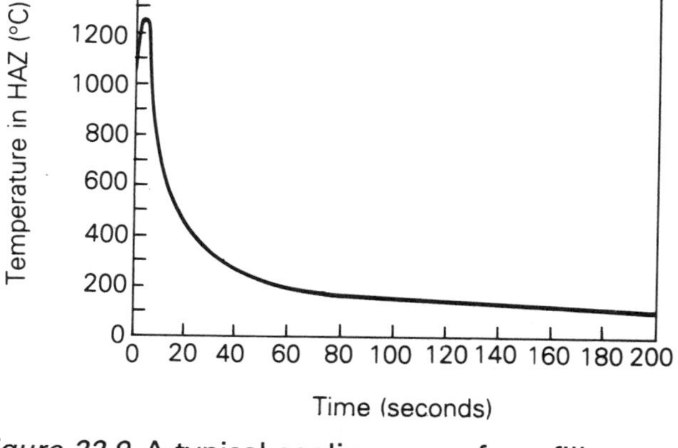

Figure 22.9 A typical cooling curve for a fillet weld between two 6 mm thick low-carbon steel plates using a 3.25 mm electrode.

Cold cracking

Parent metal cracks occur close to the weld and are usually associated with too high a rate of cooling coupled with the action of **hydrogen**. They form after the weld metal has cooled, sometimes occurring hours or even days after the weld has been made. Because of this they are called **cold cracks**.

Cold cracking is likely to occur in all ferritic steels that arc welded if the alloy content is above a certain level and if adequate precautions (mainly preheating) have not been employed. These cracks are not normally visible on the surface and are therefore difficult to detect. Because of the dangers that hidden cracks could cause, it is very important that suitable welding procedures are established and followed carefully.

When a steel is fusion welded by the arc process, some of the parent material will mix with the weld metal (dilution). If no filler metal is added (an upturned edge weld), the weld will be classed as **autogenous** as it will consist entirely of melted parent material.

Because the material is heated to its melting point, there will be a temperature gradient from the weld through the material that is some distance away. The whole area of the weld will cool down as soon as the arc has been removed and the hottest material will cool most rapidly from the higher temperatures. A typical cooling curve is shown in Figure 22.9.

The **heat-affected zone** (HAZ) will contain material that has been affected structurally by the heating and cooling associated with the welding cycle. Figure 22.10 shows a photomacrograph of an HAZ containing a cold crack. Part of the HAZ becomes heated to the austenitic condition and transforms to martensite if cooled rapidly. Cooling is mainly by conduction into the surrounding metal and, as shown in Figure 22.9, it can be very rapid in welds that have not been preheated, particularly when heavy sections are being welded. This rapid cooling results in the formation of martensite, which is an extremely hard substance and is more easily formed in steels with a high carbon content. Martensite also forms more easily when alloying elements are present in the material.

The existence of the hard and brittle martensite means that there is a structure present that is susceptible to crack formation. Any cracks that do form in the region are generally associated with hydrogen.

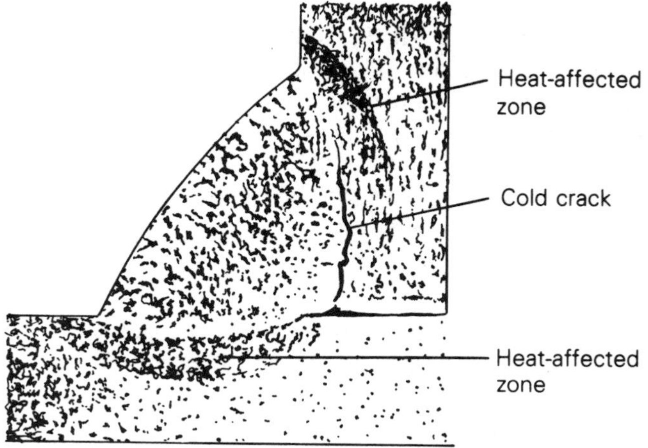

Figure 22.10 A typical cold crack in the heat-affected zone of a fillet weld (magnification × 5).

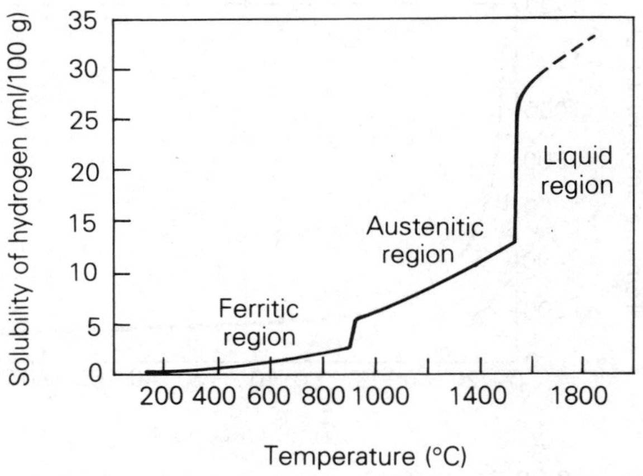

Figure 22.11 The solubility of hydrogen in steel.

Figure 22.11 shows the solubility of hydrogen in steel at various temperatures. Hydrogen is much less soluble in the products of transformation and tends to get trapped in the HAZ. Atoms of hydrogen tend to combine and form molecular hydrogen, which builds up to exert tremendous pressure, causing cracks some time after welding. The extent of cracking will be aggravated by any residual stresses that may be present due to restraint.

Hydrogen must be eliminated as much as possible, and the rate of cooling should be slow enough to prevent the formation of martensite and to allow any trapped hydrogen to diffuse out of the weld and HAZ. Low-hydrogen electrodes and processes such as MAGS help in the reduction of hydrogen present.

The composition of a steel determines its response to heat treatment and therefore its susceptibility to cracking. The element **carbon** has the biggest effect of all, and other alloying elements may be expressed in terms of the percentage of carbon. In this way, the susceptibility of a steel to hard zone cracking (or cold cracking) may be given by a single number known as the **carbon equivalent**. One simple formula for calculating the carbon equivalent is:

$$\text{Carbon equivalent} = \text{C} + \frac{\text{Mn}}{6} + \frac{\text{All other elements}}{14}$$

(See also the definition of carbon equivalent in 'Key words and definitions' for the British Standards formula.)

A mild steel will generally have a carbon equivalent in the range 0.21–0.40 and may be welded without any special precautions. If the carbon equivalent is about 0.40 you are strongly advised to use a low-hydrogen process. It is generally accepted that steel up to 0.47 carbon equivalent can be welded without preheat using a low-hydrogen process, provided the temperature is above freezing. Steels with carbon equivalents above 0.47 will usually require preheating (even when using a low-hydrogen process or electrode).

CHECK YOUR UNDERSTANDING

- When designing welded structures, take care to keep the amount of welding to a minimum. This will not only help keep costs down, but also tend minimise possible distortion.
- When welding, take care not to put too much heat into one part of a fabrication. The heat input should be balanced and spread out evenly; this can be achieved by using a welding sequence.
- Distortion can also be controlled by presetting of plates and the use of 'chills'.
- Cracking in welds is a very serious problem.
- There are two main types of crack. Those that have occurred at elevated temperature are known as hot cracks. Those that occur at room temperature are known as cold cracks.
- The main element that causes hot cracking is sulphur. Manganese can help to prevent this type of cracking.
- The use of low-hydrogen processes or electrodes combined with controlled cooling can help to eliminate cold cracking.

REVISION EXERCISES AND QUESTIONS

1. Describe how the presetting of plates can be used to eliminate the effects of distortion in a butt-welded joint.
2. Name the main element that is likely to cause hot cracking.
3. Name the main element that is likely to cause cold cracking.
4. How does the addition of managanese help to prevent hot cracking?
5. How can the susceptibility of a steel to cold cracking be expressed as a number?

(Further practice questions can be found on page 202.)

23 Examining and testing welds

Introduction

When learning to weld it is important to be able to recognise weld defects, to understand the possible causes of the defects and to apply corrective measures to avoid them. The ultimate aim of every welder is to produce welds free of any defects.

Some defects will be easily visible by visual inspection as they are present at the surface. Other defects are more difficult to find as they can be inside the weld and will not be indicated at all by a visual inspection.

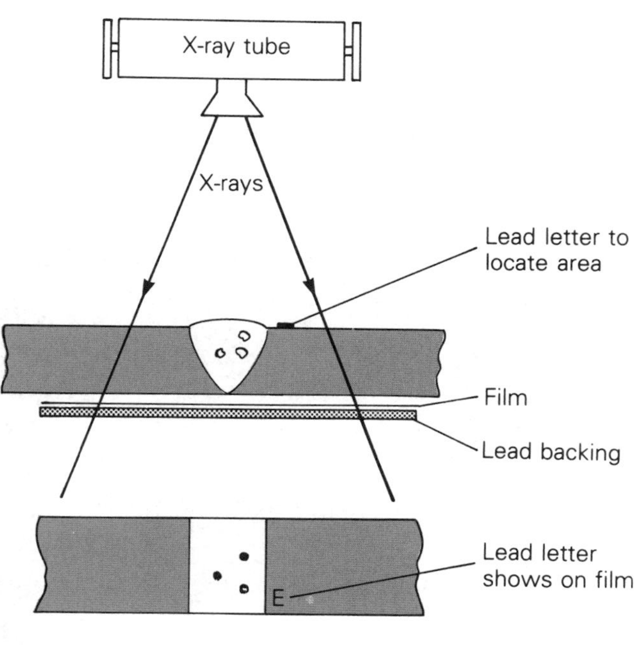

Figure 23.1 X-ray inspection (full precautions against radiation to be employed).

Non-destructive testing

The methods used in examining and testing welds are common to all welding processes. One of the biggest breakthroughs in this area has been the progress made in **non-destructive testing** (NDT). Powerful **X-ray** equipment or the use of **radioactive isotopes** enable us to look right inside a weld and examine the results on a film in much the same way as a surgeon would examine a medical X-ray (Figure 23.1).

Ultrasound (pulses of high-frequency sound) can also be used (Figure 23.2). When the equipment is used by a skilled operator, it can produce information about the quality of a weld without the stringent safety precautions required for the use of X-rays and radioactive isotopes (Figure 23.3).

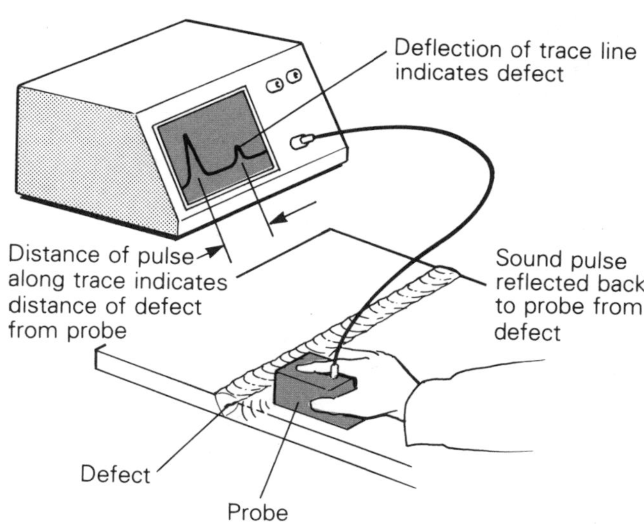

Figure 23.2 Ultrasonic inspection.

Figure 23.3 On-site inspection of a node joint using ultrasonic equipment. (Courtesy of TWI, UK)

Miniature **television cameras** are often used to inspect the penetration of welds in small-diameter pipes.

Special dyes are employed in the **dye penetrant** test. These dyes will find their way into any surface defects and highlight them on subsequent inspection as, after the work has been wiped, the dye will remain in the defect. Some dyes are fluorescent in ultraviolet light.

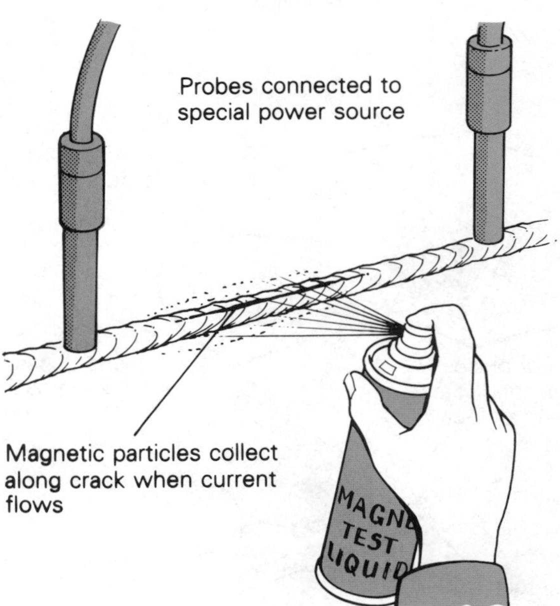

Figure 23.4 Magnetic particle inspection. Use in a well-ventilated area; never spray on a hot surface.

Magnetic particle inspection works in a similar way, when oil containing iron powder is spread over the weld area and the work magnetised. The particles will gather around any surface or near surface defect (Figures 23.4 and 23.5).

Standards

X-rays or radiographs are required when welding to certain standards, and welders have to submit their test welds to radiographic inspection and

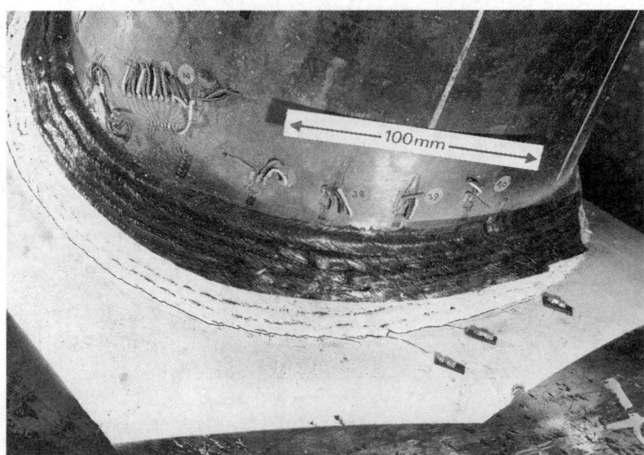

Figure 23.5 Cracking revealed by magnetic particle inspection. (Courtesy of TWI, UK)

various destructive mechanical tests in order to gain higher levels of welder approval.

The Comité Européen de la Normalisation (CEN) is working towards common welding standards for Europe. However, at present, students training to become welders in the United Kingdom usually work towards the standards given in BS 4872 Part 1 (1982). All welds are first subject to a visual examination under this standard before any destructive tests are carried out.

The existing British Standards BS 4870 and BS 4871 governing welding procedures and welder approval are now replaced by European Standards EN 287 (Parts 1 and 2) and EN 288 (Parts 1 to 4).

Destructive testing

When training or when taking a welding test, different types of destructive test can be employed to determine the quality of a welded joint. Many of these tests (such as the bend test and tensile test) will fail if there are internal defects present. Other tests, such as the nick break test, break open the weld so that we can see inside it. The macro-etch test will show fusion faces and internal defects.

Table 23.1 lists destructive tests for approving welds and welders to BS 4872 standards.

Methods of examination

Visual examination of welds

Visual examination of welds is used to check for size of weld, profile or weld face shape, any surface defects, undercut and overlap, any root defects and weld penetration.

Macro-etch examination

This is a destructive test, in which level, polished sections of welds are examined after etching, using up to 10 times magnification.

Figure 23.6 shows the stages involved in performing a macro-etch examination of a weld specimen. Cut the specimen out by sawing, and prepare a small cross-sectional area by filing or grinding the surface flat (using a coarse file). Remove the coarse file marks with a smooth file.

Using either emery paper laid on plate glass, or in the workshop wrapped round a file, polish with M, F and O grade papers. Continue until all scratch marks are removed. Alternate the direction of filing and polishing at right angles.

Immerse the polished surface in an etching solution of 10 per cent nitric acid in alcohol (used for low carbon steels).

When you have obtained a good definition of

Table 23.1 Destructive tests to BS 4872

Test number and type	Destructive test(s) required
1 Butt weld in sheet	One macrosection to include the stop/start position.
2 Fillet weld in sheet	Three fracture tests after the end face at the stop/start position has been used for macro-examination.
3* Butt weld in plate (without backing, welded from one side)	One bend test to be taken from a location showing full penetration other than the central 50 mm. One fracture test to include the stop/start position.
4* Butt weld in plate (welded from both sides)	One bend test selected from other than the central 50 mm. One macrosection to include stop/start position.
5* Butt weld in plate (with backing)	One bend test selected from other than the central 50 mm. One fracture test from the central 50 mm.
6 Fillet weld in plate	Three fracture tests after the end face at the stop/start position has been used for macro-examination.
7 Butt weld in pipe (without backing)	Two root bend tests taken from locations having full penetration, but for MIG welded pipe 10 mm thick and over two side bends.
8 Butt weld in pipe (with backing)	Two root bend tests, but for MIG welded pipe 10 mm thick and over two side bends.
9 Branch connection (fillet weld)	Four macrosections (one at each crotch and flank).

* In tests 3, 4 and 5, for plate less than 10 mm thick a root bend test shall be used; and for plate 10 mm thick and over a side bend test shall be used.

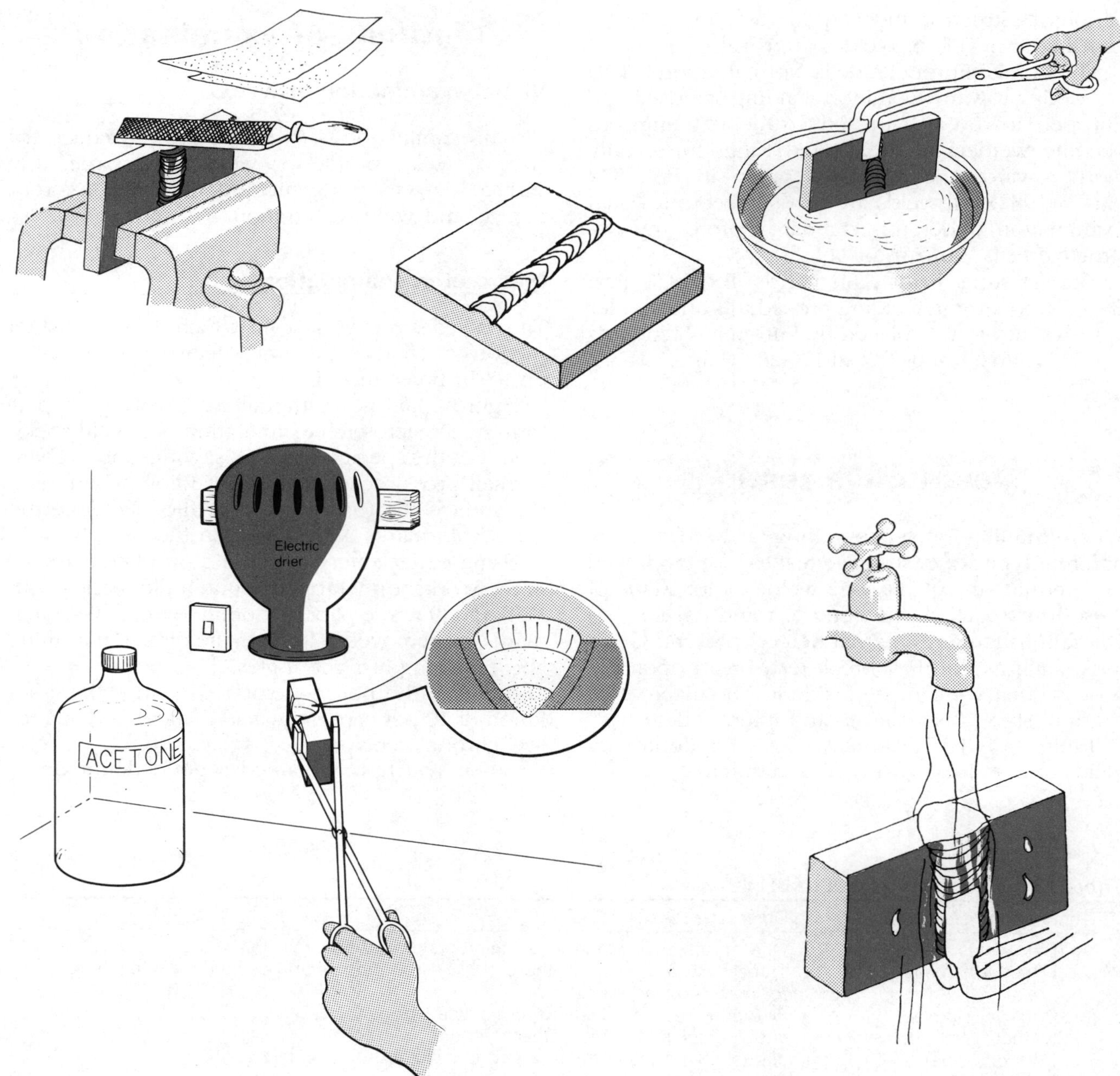

Figure 23.6 The stages involved in performing a macro-etch examination on a weld specimen.

the weld structure with the etching fluid, wash the specimen in hot water. After washing, rinse with acetone and dry using a hot air dryer.

You can preserve an etched specimen by painting it with a layer of clear varnish.

Figure 23.7 shows a macro-etch on a single 'V' manual metal arc weld. Note the two large slag inclusions and the excessive penetration. Figure 23.8 shows the typical structure of a single-run weld, while Figure 23.9 shows a multirun weld. In the as-welded state this would tend to show grain refinement in consecutive weld runs, with larger columnar crystal formation only in the final capping run.

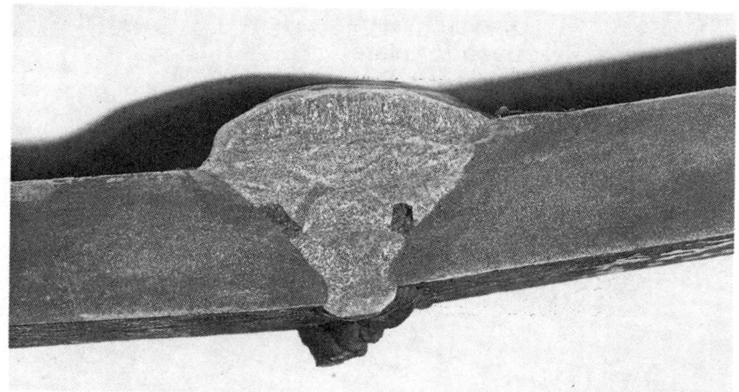

Figure 23.7 A macro-etch on a single 'V' manual metal arc weld.

The nick break fracture test

Breaking the weld open allows examination of internal defects. For this reason, the nick break test is often used during the training of welders (Figures 23.10 and 23.11). It shows the welder any faults in technique, and points the way to overcoming them.

A good weld should fracture along the sawcut, leaving equal halves of the weld fused to their respective plates.

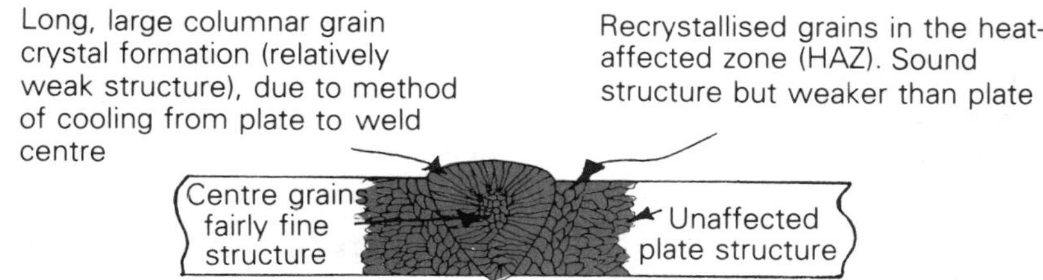

Figure 23.8 Typical macrostructure of a single-run weld.

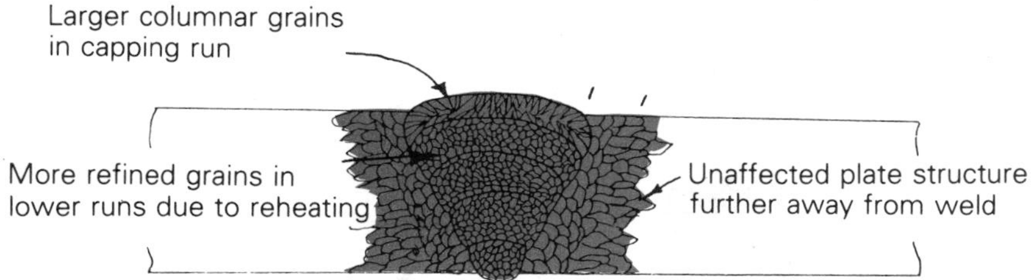

Figure 23.9 Typical macrostructure of a multirun weld.

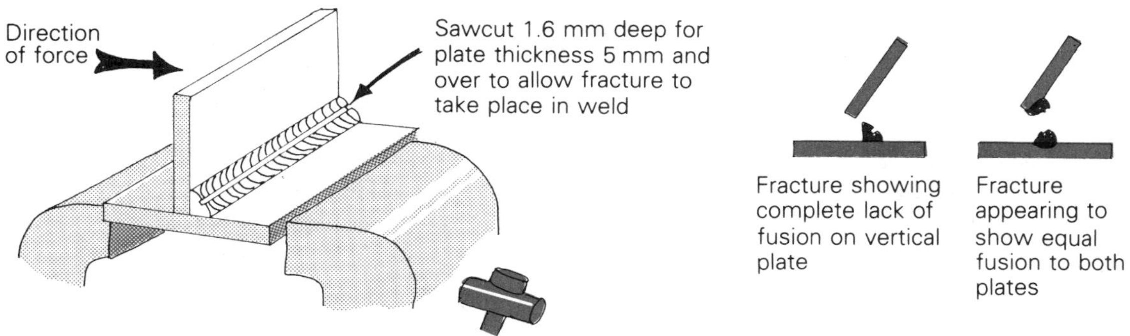

Figure 23.10 A fillet weld specimen prepared for a nick break test.

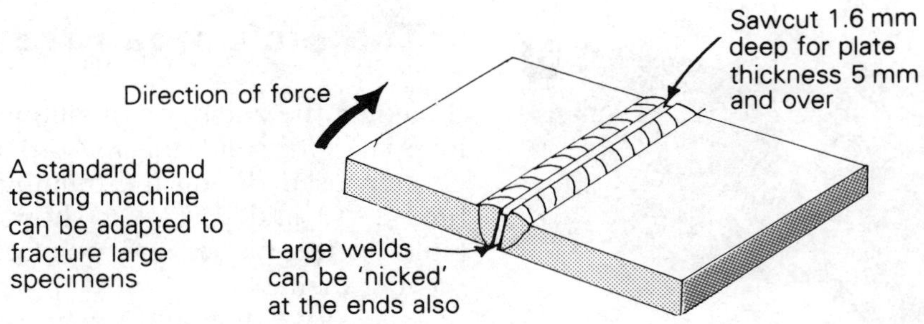

Figure 23.11 A butt weld specimen prepared for a nick break test.

The bend test

The bend test, in one of the forms shown in Figure 23.12, is used to test the skill of the welder. If there is a fault in the weld, such as lack of fusion, slag inclusion, or severe porosity, the bend test will probably reveal it by failure of the specimen.

Specific sizes of specimen and formers are given with each welding code requiring a bend test or tests, and these sizes should be strictly adhered to.

(See also the section on tensile testing in Chapter 13.)

Testing spot welds

X-rays can be used to determine the quality of spot welds, but generally one or more of the tests shown in Figure 23.13 is used to check welding procedure.

CHECK YOUR UNDERSTANDING

- In an actual welded job, non-destructive testing methods such as X-ray, gamma-ray and ultrasound

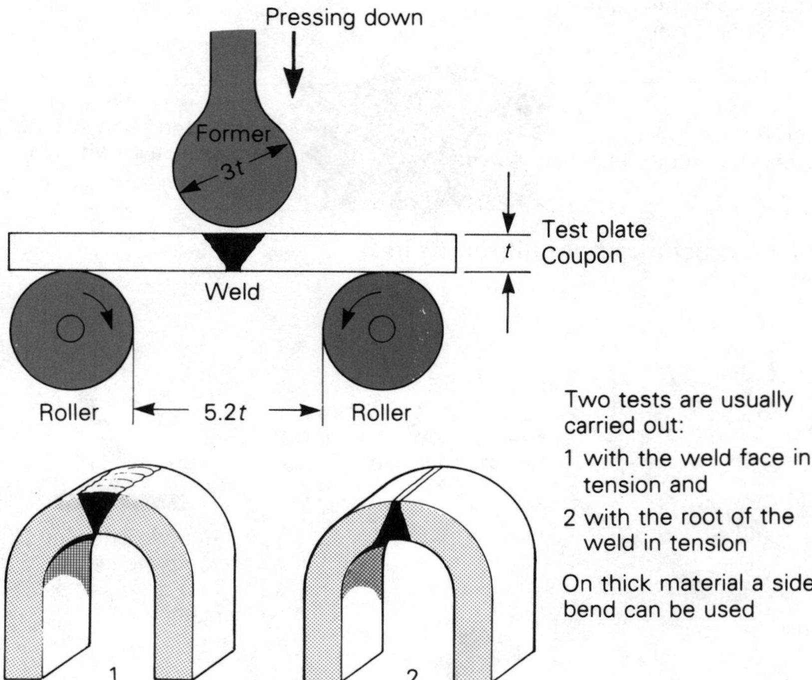

Figure 23.12 The principle of the bend test.

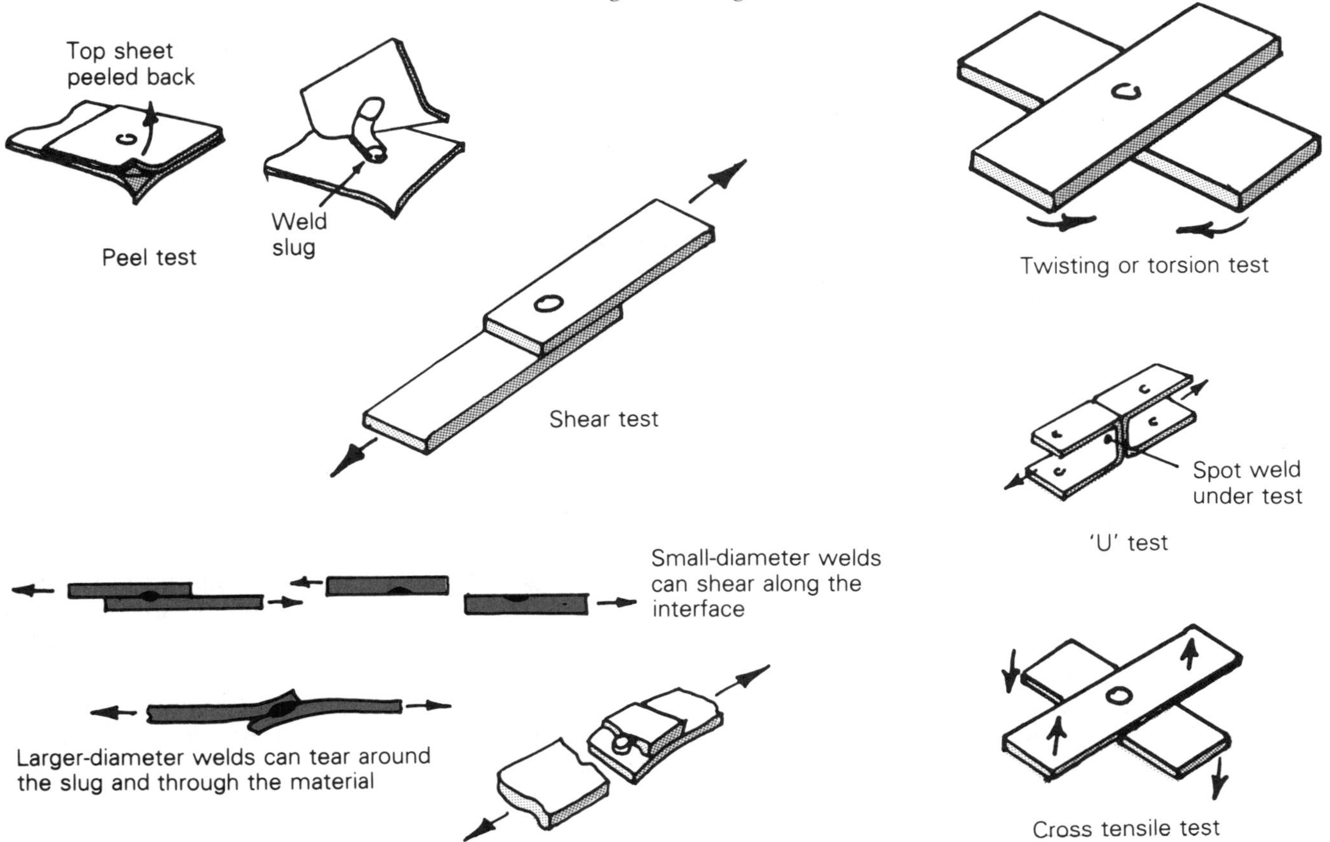

Figure 23.13 **Destructive tests used to check spot-welding procedure.**

can be employed to determine the quality of the interior of welds.

● Other non-destructive methods such as magnetic particle and dye penetrant can be employed to check for surface defects that are difficult or impossible to see with the naked eye, such as very fine surface cracks and even cracks just below the surface in the case of magnetic particle inspection.

● Non-destructive tests allow the completed work to be examined without damaging it. Destructive tests, such as bend, tensile, macro etch and nick break, are often employed during welder training. They complement the non-destructive methods when examining a welder's testpiece that has been submitted to approve the standard of welding to particular codes or standards.

● When a testpiece is successful in passing the required testing procedures, a certificate is issued for insurance purposes. This certificate lists the date of the test, the welder's name and identification number, and exact details of the process used, type of weld and welding position.

REVISION EXERCISES AND QUESTIONS

1 When examining a single 'V' butt weld that has been made by the manual metal arc process you notice that there is undercutting on the surface and lack of penetration at the root. Give two possible causes for each of these defects.

2 Which of the following would *not* be found by a visual inspection:
undercutting, excessive spatter, internal slag inclusions, lack of penetration?

3 Name three destructive weld tests.

4 Name three non-destructive weld testing methods.

(Further practice questions can be found on page 202.)

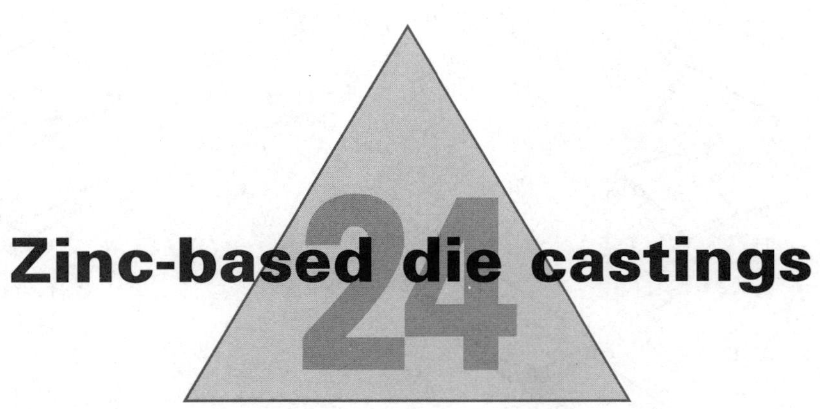

Zinc-based die castings

Introduction

Many small components, such as door handles, carburettors and sewing machine parts, are made from zinc-based materials. These can be quite difficult to weld, but success is often achieved by use of either the oxyacetylene process or the TAGS process. The alloy content very often varies, but if the component is scrap unless it can be repaired, then it is sometimes worth attempting a repair (Figures 24.1 and 24.2).

Preparation

The preparation will be determined by the size, shape and thickness of the casting and the actual location of the fracture. If required, a 'V' preparation of 60–80° can be made on the fracture area, leaving small areas of the original fracture faces as 'location' spots for alignment of the components. The preparation can be made by a **spatula** (Figure 24.3) and two types of spatula should be available, or made before carrying out this type of repair.

File about 6 mm either side of the upper fracture surfaces to remove oxide, until bright metal is exposed. Support the weld area with suitable moulding material or metal inserts, and plug any holes near to the weld area. For some repairs it may be best to support the whole component, and there is a 'carbon putty paste' available for this purpose.

Welding technique

Use a filler rod of zinc base alloy and file off the oxide on the rod, again until bright metal is exposed, before you start welding. Use a very slightly carburising flame. (This ensures that there is no excess oxygen in the flame. Strictly speaking, the flame should be neutral. However, on older equipment when using a small size nozzle a neutral flame can sometimes become slightly oxidising, preventing welding.) No flux is required.

Preheating will not be necessary on small cast-

Figure 24.1 Typical repair of zinc die-cast carburettor.

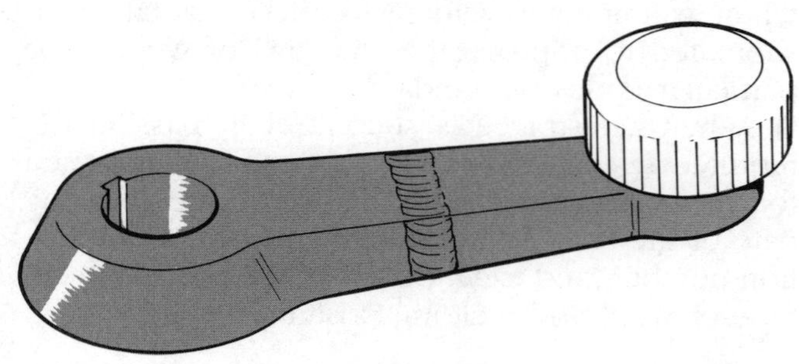

Figure 24.2 Welded repair of zinc die-cast door handle.

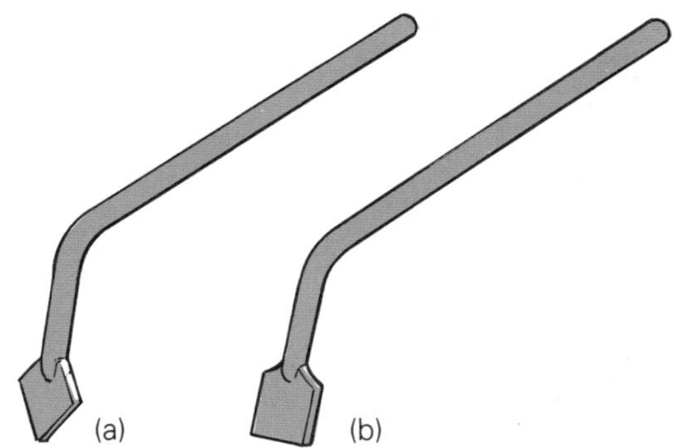

Figure 24.3 (a) Diamond-shaped spatula for forming 'V' preparations. (b) Square-shaped spatula for pushing molten metal into place.

ings or thin sections but may be applied, with the blowpipe flame only, on slightly larger or more complex shapes (larger than, say, an engine carburettor). Use the leftward welding technique. Melt at the starting point and use a spatula to remove oxide from each face. Add the filler material without agitating the rod and allow the metal to 'flow' into the weld pool underneath the oxide skin. You can also use a mould to contain the weld metal as well as for support.

After completing the weld, remove any surplus metal with a spatula. Always keep the weld area free of excessive oxide by use of the spatula, and keep the spatula cool (avoid its being heated by the oxyacetylene flame); if it becomes overheated it will vaporise zinc oxide, making the weld area dirty.

You can weld small aluminium and magnesium castings in a similar manner but, of course, you will have to use a flux and aluminium or magnesium filler rods respectively. Preheating may also be necessary.

If a magnesium casting catches fire, extinguish the blowpipe and any preheat burners. If possible, smother the flames with flux powder. If the casting

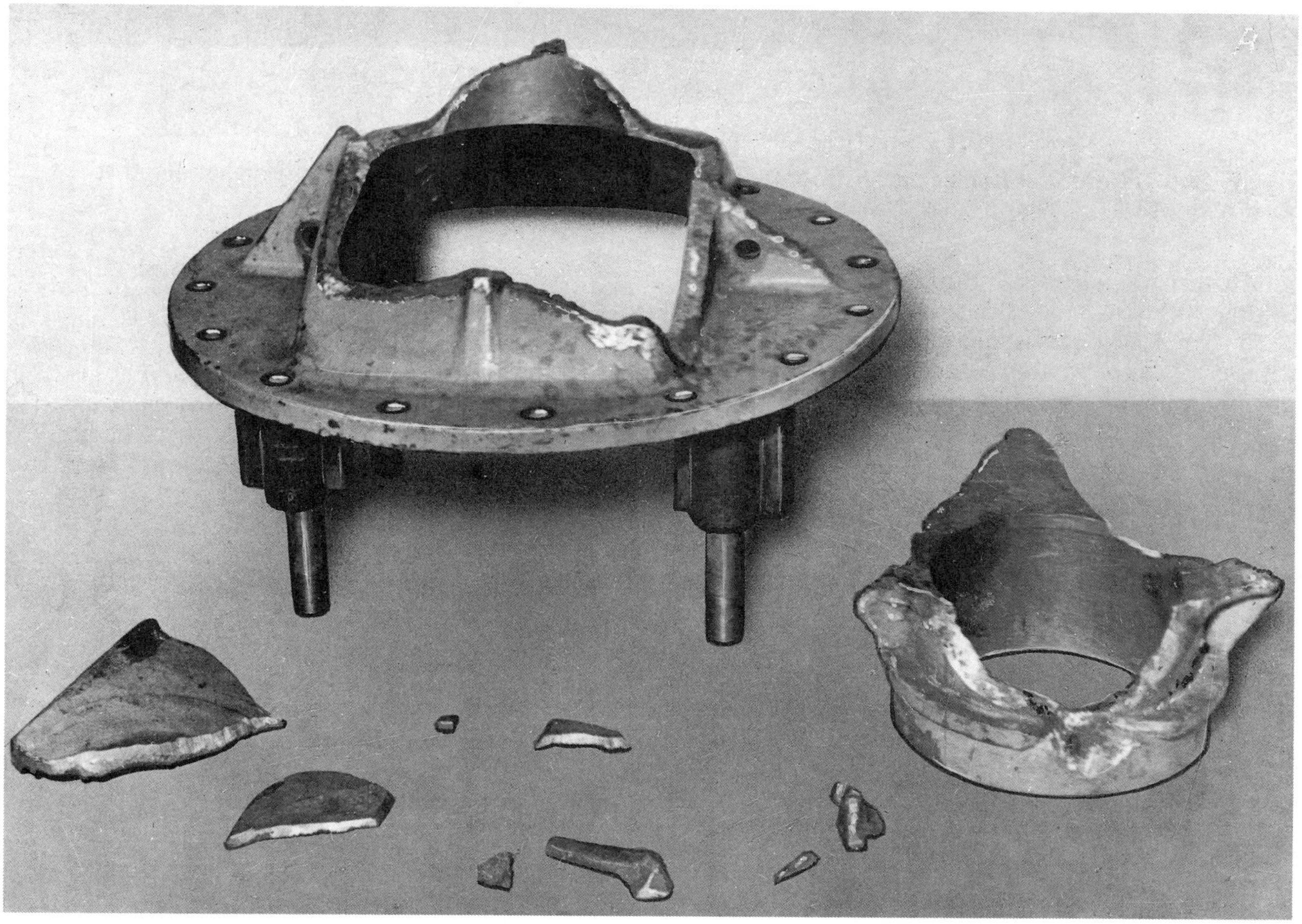

Figure 24.4 Broken differential house. (Courtesy of UTP, UK and UTC, Nigeria and Ghana)

Figure 24.5 Differential house pieced together and manual metal arc welded using nickel electrode. (Courtesy of UTP, UK and UTC, Nigeria and Ghana)

is in a furnace, close the furnace door. Cover the casting with dry sand. *On no account use water.*

The TAGS process using argon shielding, if available, will often be the best choice for repairing small aluminium or magnesium castings.

Casting repairs in general

When repairing any casting, it is important to be able to reposition all broken pieces exactly before welding. This is often achieved by only partially preparing the mating faces with a 'V', leaving the original fracture faces at the root.

The seemingly impossible repair of the differential housing shown in Figures 24.4 and 24.5 was carried out in this way. The broken pieces were tacked together and then manual metal arc welded using a nickel electrode.

CHECK YOUR UNDERSTANDING

- Many small components are made from zinc-based materials. Repair welding of such items usually requires a different approach in each case.
- It is often necessary to support the whole component with a special paste material and carry out welding with the use of a spatula.

REVISION EXERCISES AND QUESTIONS

1 Name the material that many small components, such as carburettors, some door handles and sewing-machine parts, are often made of.

2 What gas welding technique should you use for these materials?

3 Which process, if available, will often be the best choice for repairing small aluminium or magnesium castings?

(Further practice questions can be found on page 202.)

25 Rebuilding worn surfaces, hardsurfacing and Stelliting

Introduction

Oxyacetylene, manual metal arc, TAGS and MAGS welding processes can all be used for building-up operations on worn parts, by using a deposit similar to that of the parent metal.

This is an economical method for building up worn parts such as shafts and gear wheels. When depositing a layer or layers on a worn shaft, take care to balance the amount of heat input (see Chapter 22).

Hardsurfacing

For depositing a hard surface on components (both worn and new), rods that contain carbon, chromium, manganese and silicon can be used to deposit surfaces to give the required amount of hardness or resistance to wear and corrosion. These surfaces are deposited by a **sweating** method so that they do not become diluted with the softer base material. (Sweating is the melting of the surface of the metal due to the absorption of carbon from the carbon feather in the flame, which reduces the metal's melting point: see below.)

The oxyacetylene flame is adjusted to have an excess of acetylene with a white plume from 2 to $2\frac{1}{2}$ times the length of the inner cone. The work surface will absorb carbon from such a flame and its melting point will be reduced. This causes the surface to sweat. The rod is then melted on to this sweating surface, producing a sound bond between the hard deposit and the softer parent material but with a minimum amount of dilution taking place.

An extremely hard surface can be deposited using special tubular rods that contain granules of tungsten carbide. These rods can be obtained with granules of various sizes.

Stelliting

One of the best-known hardsurfacing materials is **Stellite**. Originally developed in the USA in 1900, it is an alloy of cobalt, chromium and tungsten with carbon. There are a range of Stellite materials available for different applications. Stellite has a great resistance to wear and corrosion and will maintain these properties at high temperatures. It is an extremely brittle material, but will produce extremely useful surfaces when deposited on to a more ductile metal. Stellite tips are used for machine-cutting tools, and can be brazed on to steel shanks. Stellite can also be deposited directly on to surfaces that will have to stand up to extreme wear and corrosion conditions in service.

With oxyacetylene, adjust the flame with an excess of acetylene, again 2–$2\frac{1}{2}$ times the length of the inner cone, and when the steel surface begins to sweat, bring the Stellite rod into the flame and melt a drop of Stellite on to the surface. The Stellite will spread out, making a good bond. Repeat this method, without the inner cone touching the work, until the deposit is complete. The surface should be clean before Stelliting, and it is common to use a preheat and controlled cooling to prevent cracking. When building up deposits on hardened parts such as camshafts, it is common practice to direct

Table 25.1 Electrodes for surfacing applications

Service condition required	Type of deposit	Approximate Vickers hardness (VPN)
High-impact resistance coupled with medium abrasion resistance	Low alloy steel	350 VPN
Medium impact with higher abrasion resistance	Medium alloy steel	500 VPN
Excellent resistance and work-hardening under impact conditions to resist abrasion	13% manganese steel or austenitic steel	250 VPN (500 VPN when work-hardened)
Maximum abrasion resistance with medium impact resistance	Tungsten carbide	1800 VPN
Maximum resistance to both impact and abrasion	Chromium carbide	700 VPN

small jets of water on each side of the deposit, to limit the heat flow and thus reduce distortion.

With MAGS and manual metal arc welding, it is important to select the electrode that will give the best deposit to match the required service conditions. (This is of course true for the filler rod when oxyacetylene or TAGS welding.)

The approximate hardness of the deposit will not necessarily be the only criterion for suitability. The ability to withstand impact and/or corrosion may be just as important.

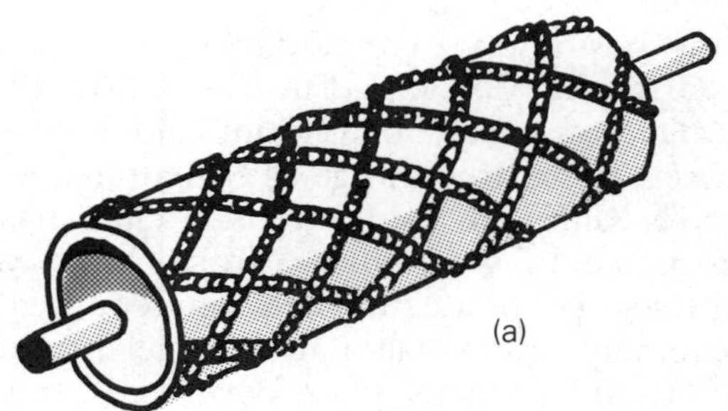

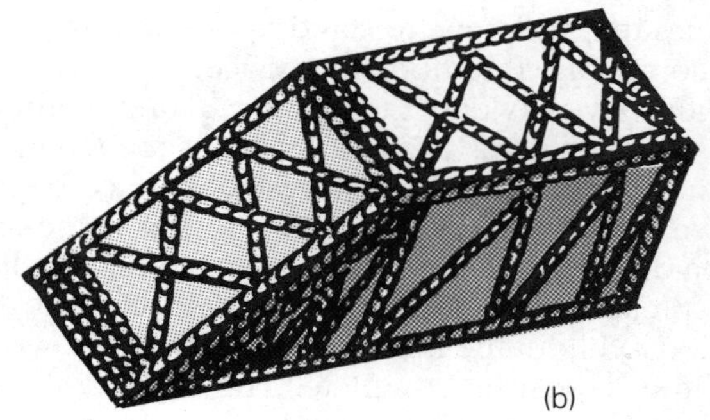

Figure 25.1 Various patterns of chequered reinforcement on (a) a crushing roller and (b) a digger tooth.

Practical considerations

Table 25.1 gives a rough guide to the electrodes available for both MAGS and manual metal arc surfacing applications.

When hardfacing new parts, you can cut some of the surface away, or prepare it to accommodate the hardsurface metal better. Build up areas where wear is likely to occur. On worn parts, first ensure that you have identified the parent material correctly. Remove any old hardsurfacing and prepare by cutting away if necessary. If you are using a tungsten carbide electrode, restrict the deposit thickness to a maximum of 6 mm, to avoid the deposit breaking off. Where damage is severe on manganese steel components, you can weld sections of metal on to the part using an austenitic electrode, thus reducing the total amount of welding required. Always plan heat input to avoid distortion. The amount of welding can often be minimised by using a chequered or rib pattern of weld runs when complete resurfacing is not required (Figure 25.1).

The series of photographs in Figures 25.2–25.9 show various rebuilding and surfacing operations using a variety of welding techniques.

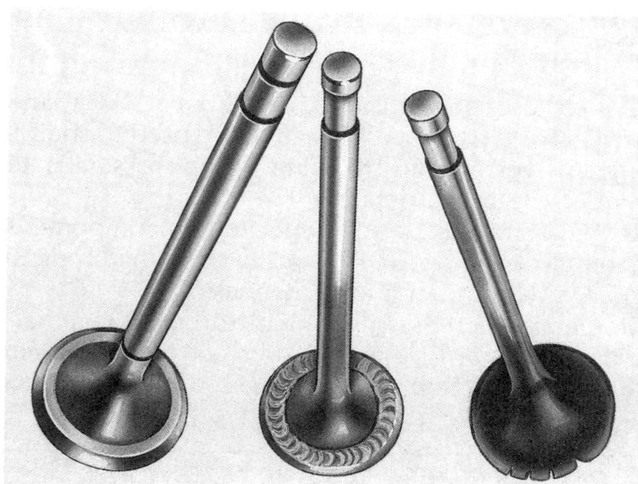

Figure 25.2 Engine exhaust valves built up using the oxyacetylene process and Stellite rod. (Courtesy of UTP, UK and UTC, Nigeria and Ghana)

Figure 25.3 Excavator bucket teeth rebuilt using high chrome–carbon hardsurfacing electrodes. (Courtesy of UTP, UK and UTC, Nigeria and Ghana)

Figure 25.5 Roll welding in operation. (Courtesy of UTP, UK and UTC, Nigeria and Ghana)

Figure 25.6 Roll built back up to size with layers of weld. (Courtesy of UTP, UK and UTC, Nigeria and Ghana)

Figure 25.4 (left) Manganese steel digger tooth repaired using austenitic chromium–nickel–manganese electrode. (Courtesy of UTP, UK and UTC, Nigeria and Ghana)

Figure 25.7 Worn sand discharge valve off a suction dredger. Valve seat rebuilt by welding and valve put back into service with minimum delay. (Courtesy of UTP, UK and UTC, Nigeria and Ghana)

CHECK YOUR UNDERSTANDING

- Oxyacetylene, manual metal arc, TAGS and MAGS welding processes can all be used for building up worn parts, by using a deposit similar to that of the parent metal.
- Hard surfaces can be deposited on components (both worn and new) by using rods that contain carbon, chromium and manganese.
- One of the best-known hardsurfacing materials is Stellite, which is an alloy of cobalt, chromium and tungsten with carbon.

REVISION EXERCISES AND QUESTIONS

1 Which processes can be used for building up worn parts with a deposit similar to that of the parent material?

2 What is the composition of Stellite?

(Further practice questions can be found on page 202.)

Figure 25.8 Mild steel extensions welded to a cast iron roller using nickel 'buttering' technique and nickel–iron electrodes. (Courtesy of UTP, UK and UTC, Nigeria and Ghana)

Figure 25.9 Building up conveyor links with hardsurfacing electrode. (Courtesy of UTP, UK and UTC, Nigeria and Ghana)

26 Welding pipes

Introduction

Before attempting to weld pipe by any process it is usual to master the welding of plate first. If the pipe can be rotated, then this is the easiest method and is known as **roll welding** (Figure 26.1). With the manual metal arc process, the arc is struck at the top of the pipe and held in this position to deposit the weld while the pipe is steadily rotated under the electrode. This method can be adopted for other welding processes, particularly if the rate of pipe rotation can be varied.

The real skill of pipewelding is when the pipe cannot be rotated, as this will involve being able to weld in the flat, vertical and overhead positions and also being able to change from one position to the next without stopping the weld.

Welding techniques

Figure 26.2 shows the various 'G' positions for welding pipe and Figure 26.3 shows one type of automatic pipewelding machine. Although automatic machines are employed on certain pipe applications, by far the largest amount of pipewelding is done by one of the manual processes.

Pipe in the horizontal position for use in industrial applications is usually welded vertically upwards from the 6 o'clock position to 12 o'clock (Figure 26.4). The preparation is usually a 60° or 70° included angle with a root gap of up to 3 mm to ensure full penetration. The technique employed for vertical-up pipe welding is the same as for the vertical welding of plate, in that a **keyhole** or **onion** is maintained in the root. For very high-quality work the root run can be deposited with the TAGS process and then the remaining runs can be deposited by manual metal arc.

Another method of pipewelding often employed for transmission pipelines across country is the **stovepipe method**. With the manual metal arc process, stovepipe welding is undertaken with cellulose or cellulose iron powder electrodes, welding downwards from the 12 o'clock position to 6 o'clock in multiple runs. The MAGS process can also be used for stovepipe welding, or for a combination technique, where the root run is deposited vertically down and then the hot pass and capping run are deposited vertically upwards. With stovepipe welding, the root gap generally need not be as wide as for vertical-up welding; a 1.5 mm root face and root gap are usually adequate.

Figure 26.5 shows the various points relating to MAGS butt welding of pipes. The root run (a) when deposited vertically down is completed without weaving but, in order to obtain uniform pen-

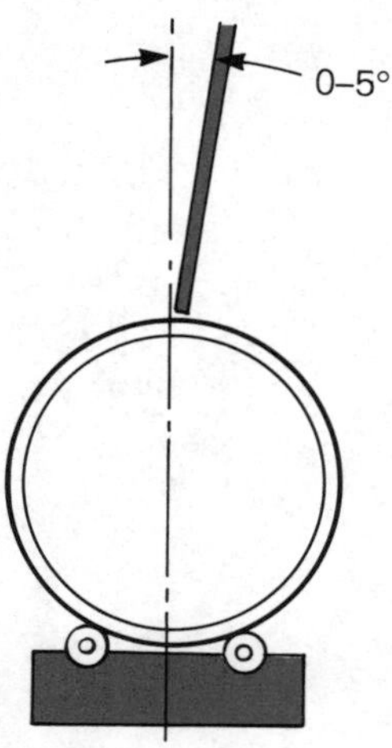

Figure 26.1 The 'roll' welding of pipe.

etration, the small keyhole or onion must be maintained at the leading edge. It is common on transmission pipelines, when using the MAGS process, to use three runs of weld; the amount deposited is increased as the pipe wall thickness increases. The root run is deposited vertically downwards, without weaving, and then the hot pass and capping run are deposited vertically upwards, using the type of weave patterns shown in Figure 26.5(d).

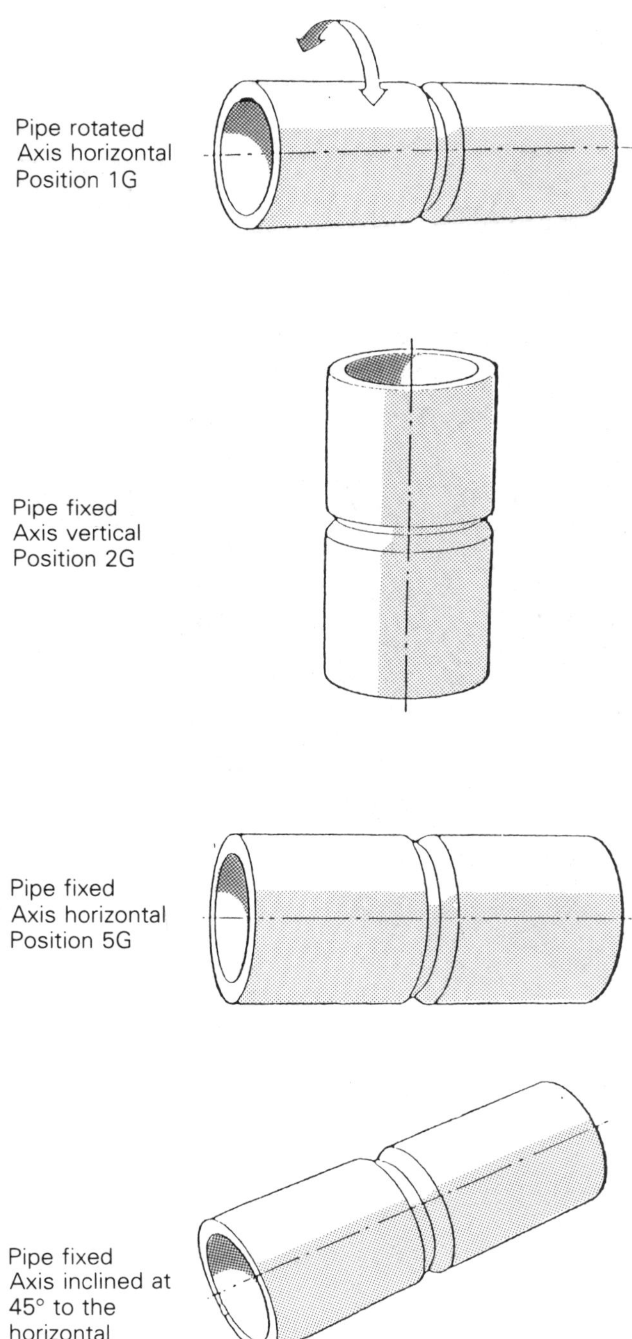

Figure 26.2 The 'G' positions for welding pipe.

The penetration bead (Figure 26.5(c)) should be uniform and not excessive, as too much penetration can interfere with the flow within the pipe. The various inspection methods used on the pipe welds and the criteria for weld acceptance will be determined by the particular welding code that is being worked to. This in turn is determined by the intended use of the pipeline.

Torch angles are shown in Figure 26.5(e) and (f). If the pipe can be rotated, then the angle can be maintained, turning the pipe one segment at a time, or the pipe can be slowly rotated with the torch in a fixed position.

When depositing the root run vertically upwards, which is more common with the manual metal arc, TAGS and oxyacetylene processes, the keyhole must still be maintained in order to obtain the required penetration (Figure 26.5(b)) and it usually takes many practice welds to perfect this. (See Figure 26.6.)

For very high-quality welds a combination of processes can be employed. For example, the root run can be deposited by the TAGS process and then filled and capped with manual metal arc welding.

Tubes can be joined to tube plates for boiler applications by a number of methods. Automatic TAGS employs a small torch that rotates at a predetermined speed, welding the end face of the tube to the plate, while explosive welding will join several tubes at once, by inserting small internal charges into each pipe to be joined. Figure 26.7 shows the welding of tubes to a tube plate by the manual metal arc process.

Oxyacetylene welding is still widely used for welding pipes and can, of course, be performed in areas where there is no electrical supply. Figure 26.8 illustrates the various welding positions in relation to the plane of the tangent. There are three oxyacetylene techniques that can be employed; leftward (Figure 26.9), rightward (Figure 26.10) and all-position rightward (Figure 26.11). Which technique is chosen will depend upon the pipe wall thickness, the welding position and whether or not the pipe can be rotated.

The leftward method is usually used on pipe with wall thickness up to 6 mm. Over this thickness, pipe is welded more satisfactorily by the rightward or all-position rightward method (Figure 26.12). Just as with the welding of plate, edge preparations are required as the wall thickness

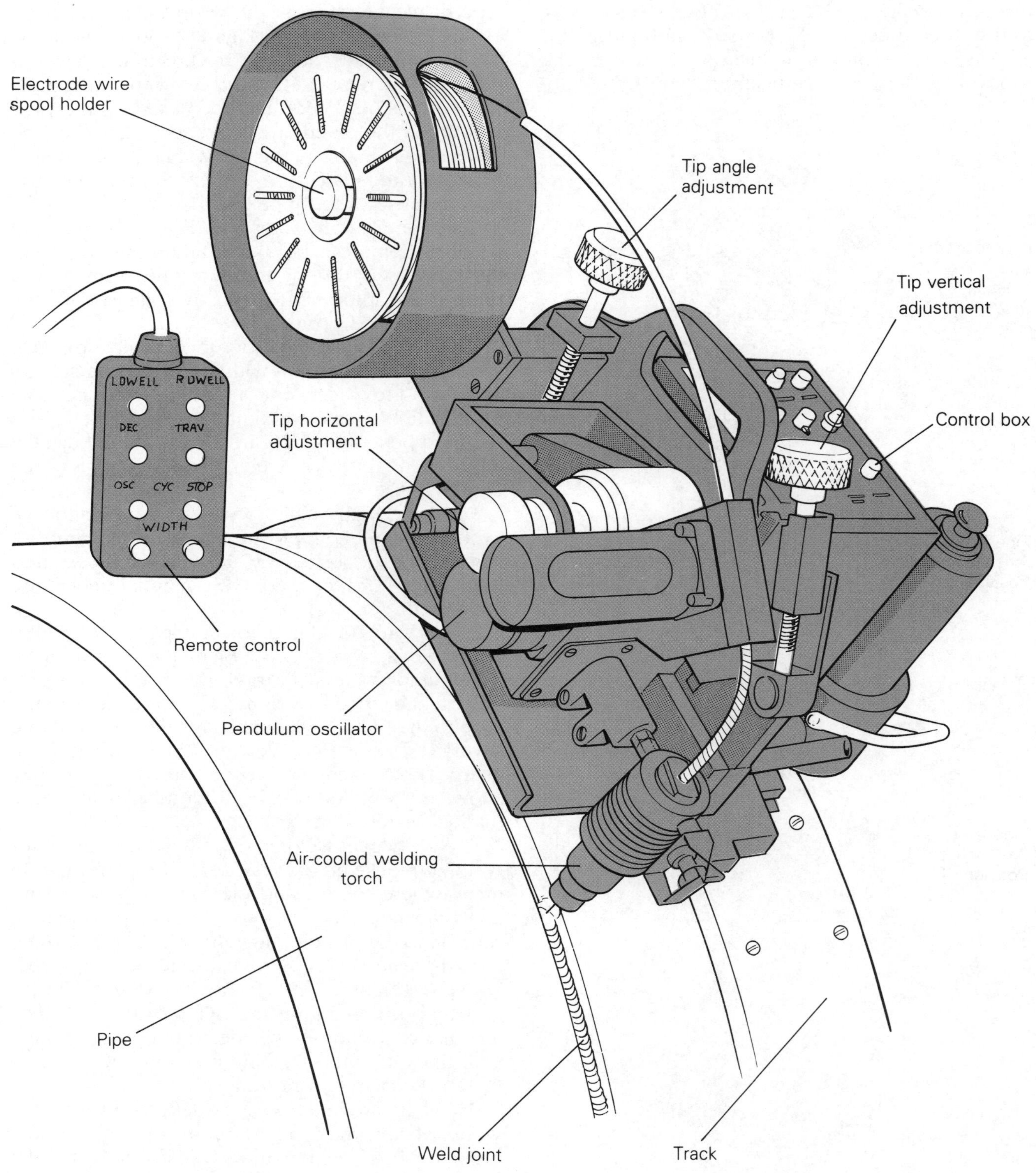

Figure 26.3 A typical automatic pipewelding machine: LH Comet Mk II.

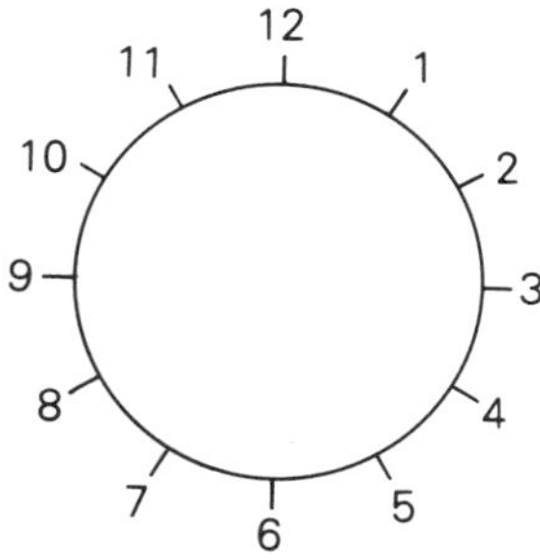

Figure 26.4 The clock positions used as reference when pipewelding.

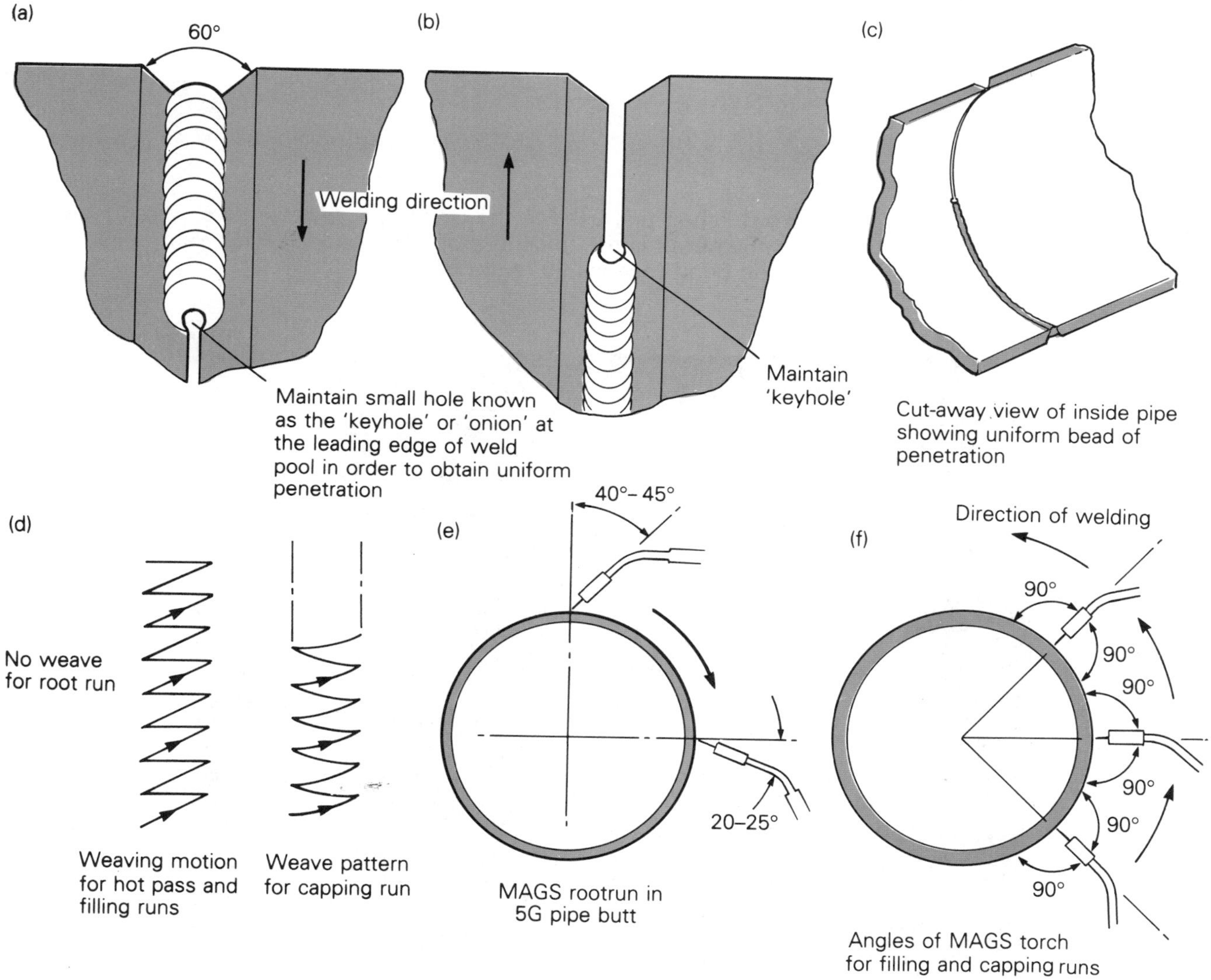

(a)
60°
Welding direction
Maintain small hole known as the 'keyhole' or 'onion' at the leading edge of weld pool in order to obtain uniform penetration

(b)
Maintain 'keyhole'

(c)
Cut-away view of inside pipe showing uniform bead of penetration

(d)
No weave for root run
Weaving motion for hot pass and filling runs
Weave pattern for capping run

(e)
40°– 45°
20–25°
MAGS rootrun in 5G pipe butt

(f)
Direction of welding
90°
90°
90°
90°
90°
90°
Angles of MAGS torch for filling and capping runs

Figure 26.5 MAGS welding of pipe butts in fixed horizontal position.

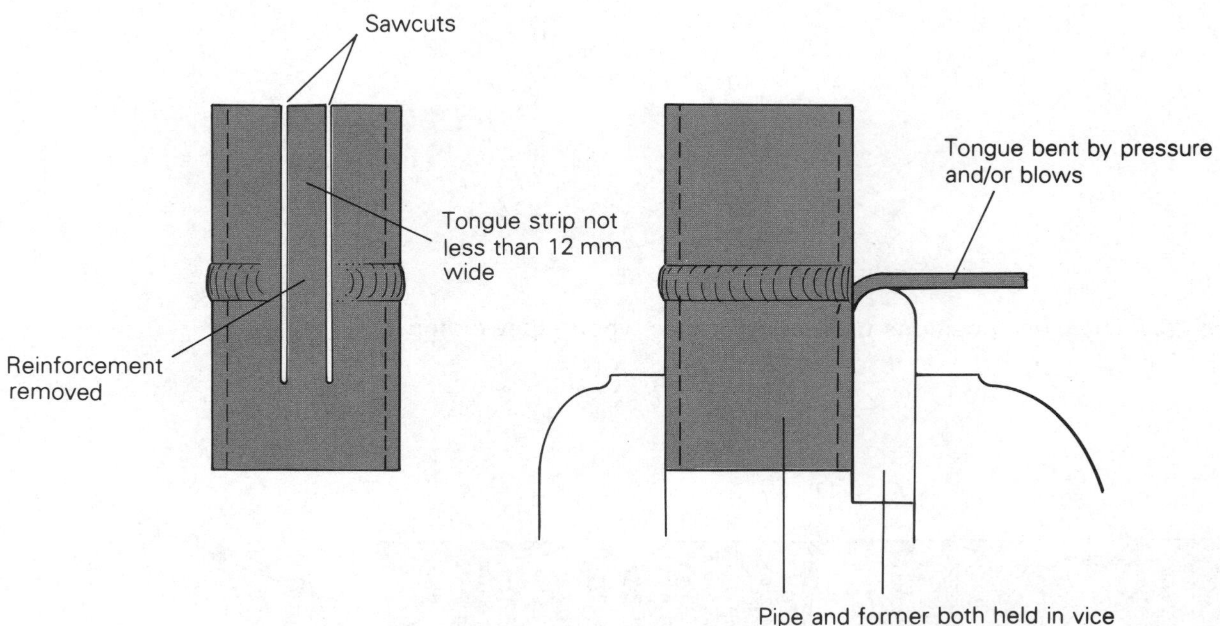

Figure 26.6 The tongue bend test is a workshop test used in the training of pipewelders. The diameter D of the former should be equal to $4 \times t$, where t is the thickness of the pipe wall. The weld is usually considered satisfactory if the angle of the bend reaches 90° without fracture.

Figure 26.7 Welding tubes to tube plate by the manual metal arc process. (Courtesy of UTP, UK and UTC, Nigeria and Ghana)

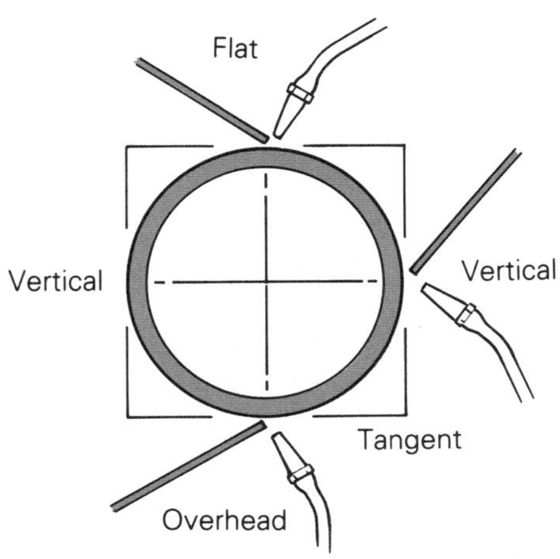

Figure 26.8 End view of a fixed pipe, showing positions of blowpipe and filler rod. If the pipe can be rotated, then the welding position can remain fixed.

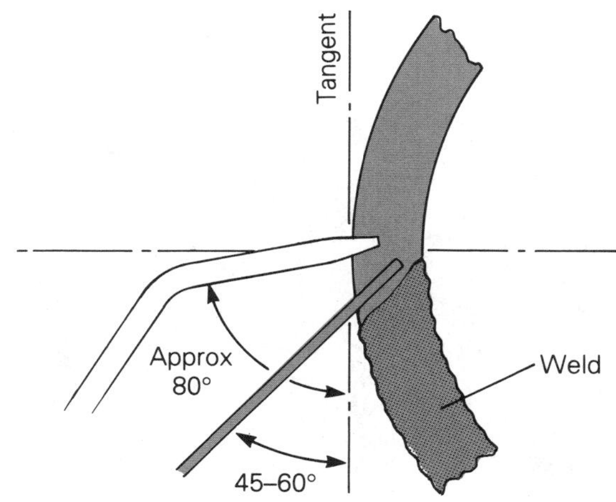

Figure 26.11 The all-position rightward technique of pipewelding.

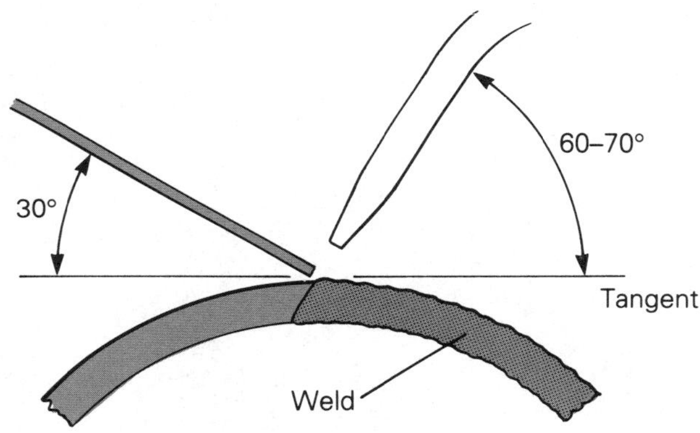

Figure 26.9 The leftward technique of pipewelding.

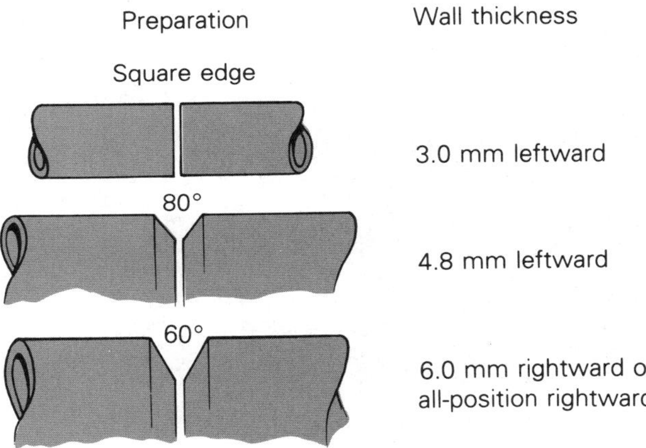

Figure 26.12 Appropriate pipewelding techniques for different wall thicknesses.

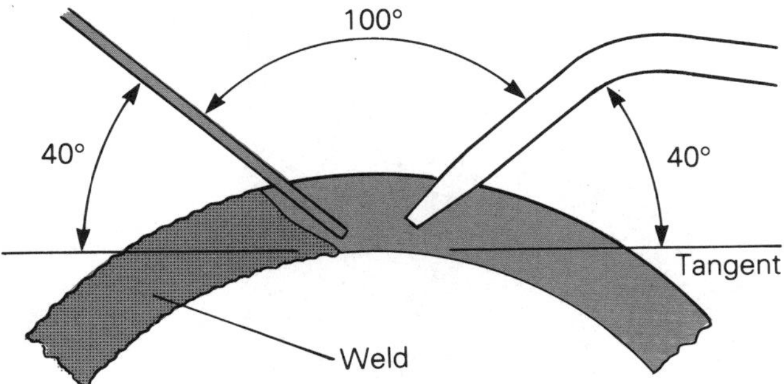

Figure 26.10 The rightward technique of pipewelding.

increases. These can be achieved either by oxy-acetylene bevelling (pipe rotated under a fixed cutting torch set at required angle, or the use of small machines that will travel round a fixed pipe) or by using large lathes.

The series of photographs in Figures 26.13–26.16 shows some scenes of the arc welding of pipelines for long-distance gas transmission.

Figure 26.13 Mobile arc welding station for use on long-distance transmission pipelines. Note the tent to give all-weather protection while each weld is being formed.

Figure 26.14 Showing the diameter of a gas-transmission pipeline under construction.

Figure 26.16 Section of completed pipeline lowered into trench ready to be covered over.

Figure 26.15 Welding of gas-transmission pipeline completed above the surface of the ground.

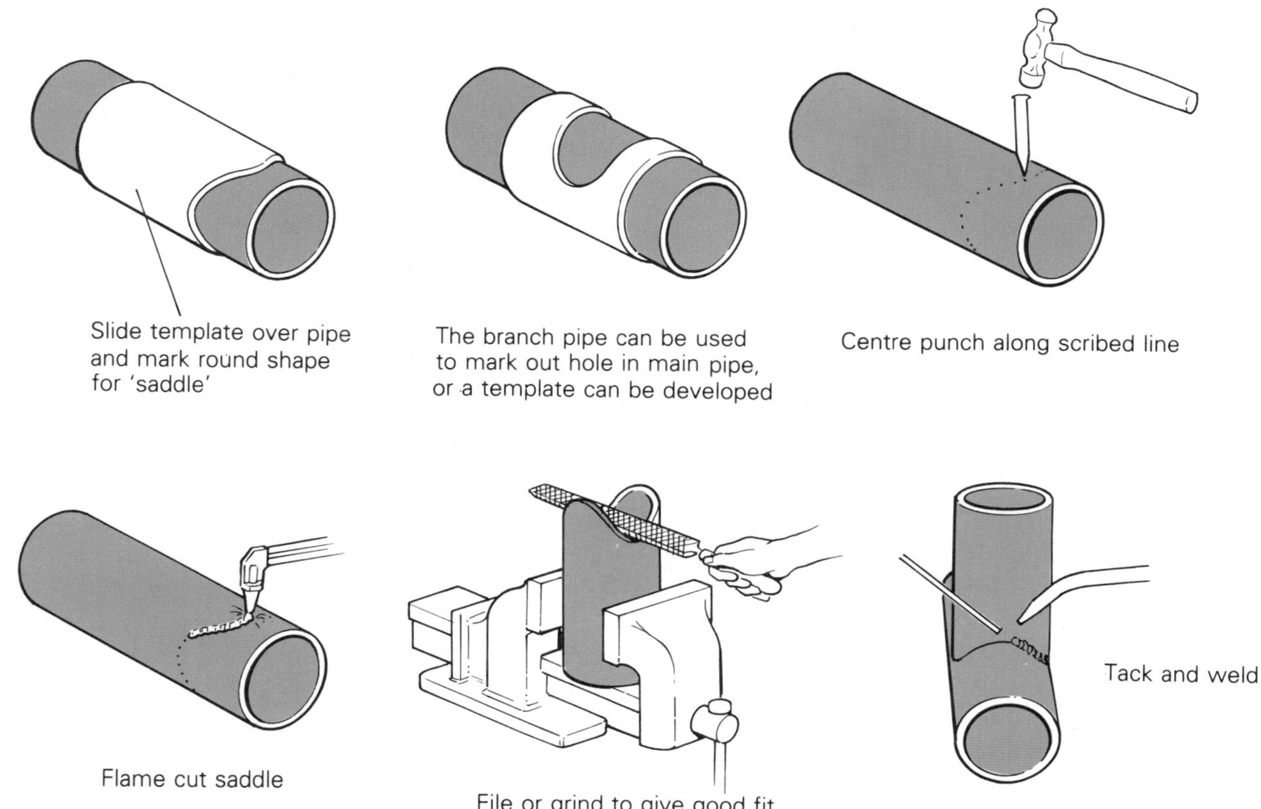

Figure 26.17 Pipe branches: using templates for marking out cutting lines for 'saddle' on branch pipe and hole in main pipe.

Pipe branches

In pipe work there is often a need to branch one pipe off from another. This work is made easier by having a set of **templates** for different sizes of pipe and types of branches (Figure 26.17).

To develop cutting templates for the hole in the main pipe and the shape of the branch pipe end, draw out the side and end views of the main pipe (or header) and the branch as shown in Figure 26.18(a) and (b). Then divide the lower half of the circumference of the branch into equal parts, and draw lines from these points, parallel to the centre line, to intersect the outside and inside diameter of the main pipe.

Draw horizontal lines from intersecting points a, b, c, d, e (Figure 26.18(a)) to intersecting points J, K, L, M, N (Figure 26.18(b)). Set out the circumference of the branch pipe as a baseline A–B–A (Figure 26.18(c)) and mark off the equal distances 1–2, 2–3, 3–4, etc. Plot from this baseline the distances from A–B to the points of intersection with the main pipe wall a–a, b–b, c–c, etc. Join these points with a smooth curve, which will give the required shape of the template for preparing the end of the branch pipe.

To develop a template for the hole in the header, lay out horizontal centre line JJ and vertical centre line NN, as shown in Figure 26.18(d). On centre line JJ, plot the distances NM, ML, LK, KJ from Figure 26.18(b), these distances being measured from intersecting points on the main pipe curve. This determines the length of the template to allow for the curve.

To obtain the required width, which will be equal to the outside diameter of the branch pipe, plot the distances from Figure 26.18(a), measured in a straight line, using e as the centre line, ei, eh, eg, ef. This will then give NN, MM, etc. Connecting the intersecting points with a smooth curve will

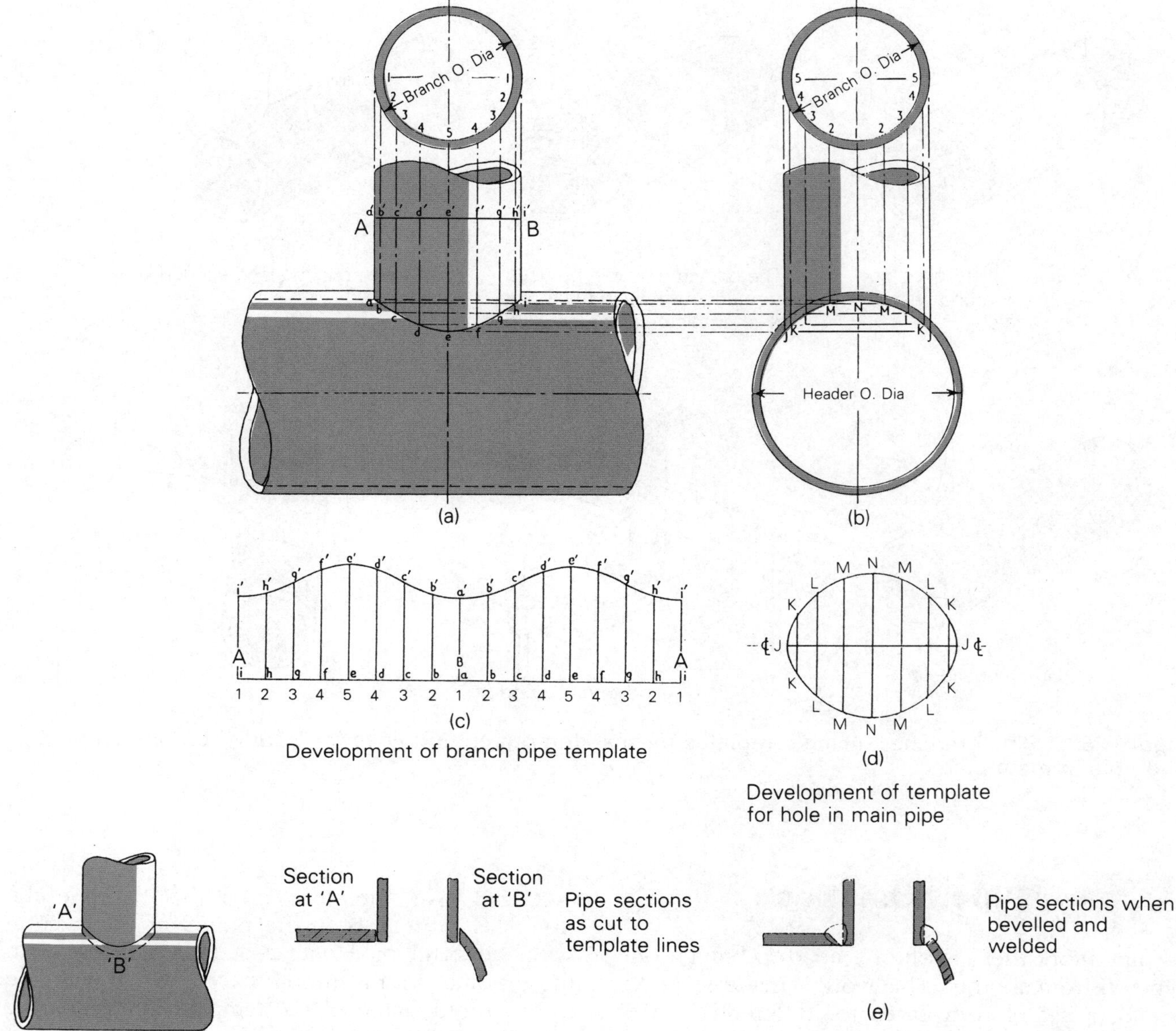

Figure 26.18 **Method of developing templates for an unequal branch pipe at 90°.**

give the template for cutting the hole. When cut, the hole in the main pipe can be prepared with the required bevel ready for welding (Figure 26.18(e)).

Figure 26.19 shows the development of template patterns for a set-on branch pipe.

CHECK YOUR UNDERSTANDING

- Before attempting to weld pipe by any process it is usual to master the welding of plate.
- The real skill of pipewelding is required when the pipe cannot be rotated, as this will involve being able to weld in the flat, vertical and overhead positions and also being able to change from one position to the next without stopping the weld.
- The technique employed to ensure full penetration when welding pipe vertical-up is to maintain a 'keyhole' or 'onion' in the root.
- Stovepipe welding is the name given to the method using cellulose or cellulose iron powder

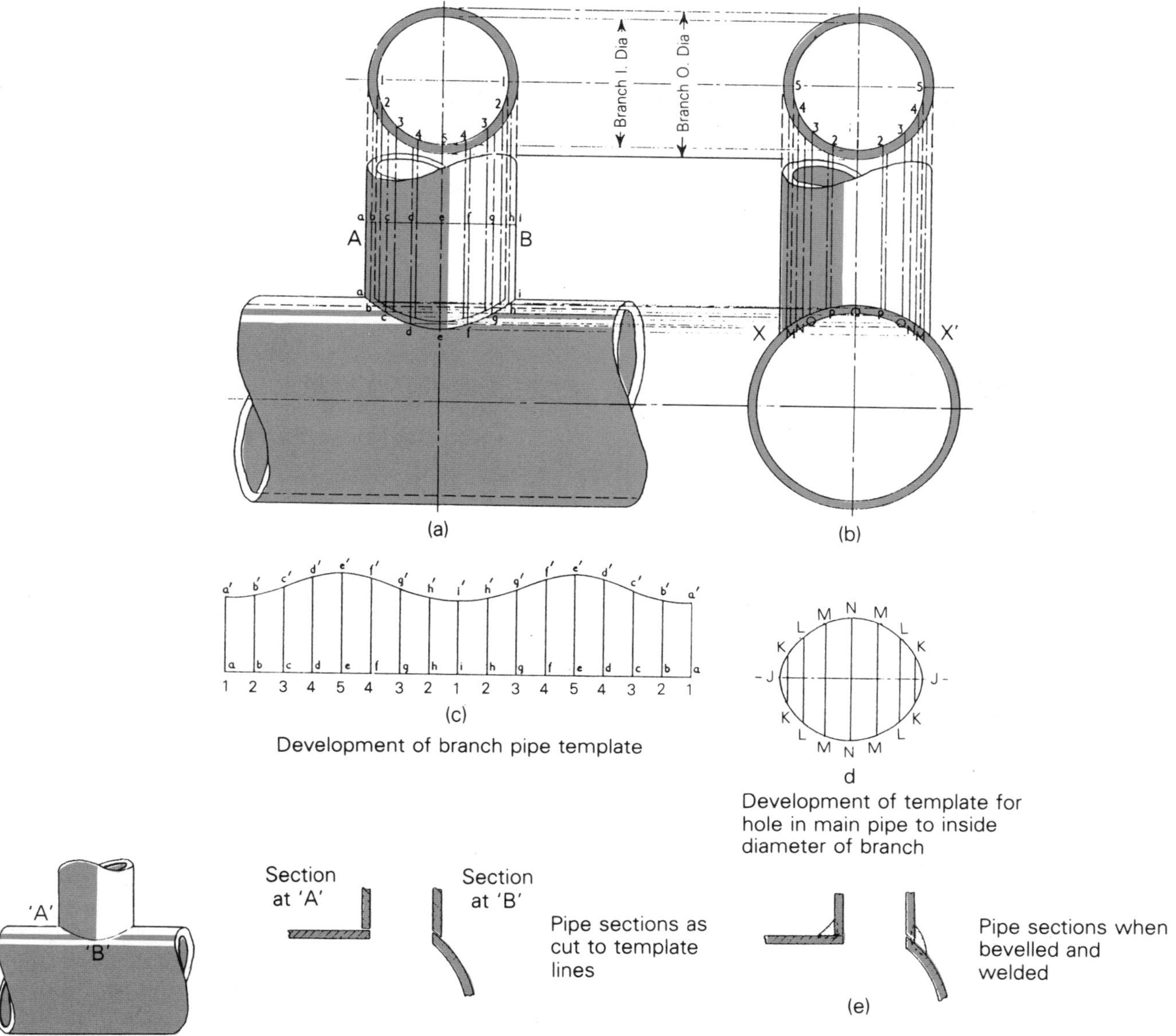

Figure 26.19 **Method of developing templates for a set-on branch joint.**

electrodes to weld downwards from the 12 o'clock position to the 6 o'clock position in multiple runs. The MAGS process can also be employed for this method of welding.

REVISION EXERCISES AND QUESTIONS

1 Why is it best to master the welding of plate fully before attempting to weld pipe?

2 Explain the technique used to obtain full penetration when welding pipe vertical-up.

3 What is meant by stovepipe welding?

4 When might you use oxyacetylene welding instead of electric welding?

5 When might you employ a combination of processes on a pipe weld joint?

(Further practice questions can be found on page 202.)

Other welding processes

Introduction

This chapter deals with two specialised welding techniques – Thermit welding and friction welding – and the special considerations involved in welding underwater. The 'key words' section, towards the back of this book, contains additional definitions and brief descriptions of some of the more advanced welding processes and techniques.

Thermit welding

Thermit welding is based on aluminium exothermic reactions (an exothermic reaction is one that gives off heat). The reduction of metal oxides by means of finely divided aluminium was demonstrated by Sainte-Claire-Deville and by Wohler in the early nineteenth century. It was not until the 1890s, however, when Herault and Hall used the electric furnace method for producing cheaper aluminium, that commercial applications of the alumino-thermic method could be considered.

In 1894 Vautin discovered that extremely high temperature (approximately 3000°C) could be obtained by igniting mixtures of finely divided aluminium with iron oxide.

Dr Hans Goldschmidt advanced the process on a commercial scale by incorporating the important development of starting the reaction with a fuse. The earlier experiments had required the heating of the whole reaction charge in order to reach ignition temperature.

This method is known as the **Goldschmidt** or **Thermit process**. (The name Thermit is derived from the word thermite, which denotes a mixture of powdered aluminium and metallic oxide.)

Although the Goldschmidt principle is applied in the extraction of certain metals from their oxides, Thermit mixtures can be used for the welding of iron and steel or in incendiary bombs.

The Thermit welding process

The basis of the welding process is the chemical reaction between the finely powdered aluminium and the iron oxide.

The chemical equation describing this reaction is as follows:

$$Fe_2O_3 + 2Al \rightarrow Al_2O_3 + 2FE + \text{heat (4187 J)}$$

The approximate proportions of the mixture by weight are three parts of aluminium to ten parts of iron oxide.

The charge is placed in a crucible, which consists of a refractory magnesia-lined conical steel pot covered with a steel lid having a large hole in the centre. At the base of the crucible is the tapping device. Modern tapping thimbles are automatic and melt on completion of the reaction.

The reaction is started by an igniter, having a flash temperature of 200°C. These igniters must always be stored and transported separately from the Thermit charges.

Once started, the reaction is rapid, and continues until all the oxygen from the iron oxide has been transferred to the aluminium. This causes the temperature to rise to approximately 3000°C (neglecting heat losses). The time taken for this reaction to complete is usually about 30 seconds.

An important factor is the difference in specific gravity between the molten iron and the molten alumina, causing them to separate and the alumina slag to float to the surface. At this stage the metal will have at least a 600°C superheat, and this allows it to be used for welding purposes.

Figure 27.1 Welding railway lines by the Thermit process (Thermit is a registered trade name). Here the reaction has been started.

Figure 27.2 Molten Thermit steel pouring into the mould to form the weld.

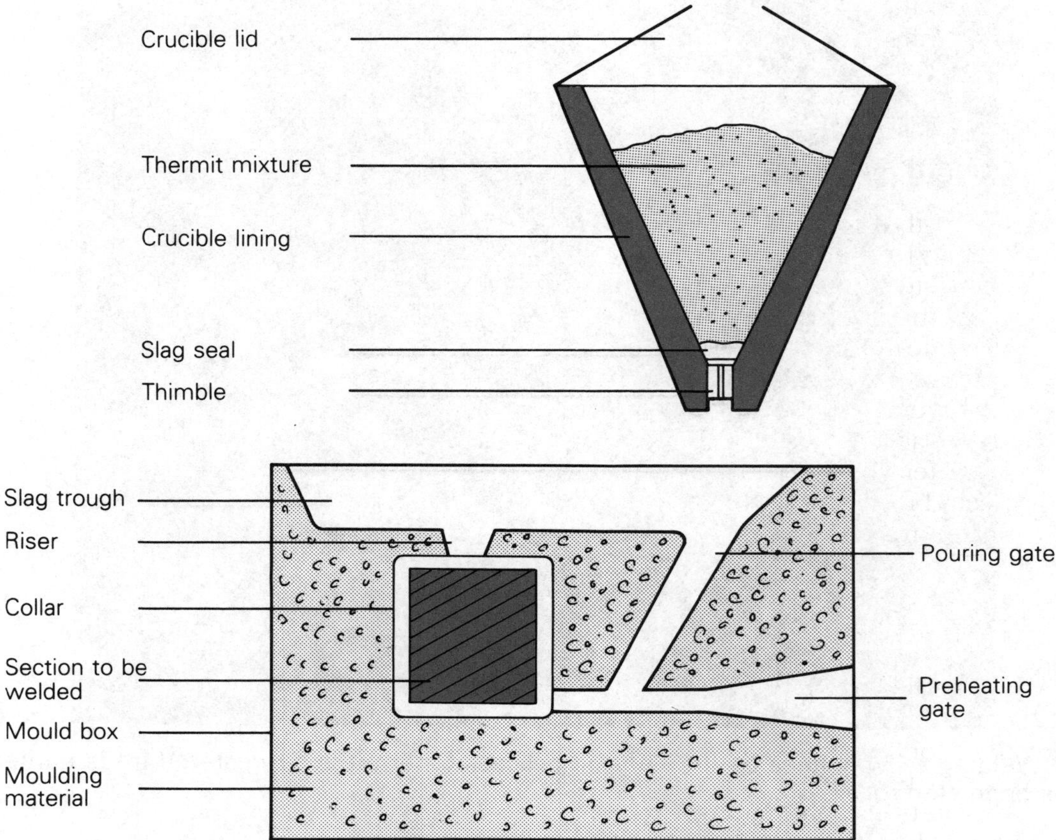

Figure 27.3 **General arrangement for Thermit welding.**

The hot liquid Thermit steel is cast into a mould, welding the ends of the workpiece by flowing between and around them.

Moulds can either be preformed to the shape of the desired weld, as for railway lines, or one-off moulds can be manufactured for repair welding using the 'lost-wax' process (Figures 27.1 and 27.2).

It is usual to preheat the mould and the ends of the work to be joined, before pouring in the hot metal. This ensures that the mould is dry and that full advantage can be taken of the superheat for welding purposes.

The first patent for Thermit welding was granted in 1897. By the early 1900s the process was well established in Germany, France and the United Kingdom. At this time it was mainly used for smelting, rail welding and repairs to heavy machine parts. These still remain the main applications of the process.

In 1909 Dr L.A. Groth published a work illustrating the applications of the Thermit process to large marine repairs.

Figure 27.3 shows the general mould and crucible arrangements for Thermit welding.

Long-life crucibles

In the UK, Europe and Southern Africa, crucible linings were made from dead burned magnesite refractory and could be used for eight to ten reactions before needing replacement.

Increased fuel costs have made the dead burning of the magnesite very expensive and the Thermit company now use a refractory made from a special form of alumina. These long-life crucibles are pressed into a thin mild steel shell and give a life of approximately 35 reactions. The whole crucible is then discarded and replaced. The magnesite-type lining required the removal of the slag coating after each reaction to prevent residual Al levels in the steel becoming too high. The long-life lining is totally inert and only requires the removal of the slag once during the life of the crucible. This helps to increase the life of the lining because mechanical damage is not inflicted by frequent slag removal.

Automatic tapping thimbles

In conjunction with the long-life crucible, automatic tapping thimbles have been developed, which release the molten steel into the mould at the appropriate time. (A thimble is a plug inserted into the crucible tapping hole. Automatic tapping thimbles melt at the desired tapping temperature.)

This relieves the welder of the responsibility of deciding when to release the steel, and also makes the process much safer, because there is no need for welders to stand near the crucible while it contains superheated molten steel.

Friction welding

In friction welding, one component is rotated in contact with the part to which it is to be joined. This produces heat at the interface. When the heat is sufficient for welding, rotation stops and an upset force is applied. Such a joint is regarded as a **forge weld** or **solid-state weld**, as it is made below the melting point of the material(s). Dissimilar metal combinations can often be made.

The process parameters are rotational speed, axial force, welding time and upset force. The process was used for the joining of plastics in 1945 and a paper was published on the joining of metals by Chudikov and Vill in 1956.

Modifications include rotating a short section between two stationary components to form a joint embodying two welds; this is known as **radial friction welding**. Non-circular parts can be joined by a further development known as **orbital friction welding**, in which heat is developed by moving one component (non-rotating) in a circular orbit around the axis of the stationary component to which it is to be joined.

Friction welding machines convert mechanical energy to heat at the joint to be welded. Most machines use rotation of one component, although a new development is the linear friction method.

The conventional method is to rotate one component and then force it against the other, which is held stationary (or the fixed component is pushed against the rotating one, as in Figure 27.4).

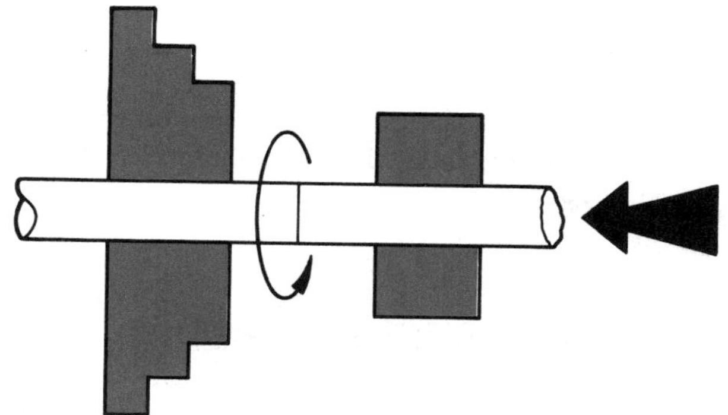

Figure 27.4 The principle of rotational friction welding.

The process takes place in three stages (Figure 27.5):

Stage 1 The cold parts are subjected to dry friction.

Stage 2 Local seizures occur, gradually increasing until each seizure is following by rupturing. The end of the second stage occurs at maximum torque.

Stage 3 In this final phase the torque may drop; the process of seizure and rupture gives way to plastic deformation and a steady state is reached. The greatest percentage of heat (85 per cent) is generated at this stage.

Metal in the plastic state is extruded from the interface to form a **flash** or **collar** around the joint. This causes a shortening of the work, known as

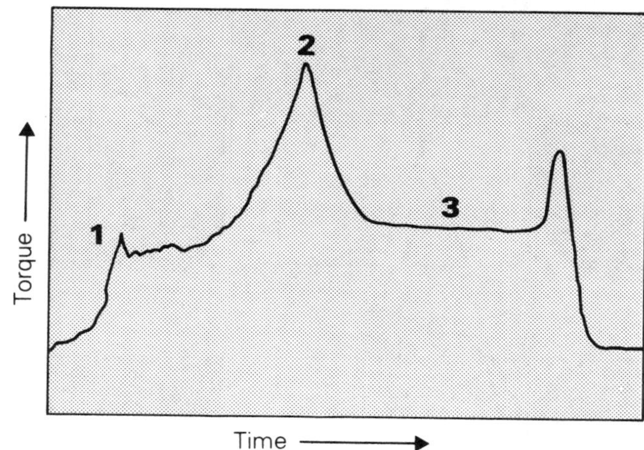

Figure 27.5 A graph of torque versus time shows that the friction welding process takes place in three stages.

the **upset**. A peak occurs in the torque curve at the end of the process; this is the result of speed reduction during braking and forging.

Because friction welding is a solid-state process (no melting takes place), it enables many combinations of dissimilar metals to be joined together.

Underwater welding

There are two types of underwater welding: **hyperbaric**, where a dry diving chamber is used, so that the actual welding can be done in the dry; and **wet welding**, where there is no protection given to the weld from the water. The biggest problem with wet welding arises from the quenching effect of the water as fast as the weld is deposited.

Although wet welding is primarily used for the repair welding of underwater structures, advances in electrode design have allowed it to be used for other applications, such as the attachment of sacrificial anodes to marine structures. It is also used for attaching lifting lugs to submerged structures during salvage operations. Electrodes are usually coated with a varnish to protect the flux. Quality control procedures and welder qualification tests are required for underwater welding, and comprehensive welder/diver training is essential.

With hyperbaric welding, special **underwater habitats** (UWH) (Figure 27.6) are used. These can be fastened around the work to be welded and, in underwater pipeline welding, the divers fasten seals at the intersection of the pipes with the habitat walls. Once the seals are installed, the water is displaced from the habitat with a gas, usually helium. Because the habitat is filled with a large percentage of helium gas and also contains an environmental control system, the welder/divers can spend long times inside.

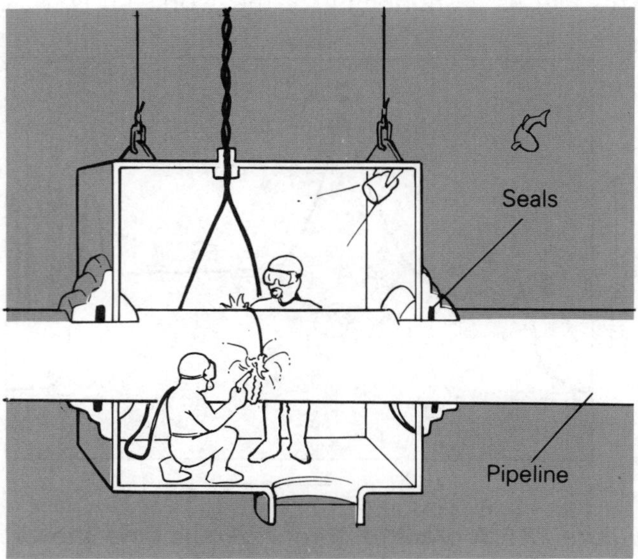

Figure 27.6 Welders working in a dry habitat.

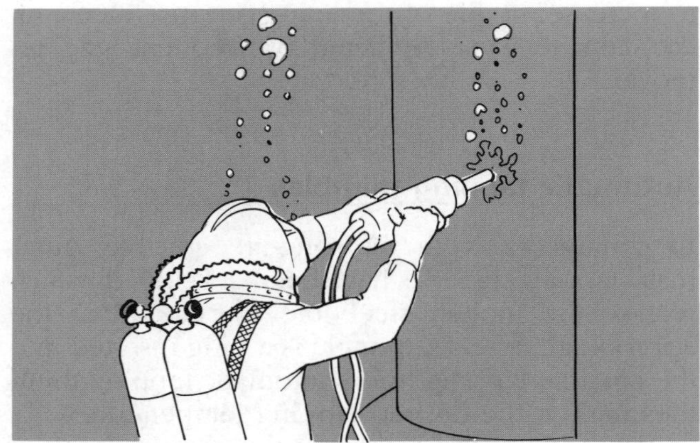

Figure 27.7 Diver-welder attaching a stud by friction welding.

Some hyperbaric systems use **robotic welding systems**, controlled from a ship on the surface, as television cameras relay the welding operation to an on-board television screen. Hyperbaric welding is very expensive and is therefore only employed when no other system will suffice.

Development work in underwater welding is constantly being carried out. One fairly recent idea is the use of underwater friction welding for the attachment of studs (Figure 27.7). This has proved very effective.

REVISION EXERCISES AND QUESTIONS

1. Give a typical application for the Thermit welding process.
2. What is meant by a 'solid-state weld'?
3. Name a solid-state welding process.
4. What is the name given to the type of underwater welding carried out using a dry diving chamber?
5. When wet welding underwater, what is the biggest problem affecting weld quality?

(Further practice questions can be found on page 202.)

Answers to questions and answering hints

Introduction

This section provides you with all the answers to the variety of questions and exercises given in the book. Always try a question or exercise yourself before you look at the answer. This will increase your understanding of the topic and give you practice in answering questions. If you are not sure of a particular answer, re-read the relevant section or chapter in the book to revise the work. You need to understand why a question has a particular answer, so that you can apply your understanding to similar types of question or exercise in your examinations and course assignments.

The book contains a variety of types of question and exercise. Find out the types of question that you will be expected to answer and their pattern. If possible, obtain past papers to support your work and revision. Some of the questions in the book require longer answers. We have provided hints on how to tackle these questions, and on the range of topics that you should include. Practise giving full answers to these questions and then check the answering hints to see that you have included all the relevant topics.

To revise a topic quickly you can also refer to the 'Check your understanding' sections given at the end of each chapter, and the list of key words with definitions given at the end of the book.

Hints to answering questions in examinations and course work

- ☐ Read all the questions carefully before you try anything. Make sure that you understand what each question is asking you to do.
- ☐ Plan the time that you will spend on each question. Use the marks as a guide: the more marks a question is worth, the more time it is worth spending on it.
- ☐ If you have a choice of questions, try to make your choice and stick to it. Don't change your mind halfway through the examination.
- ☐ Make sure that you earn all the 'easy' marks. Do not spend too long on a question you find difficult. Leave it; if you have time, you can try it again later when you have finished all the other questions.
- ☐ Keep an eye on the time. Make sure that you try all the questions you are required to answer.
- ☐ Always present your work as clearly as you can, whether you are writing or drawing. Make your work easy to follow for the examiner or assessor.
- ☐ Try and allow some time at the end to check your answers and improve them.
- ☐ In practical work, make sure that you understand what you are being asked to do by re-reading the question before you start. Follow all instructions carefully.

A note from the author

At the end of the answers is a section of further questions that you can try when you have completed all the exercises. These questions are to help you revise the subject; no specific answers are given, as you will find the full answers by referring to the relevant section of the book.

Chapter 1

1 The word 'weld' means to join materials together into one piece.
2 Any 20 items including those from the chapter

such as: cars, lorries, trains, metal-framed buildings, ships, metal chairs, metal tables, metal bridges.

3 Ship, oil platform, metal-framed building etc.
4 Electrical components such as transistors.
5 Oxyacetylene welding (also known as gas welding), manual metal arc welding, tungsten arc gas-shielded welding, metal arc gas-shielded welding, resistance welding.
6 Any two from: X-ray, gamma-ray, ultrasound.
7 The rods are precoated with flux and are called electrodes.
8 Brazing, bronze welding.

Chapter 2

1 Immerse the area under cold water or cold running water for at least 10 minutes.
2 Make sure that the electric current has been turned off or that the casualty is removed from the source of the electric shock.
3 By carrying out mouth-to-mouth ventilation. (If the heart has stopped, the application of external chest compression will also be required.)
4 Reassure and comfort the casualty. Loosen any tight clothing, but keep them warm with extra clothing or a blanket. If they are thirsty, moisten their lips with water but do not give them anything to drink.
5 If bandages are tied too tightly they can stop the blood circulation.

Chapter 3

1 Everyone is responsible for safety.
2 To protect other people passing by (from 'arc-eye').
3 If an electrical fault develops, electricity takes the shortest route to earth. When equipment is correctly earthed, the electricity will use this route. If there is no proper earth, the electricity can pass through the human body to earth, causing electrocution.
4 State the type(s) of fire extinguisher(s) in your company or college workshop.
5 The vapours from degreasing operations can decompose by the action of the rays from an electric arc and will form phosgene or other poisonous gases.
6 Copper in contact with acetylene gas will form a contact explosive.

Chapter 4

1 Left-hand thread.
2 3250°C
3 Soapy water.
4 Correct sketch of neutral, oxidising and carburising flame correctly labelled (check with illustrations in chapter).
5 The biggest safety factor of all is the operator turning off the cylinder valves when there is any doubt.
6 The rightward method.

Chapter 5

1 A material that is capable of carrying an electric current with a minimum of resistance.
2 An insulator.
3 Voltage = V, Current = I, Resistance = R.
4 $I = \frac{V}{R}$
5 The process by which iron can be magnetised is called induction.
6 Alternating current.
7 Because a direct current arc will be travelling in one direction only.

Chapter 6

1 To suit different types of weld joint and plate thickness.
2

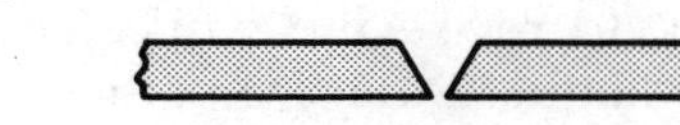

3

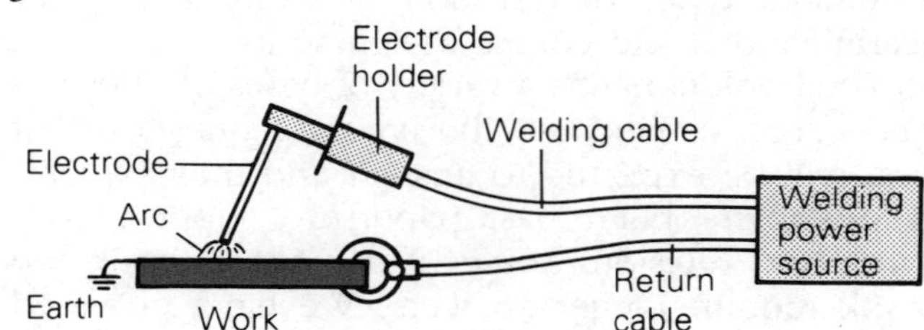

4 The classification is given in writing and as a letter and number code.

Chapter 7

1 The TAGS process uses an inert gas shield to protect the weld from atmospheric contamination.
2 The light intensity can be greater with a tungsten arc.
3 A.c. is required for TAGS welding aluminium to remove the oxide electrically from the surface of the metal so that it can be welded. (The oxide has a higher melting point than the aluminium metal.)
4 A 'gas lens' allows a greater extension of the tungsten electrode. It might therefore be needed when welding in an awkward situation. (Deep groove etc.)

5 Thoriated.
6 High-frequency starting will reduce the risk of electrode contamination, which is possible when touch starting is employed.

Chapter 8

1 Direct current.
2 Electrode positive.
3 Any variation in the arc length produces a change in the burn-off rate of the electrode, returning the arc rapidly to its original length.
4 Carbon dioxide, argon (any others correct).
5 Spray, pulsed and dip.

Chapter 9

1 Current, resistance and time.
2 Seam welding.
3 Economy and speed.
4 Because arcing takes place.
5 Copper.

Chapter 10

1 i) Preheating the metal to be cut to ignition temperature.
ii) Oxidising the preheated metal with a stream of high-pressure oxygen.
2 Kerf: the width of the cut; or the space left from which metal has been removed by a cutting process.
3 Nozzles for gas cutting have six or eight holes to give six or eight neutral preheating flames and one central hole for the high-pressure oxygen. A gas welding nozzle has just one hole to give one flame.
4 When the same shape is required, several plates can be cut at once by stacking them and clamping them tightly together before placing them under the cutting head.
5 Description of two processes from: air arc, oxygen arc, manual metal arc or carbon arc. (Plasma is also an arc-cutting process, employing a variation of a plasma welding torch.)
6 Machines would tend to be used to increase production speed, where several items of the same shape were required to be cut within close limits.

Chapter 11

1 By using the freezing point of water as 0°C and the boiling point as 100°C.
2 The joule.
3 Conduction, convection and radiation.
4 i) Temperature-indicating crayons.
ii) Seger cones.
5 It consists of a probe, which is touched to the work. Inside the end of the probe is a joint between two wires made of different metals. The other ends of these wires are connected to a millivoltmeter calibrated in degrees Celsius. According to the temperature of the metal surface, an electrical voltage is produced at the junction of the dissimilar metals: the hotter the surface, the greater the voltage. This is measured on the millivoltmeter and, because it is calibrated in degrees Celsius, a direct temperature reading is given.

Chapter 12

1 An element is a substance that cannot be broken down into any simpler substances.
2 Solid, liquid or gas.
3 Amorphous.
4 Lead.
5 Two.

Chapter 13

1 Any three correct from: ductility, plasticity, brittleness, malleability, hardness, tensile strength, etc.
2 Larger grains.
3 A weaker grain growth structure.
4 Tensile test.
5 By using the formula $\frac{\text{Load}}{\text{Cross-sectional area}}$
6 i) Body-centred cubic; ii) face-centred cubic; iii) close-packed hexagonal.

Chapter 14

1 A metallurgical microscope has an illuminator built into it.
2 A 5 per cent solution of nitric acid in alcohol, which is called nital.
3 Face-centred and body-centred.
4 Around 0.25 per cent carbon.
5 The greater the carbon content, the more brittle the material is likely to be and therefore the greater the risk of cracking if precautions are not taken.

Chapter 15

1 It is important to be able to identify metals because, until you know what the metal is that you are going to weld, you cannot plan how you are going to weld it.
2 By their colour and weight.
3 A worn file will give misleading results.
4 It can be used to distinguish between most ferrous and non-ferrous metals.

5 A dull thud.

Chapter 16
1 Multipass welds have the effect of refining the grain structure in the lower deposits.
2 By use of the carbon equivalent formula.
3 The clip test.
4 This occurs when carbon from the parent metal diffuses into the weld metal.
5 Buttering.

Chapter 17
1 The fumes can cause 'Galvo' or zinc fume fever. This is a condition that can last a couple of days, causing sickness and dizziness.
2 Capillary attraction describes the way a liquid travels into a narrow gap. It does not occur if the gap is wide.
3 A transition piece is a material, or combination of materials, which can be used to join dissimilar materials. It forms an insert to which both materials being joined can readily be welded.
4 Clad steel.

Chapter 18
1 Grey cast iron.
2 650°C or higher if a complicated casting.
3 Because the fracture surfaces in this material have a white appearance.
4 White cast iron can be difficult or at times impossible to weld because it is an extremely hard and brittle material in which the carbon is combined as either cementite or martensite.
5 Strictly neutral.

Chapter 19
1 Chromium and nickel.
2 Austenitic stainless steel.
3 Stainless steels have a high coefficient of expansion and much lower heat conductivity than mild steel.
4 By using a filler rod/electrode that will produce 4–5 per cent ferrite in the weld deposit.
5 By adding stabilizing elements such as niobium to the material and the electrode or filler wire.

Chapter 20
1 A flux is not necessary because the oxide is removed by the electrical action of the arc, and further contamination is prevented by the use of an inert gas shield.
2 By using a spool-on-gun arrangement.
3 Duralumin is a very useful engineering material because it has the strength and hardness of mild steel but is much lighter.

Chapter 21
1 Because copper has a very high heat conductivity.
2 When very heavy sections are being welded.

Chapter 22
1 Plates can be set a predetermined amount in the opposite direction to that in which they will be pulled by the weld contraction. The amount can be determined by tests so that, when welded, the plates pull straight (or sketched alternative).
2 Sulphur.
3 Hydrogen.
4 Manganese will tend to globularise the sulphur and therefore prevent the formation of low-strength sulphide films.
5 By using the carbon equivalent.

Chapter 23
1 i) Undercutting – any two from: current too high, incorrect manipulation, arc too long, welding speed too rapid.
ii) Lack of penetration – any two from: joint design fault (insufficient root gap), welding speed too rapid, insufficient welding current, too large an electrode (not able to reach root of weld).
2 Internal slag inclusions.
3 Bend test, macro-etch, nick break (or others correct).
4 X-ray, gamma-ray, ultrasound (or others correct).

Chapter 24
1 Zinc-based.
2 The leftward welding technique.
3 The TAGS process.

Chapter 25
1 Oxyacetylene, manual metal arc, TAGS and MAGS welding processes can all be used for building up worn parts by using a deposit similar to that of the parent material.
2 Stellite is an alloy of cobalt, chromium, tungsten and carbon.

Chapter 26
1 It is best to master the welding of plate fully before attempting to weld pipe, because the

welding of pipe that cannot be rotated will involve being able to weld in the flat, vertical and overhead positions.

2 The technique employed to obtain full penetration when welding pipe vertically is to maintain a 'keyhole' or 'onion' in the root.

3 Stovepipe welding is the name given to the method using cellulose or cellulose iron powder electrodes to weld downwards on a pipe from the 12 o'clock position to the 6 o'clock position in multiple runs. The MAGS process can also be employed for this method of welding.

4 In areas where there is no electrical supply.

5 For very high-quality welds a combination of processes can be employed. For example, the root run may be deposited by the TAGS process and then the joint filled and capped by the manual metal arc process.

Chapter 27

1 The welding of railway lines.

2 This is a weld in which no melting has taken plce.

3 Friction welding.

4 Hyperbaric.

5 The biggest problem with wet welding arises from the quenching effect of the water on the deposited weld.

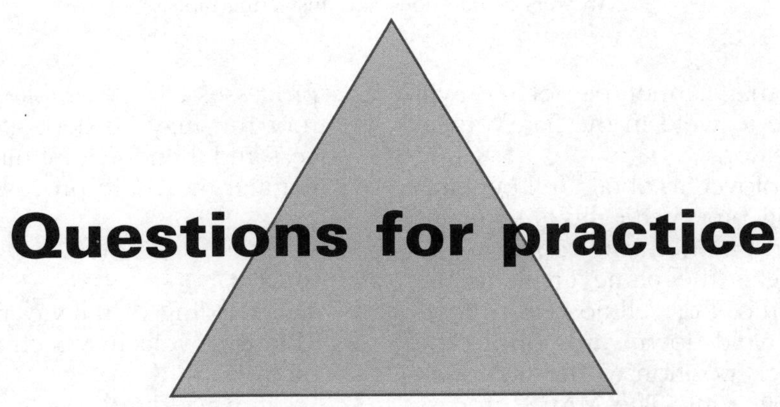

Questions for practice

Answer questions one at a time, then check your answer with the appropriate section or chapter of the book.

1 State the safety precautions to be taken before welding or cutting tanks that have contained inflammable or explosive liquids.
2 Describe how you would perform a nick-break test on a fillet weld.
3 Make sketches of a cross-section of a single 'V' butt weld between two pieces of low-carbon steel. Indicate on the sketches the following points:
 i) reinforcement of weld deposit
 ii) included angle of bevel
 iii) heat-affected zone
 iv) fusion face
 v) root face
4 Describe how to prepare a weld specimen for a macro examination.
5 State two safety precautions to be taken if an oxyacetylene blowpipe becomes overheated.
6 State two advantages of bronze welding cast iron.
7 Give one possible cause of undercut in a fillet weld.
8 Sketch the edge preparation for a butt weld between two pieces of 6 mm low-carbon steel plate in the flat position to be welded by the rightward technique.
9 Draw a neat cross-sectional sketch of a high-pressure gas welding blowpipe and label the main parts.
10 Explain any three safety precautions to be taken before starting oxyacetylene fusion welding.
11 Draw a neat sketch of a tungsten arc gas-shielded welding torch and label the main parts.
12 Name four destructive weld tests.
13 State one reason why it is important that a dissolved acetylene cylinder should always be used in the upright position.
14 Give one example of a situation when post-heating might be required.
15 List four desirable characteristics of a welded joint, regarding its quality.
16 Give two reasons for avoiding a crater at the end of a joint made by MAGS welding.
17 Describe with the aid of sketches three methods of measuring temperature that would be suitable for use in welding.
18 Explain how thermal gouging differs from thermal cutting.
19 Name any two safety devices incorporated in an oxyacetylene welding system.
20 Why is it dangerous to use arc welding processes near degreasing agents?
21 Give one reason for controlling the sulphur content in steels that are to be welded.
22 Explain the term 'weld decay' when associated with stainless steel welding.
23 Sketch a carbon dioxide siphon cylinder.
24 Why is a heater needed when using CO_2 shielding?
25 Name the correct oxyacetylene flame adjustment for fusion welding low-carbon steel.
26 Why are low-carbon steel filler rods usually coated with a thin layer of copper?
27 Describe how you would braze two strips of 1.5 mm low-carbon steel plate together to form a lap joint.
28 Describe any three methods of controlling distortion.
29 Explain the precautions that must be taken when welding or cutting in a confined space with particular reference to:
 i) asphyxiation

ii) toxic fumes
iii) oxygen enrichment

30 Draw neat labelled sketches of:
i) a low-pressure gas welding blowpipe
ii) an air-cooled MAGS welding torch
iii) a flow meter.

31 By means of a sketch, explain the dip method of metal transfer used in MAGS welding.

32 Describe the full procedure for welding a 100 mm crack in a cast iron cylinder block using oxyacetylene welding.

33 Explain a suitable application for pulsed MAGS welding.

34 Describe the Thermit welding process and state two applications.

35 Two pieces of 300 mm diameter low-carbon steel pipe with 6 mm wall have to be welded with the pipes in the fixed horizontal position.
i) Describe a suitable welding technique and process.
ii) Explain one non-destructive method of indicating weld quality.

36 Explain the following terms:
i) peening
ii) residual stress
iii) grain growth
iv) normalising

37 Name three variables that can affect the quality of a MAGS weld.

38 Describe the resistance spot welding process.

Key words and definitions

This section contains brief descriptions of key words and welding terms used in the text. It also includes brief summaries of other welding processes that are not covered in the text.

A.c. Alternating current

Acetylene A gas (C_2H_2) made by adding water to calcium carbide (or calcium carbide to water). For use in welding, it is available in cylinders (dissolved in acetone) for the high-pressure welding system or from acetylene generators at a pressure slightly above atmospheric for the low-pressure welding system. Acetylene cylinders are painted maroon in most countries. They should always have a clear label stating their contents.

Acetylene generators The equipment for making acetylene gas. There are two types: carbide to water and water to carbide.

Alclad *See* **Duralumin**.

Alloy Formed by an intimate mixture of two or more metals.

Alloy steels Steels that contain various additions such as nickel, chromium, molybdenum or other metals in order to give the material special properties.

Alternating current welding arc An arc welding process in which the power supply at the arc is a.c.

Annealing A heat treatment that is applied to relieve the internal stresses in a component.

Arc A sustained electrical spark; a discharge of electricity across a gap.

Arc brazing An electric brazing process in which the heat is obtained from an electric arc between the base metal and the electrode, or between two electrodes.

Arc crater A depression caused by the arc in the molten metal surface directly under the end of the electrode.

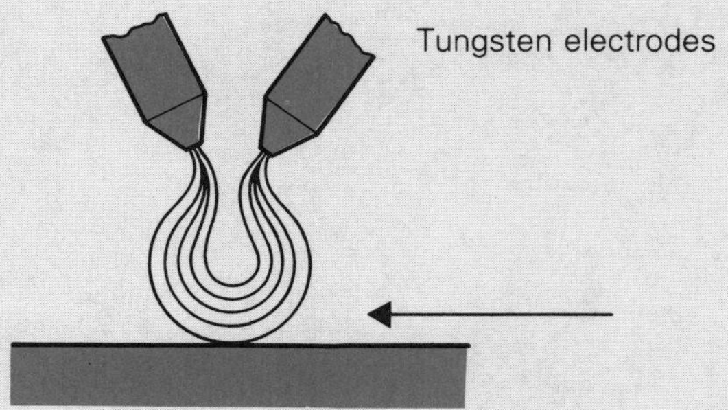

Atomic-hydrogen welding: shape of arc.

Arc p.d. Arc potential difference. *See* **arc voltage**.

Arc stream voltage The drop in voltage in the part of the arc that is liquid or gaseous and considered in a central stream.

Arc voltage This is given by the sum of the voltage drop near the positive (anode drop zone), the arc stream voltage and the voltage drop near the negative (cathode drop zone).

Arc welding A fusion welding process in which the heat is obtained from an electric arc formed either between the parent metal and an electrode or between two electrodes.

Atomic-hydrogen welding This is a fusion welding process in which hydrogen is passed into an electric arc formed between two non-consumable tungsten electrodes. The hydrogen is dissociated in the arc and then recombined to supply the heat for welding.

Austenitic stainless steel A steel containing alloying elements of up to 18 per cent chromium, 8 per cent nickel and 0.1 per cent carbon. Such steels are known as 18/8 stainless steels.

Austenitic steel A steel containing austenite, which is a solid solution of carbon in iron. Austenitic steels are non-magnetic and cannot be hardened by heat treatment. They will, however, become hardened by cold working, such as rolling and hammering.

Automatic arc welding Electric arc welding in which the arc length, feed rate and travel speed of the electrode are automatically controlled. Such machines can either have the welding head moving over the work, electrically driven along a small track, or the welding head can be fixed and the work moves along or rotates beneath it at a controlled rate.

Axis of a weld An imaginary line drawn through a weld parallel to the root.

Backing bar A piece of metal or other material placed under a weld to aid good penetration formation but not intended to become part of the welded joint.

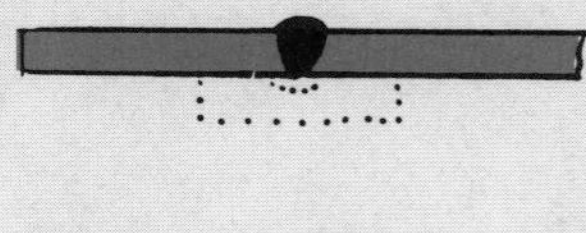

Backing bar.

Backing strip.

Backing strip A piece of metal positioned at the root of the joint and becoming part of the welded joint.

Back-step welding A welding technique that uses a sequence of weld depositions so as to help control heat input and minimise distortion. The welds are deposited in an opposite direction by leaving a space equal to the deposition length of one electrode and welding back to the start of the previous weld run.

Back-to-back welding A method used to help reduce distortion by clamping and welding two similar parts back to back.

Bare wire electrode A solid metal electrode with no flux coating.

Base metal (parent metal) The work, metal to be welded or cut.

Base metal testpiece A specimen for testing that is machined wholly from the base (parent) metal.

Bead A term often used to signify a run of weld metal.

Bead weld A weld made with one pass of the electrode or welding rod.

Bend test *See* **Free bend test** and **Guided bend test**.

Block welding A technique used on pipes, in which the weld is deposited in layers to the full depth of the wall thickness. These increments of the full size of the weld are deposited at definite intervals, the ends of which are stepped back. Rotation of pipe is minimised and welding rate increased because of greater concentration of heat.

Blowpipe (torch) The piece of gas welding equipment in which the gases are mixed, ready for burning at the nozzle or tip.

Bond The junction of the weld and parent material; in fusion welding can also be known as the fusion face or fusion line.

Brass Alloys of copper and zinc.

Brazing A group of joining processes that employ a non-ferrous filler metal or alloy with a melting point higher than 540°C, but lower than the melting point of the metals or alloys to be joined.

Brinell hardness A test that can be used to give a comparative hardness value, which is obtained by measuring the diameter of the indentation made by a steel ball, of a fixed diameter, forced into the surface of the testpiece using a fixed load. The method becomes inaccurate on very hard materials, such as heat-treated steels, owing to deformation of the ball.

Bronze Alloys of copper and tin.

Bronze welding A comparatively low-temperature process (compared with fusion welding) suitable for joining certain metals of the same composition and some dissimilar metal combinations.

Build-up (sequence of) The order of weld run deposition in a multipass weld. Usually illustrated by numbering individual runs on a cross-sectional drawing of the weld.

Buttering Weld metal of a different material from the parent metal, which is deposited on the face or faces of a joint before any joining welds are made. Sometimes employed when welding dissimilar metals to allow the use of filler metals of different composition, or when welding alloy steels and cast iron, as it can help to reduce carbon pick-up in the joining run(s).

Butt weld A weld between two components that have been placed face to face or edge to edge (depending on shape) in the same plane.

Cable (return) Return cables often do not require the same flexibility as the welding cable. The inner conducting core can therefore be of the same cross-sectional area as the welding cable but made from thicker wire, reducing cost.

Cable (welding) The cables used to conduct the electric current required for arc welding consist of an inner core of copper or aluminium wires covered with an insulating sheath (usually thick rubber). The inner core conductor is made from several strands of small-diameter wire to give flexibility and lightness.

Calcium carbide A chemical compound that, when in contact with water, will release acetylene gas.

Capping run The reinforcement or final run of a welded joint. Depending on the size (width) of weld and type of finish required, it can be deposited with a weaving action.

Carbon arc cutting Using the arc heat of the carbon arc process to melt metals and cut through them.

Carbon arc welding Using the arc produced between a carbon electrode and the work, a molten pool is formed. This pool can be moved along the joint to fuse the edges together. Filler metal can be added to the molten pool in order to allow the welding of thicker sections.

Carbon dioxide (CO_2) flux welding This process is the same as **carbon dioxide welding** but the electrode wire also has additions of flux. A flux-cored electrode can be employed (with the flux in the centre) or the flux can be picked up by the wire by magnetic attraction after the wire has passed through the feed rollers.

Carbon dioxide (CO_2) welding A semi-automatic metal arc welding process in which a bare wire electrode, fed from a spool, is used. The arc and molten pool area are shielded from the atmosphere by carbon dioxide gas, which is fed through a nozzle surrounding the wire electrode.

Carbon equivalent The effect of the addition of elements such as Mn, Ni, Cr, Mo, V and Cu on the weldability of a steel can be considered to have the same effect as an increase in the carbon content. There are different formulae for calculating the carbon equivalent when the steel composition is known. The formula below is to British Standards:

$$CE = C + \frac{Mn}{6} \frac{Cr + Mo + V}{5} + \frac{Ni + Cu}{15}$$

A calculated carbon equivalent gives guidance as to whether or not preheat is required. The following table gives a guide:

CE of parent material	Electrode type	Preheat required
Less than 0.41	Rutile	No
0.41–0.45	Rutile	Yes
	Low hydrogen	No
Greater than 0.45	Low hydrogen	Yes

Carbon steel Formed when iron is combined with 0.1–1.5 per cent carbon, with small percentages of manganese and other elements.

Carburising flame An oxyacetylene flame containing excess acetylene.

Cast steel Steels containing 0.9–1.5 per cent carbon, having the properties of strength and toughness and being used mostly for tools.

Chill Usually a large block of metal suitably placed to conduct heat away from the welding area quickly, in order to minimise distortion. Copper in the form of a block or strip is sometimes used as a chill, because copper is a good conductor of heat.

Chipping hammer Tool used for chipping the slag from a completed weld when flux-coated or flux-cored electrodes have been used. The hammer head generally has a chisel edge at one end and a point at the other.

Clad steel Steel plate or sheet with one or both surfaces faced with another metal (for example, low-carbon steels can be clad with a layer of stainless steel).

Cold crack Can form in all ferritic steels when arc welded when the alloy content is above a certain level if precautions such as preheating have not been taken. Cold cracks are difficult to detect as they are usually subsurface. The main cause is the build-up of molecular hydrogen in or near the heat-affected zone. The hydrogen exerts a pressure that can cause cracks to occur after welding has taken place. Residual or external stresses can aggravate this cracking effect.

Columnar grain structure Long elongated crystal growth, which can be found in castings or large single-pass welds, where the cooling has started at the surface and progressed inwards. The columnar crystals point in the direction of cooling.

Concurrent heating Supplementary heat (heat additional to that from the welding process) applied to the work (or local area of the work) during the welding operation.

Constant voltage (welding power source) A welding set with an output voltage that remains constant within specified percentage limits from no load to full load.

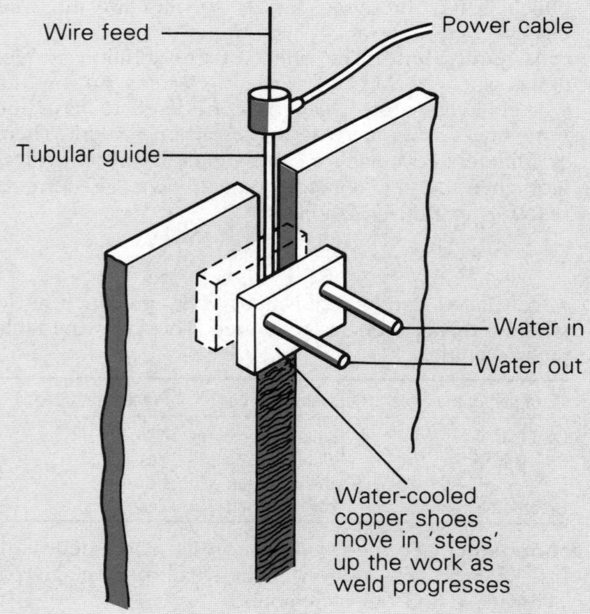

Consumable guide welding: basic set-up.

Consumable guide welding/consumable nozzle welding A modification of the **electroslag welding** process. The welding wire is guided into the molten slag pool by a steel tube (or nozzle), which also becomes progressively melted by the slag pool. The current connection is made to the consumable nozzle/guide tube in the same way as a non-consumable nozzle. The water-cooled shoes are usually moved in increments or steps up the joint with this method, instead of continuously as in electroslag welding. One variation is to use a flux-coated mild steel tube as the consumable nozzle.

Contact welding Welding carried out with a flux-coated electrode resting on the work (in the joint) as it is moved along the joint. The arc is first struck and then the electrode is brought into contact with the work and held at the correct angles of slope and tilt. This type of welding is sometimes used for a sealing run on non-critical components, as it will only give minimum penetration/fusion. Known also as touch welding and drag welding.

Continuous weld A weld that extends without interruption for the entire length of the joint (opposite of space weld).

Controlled bend test *See* **Guided bend test**.

Controlled thermal severity test (CTS test) These tests are one way of checking how susceptible steels are to cracking in the heat-affected zone. Test welds are deposited around a block of metal to a predetermined sequence and under conditions of severe restraint.

Core (wire) The central metallic part of a flux-coated electrode.

Cored electrode A metal electrode with a core of flux.

Covered electrode A metal core with a covering of flux, either applied as a paste under pressure (paste-covered electrode) or wound on (spirally wound electrode). With stick electrodes, one end is left free of flux coating in order to grip and make electrical contact in the electrode holder.

Cover glass A clear glass or plastic used to protect the filter lens in gas welding goggles and electric welding faceshields and helmets from damaging spatter material. The clear cover is much less expensive than the shaded filter lenses. In arc welding shields it is common to sandwich the expensive filter between two clear cover glasses.

Covering or coating (electrode) The flux material applied around a wire core to stabilise the arc, protect it from the atmosphere and improve the properties of the weld metal.

Crater A hollow that can be left at the end of a run of weld metal if the correct finishing procedure is not performed.

Crater-eliminating device An electrical device mostly used on TAGS welding, in which the current is reduced just before the electrode is drawn away at the end of a weld run, thus preventing the formation of a crater, which in some materials may contain cracks. Alternatively, the weld should be finished on a piece of scrap material placed at the end of the joint, known as a 'run-off plate'.

Cruciform A type of welded joint, in which plates meet to form the shape of a cross.

Current Flow of electricity (measured in amperes).

D.c. Direct current.

Deep penetration electrode (DP electrode) An electrode in which the flux coating burns in such a way as to increase the penetration effect of the arc, producing deeper-than-normal fusion at the root of a joint.

Dense slag (solid slag) A slag that has limited porosity and which may exert pressure in order to produce a smooth weld face. *See* **Slag**.

Deposited metal Metal that has been added by the welding process to become part of a welded joint.

Deposition efficiency The ratio of the weight of the metal deposited to the net weight of the electrode(s) consumed (excluding stubs).

Depth of fusion The distance from the original surface of the parent metal face to the point within the joint where fusion ceases.

Descaling The removal of an oxide film or scale from the surface of steel by flame or sand blasting, etc.

Design throat thickness This is a minimum dimension of a given throat thickness for the purposes of design.

Deslag To remove the slag (burnt flux) from the surface of a weld.

Dipped electrode An electrode in which the flux coating is built up by repeatedly dipping the core wire into a liquid or paste flux.

Dip transfer Method of metal transfer in MAGS welding in which the electrode wire repeatedly short-circuits with the molten pool of the weld. This short-circuit current melts a particle from the electrode into the molten pool, the arc re-ignites and the cycle rapidly repeats. It is employed with low welding currents and allows all-positional welding. If the welding current is increased, the metal transfer mode will change to **spray transfer** (or pulsed if a pulse unit is fitted).

Distortion The warping or twisting of metal out of shape due to uncontrolled expansion and contraction forces caused by welding heat input.

Drooping characteristic welding set A welding power source in which the voltage will automatically fall (or droop) from the striking voltage to the arc voltage as the current increases.

Ductile Can be drawn out or stretched into a smaller section.

Duralumin An aluminium alloy containing approximately 3 per cent copper, up to 1 per cent manganese and 2 per cent magnesium. When it is coated with pure aluminium, this product is known as Alclad.

Duty cycle The duty cycle gives the amount of time a welding set or unit can operate before requiring a period to cool down. Many small welding sets incorporate a thermal cut-out device, which switches the set off automatically if it is in danger of overheating. The device automatically cuts in again once the set has cooled down and welding can recommence. The duty cycle is usually based on a 10 minute period and given as a percentage. For example, in a 10 minute period, a 60 per cent duty cycle would mean that the unit could be used for 6 minutes welding and would then require 4 minutes to cool down. Large welding units, particularly those used for semi and automatic welding, have duty cycles of, or approaching, 100 per cent. In normal manual metal arc welding, it is impossible to use a welding unit at 100 per cent, because the operator has to keep stopping to change the electrode, chip off the slag and reposition work.

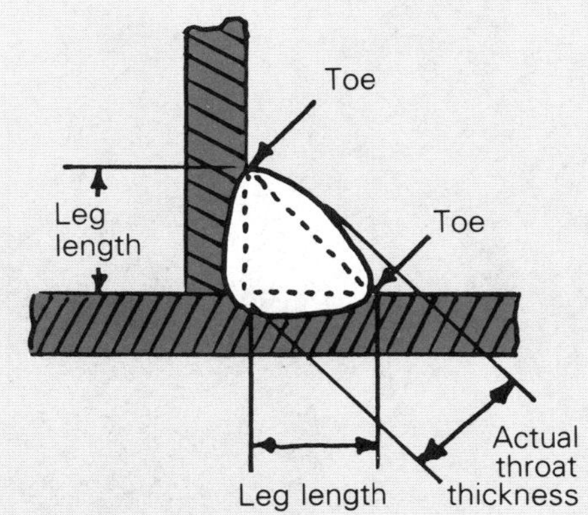

Design throat thickness.

Dye penetrant testing A method of testing for surface defects which is non-destructive. A highly penetrating

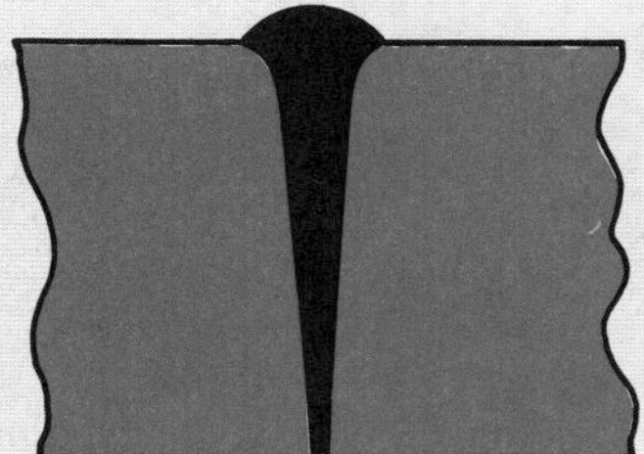
A typical cross-section showing profile of an electron beam weld

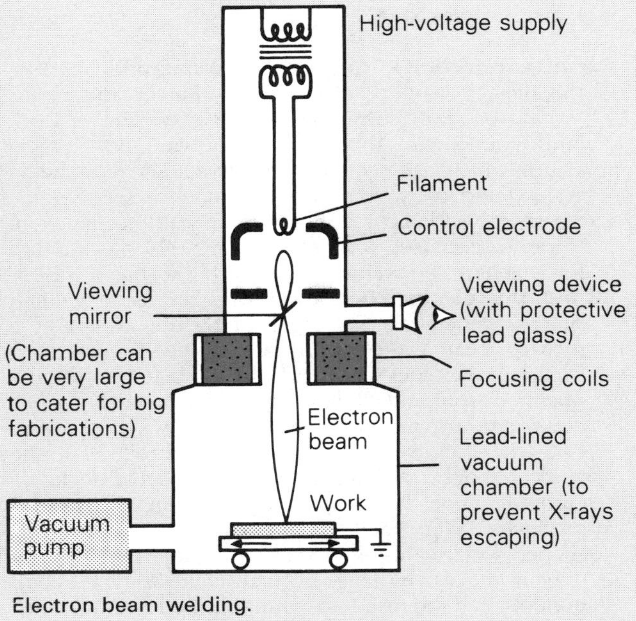

Electron beam welding.

Electron beam welding: EB welder, showing the 150 m^3 vacuum chamber in which work is carried out. (Courtesy of TWI, UK)

dye is applied to a precleaned weld surface and then wiped off. A developer is then applied and highlights any surface defects, such as cracks, that the dye has seeped into. Some dyes are highlighted by an ultraviolet lamp. *See also* **NDT**.

Earth (connection) An electrical connection between the metal casing of electrical equipment and earth/ground or an electrical connection between the work and ground. Not to be confused with the welding return, which is the connection between the work being welded and the welding power source or set.

Earth clamp Clamp for attaching an earth connection. Not to be confused with return clamp, which is a clamp for attaching the welding return cable to the work.

EB welding (electron beam welding) A fusion welding process generating welding heat by the impact of a focused beam of electrons. Usually performed in a vacuum chamber, which is lead lined to protect the operator from radiation. Some machines have been developed to work in the open air. EB welding is very fast. The gun is usually computer-controlled, or the work is moved beneath the beam. Weldable thickness currently ranges between 0.2 and 100 mm. The process produces a very high-quality *steigerwald* – a dagger-shaped weld with low distortion. It can weld normally difficult metals, and is so accurate that machined components can be used to form finished components. Typical uses: turbine blade welds, jet engine components, gears to shafts and salvage welding.

Economiser The gas economiser is designed for use with pipeline distribution of oxygen and acetylene to welding points. It will automatically extinguish the flame when the operator hangs the blowpipe on the control lever. The blowpipe can then be reignited from the pilot light when next required. The method is only for use when brief stops between welding are envisaged; all the equipment should be switched off and shut down when welding is to stop for more than a few minutes.

Edge preparation The shaping of the edges of the metal to accommodate the required amount of weld metal, allowing for fusion and penetration.

Electric brazing Processes obtaining heat for brazing from the use of an electric current.

Electrode (arc welding) Either consumable (as a rod or wire, with or without flux) or non-consumable rod (of tungsten or carbon). The arc is formed between one end of the electrode and the work or another electrode.

Electrode holder A device for holding the electrode and for supplying the electrode with current.

Electrogas welding An arc welding process using a consumable flux-cored electrode to deposit metal into a molten pool. The weld progresses vertically. The molten pool is held in place by water-cooled copper shoes that move upwards as the weld is deposited. Shielding gas (usually CO_2) is fed over the molten pool through tubes

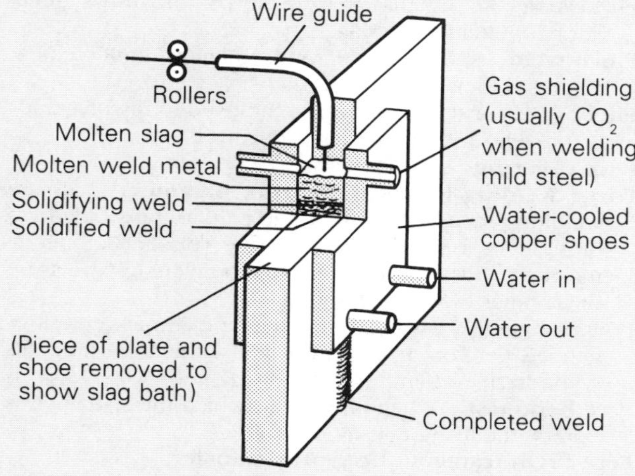

Electrogas welding: basic arrangements.

in the shoes. This is used for welding plates of thinner section (10 mm, $\frac{3}{8}$ in) than the electroslag process.

Electroslag welding This is a fusion welding process that utilises the combined effects of current and electrical resistance in a consumable electrode or electrodes and a conducting bath of molten slag, through which the electrode(s) passes into a molten pool. The whole molten area (metal and slag) is kept in the joint by water-cooled copper shoes, which move upwards as the weld progresses. The process commences with an arcing period and then the end of the electrode(s) becomes covered by slag. Melting then continues in this way until the joint is completed. The process is used mostly for welding in the vertical position, with the weld being completed in one pass. Circumferential welds can also be undertaken on thick material. It is usual to employ more than one electrode wire, in case one jams; the other(s) can be speeded up, thus saving the weld, as this process cannot be stopped and restarted once a joint has commenced.

Equiaxed structure Metal crystals, of approximately equal size, formed throughout a weld or casting when solidification has started at a number of locations within the cooling metal. An etched surface of a weld or casting will generally reveal columnar crystals on the outer surfaces (cooling inwards) and more equiaxed formation in the inner region.

Etching A method of revealing the structure of a metal (or a cross-section of weld and parent metal) by using acid to attack the surface (which has usually been smoothed and polished).

Everdur An alloy containing 96 per cent copper, 3 per cent silicon and 1 per cent manganese.

Explosive welding A welding process using the force of a controlled explosion to effect a weld. Used to bond plates for cladding operations and to weld tubes into tube-plates. A jetting action takes place and the resulting weld consists of an alternate line of fusion and solid state between the components.

Face bend test A bend test in which a specified side of a weld specimen is in tension; for example, the side opposite the root or opposite the side to which the root is nearer, or either weld face when the root is central.

Fatigue A term for the action of repeated, reversed or fluctuating stresses on a material or component. Such repeated stresses can cause failure by the gradual development of cracking at stress levels below the normal UTS (ultimate tensile strength) of the material. Fatigue strengths of welded joints are generally less than that of the parent metal. However, fatigue resistance can be improved by ensuring the absence of undercutting and other surface and internal defects. Attention to smoothness of structures by finish and design, by eliminating sharp edges and notches, will reduce or eliminate stress raisers and increase fatigue strengths.

Faying surface Part of a metal surface specially prepared to fit an adjoining part.

Ferrite The name given to pure iron and one of the microstructural constituents of steel.

Ferritic steel In the main, mild and low-alloy steels fall into this category, having a structure of **ferrite** and **pearlite**.

Ferrule A refractory sleeve that fits around the base of the stud used in arc stud welding. The ferrule contains and shapes the molten metal as well as protecting it.

It is always best to use more than one electrode as the weld will be scrapped if it has to be stopped before the finish. If two or more wires are used one can be speeded up if a 'jam' occurs

(Oscillating mechanism can be used)

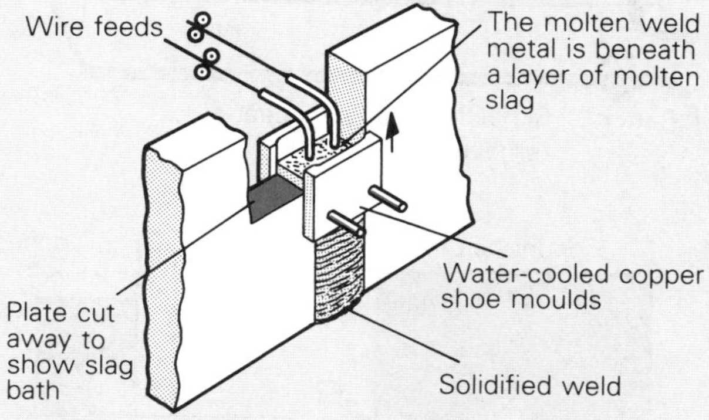

Shoe moulds and wire feed mechanism rise automatically adjusted to speed of welding
Flux is added either manually or automatically

Electroslag welding: basic arrangements.

Filler metal (rod or wire) Metal added during welding, brazing or surfacing.

Fillet (weld) A weld that, when viewed in cross-section, is virtually a triangular deposit joining two faces of parent metal, which are usually at right angles.

Filter lens A glass fitted in goggles, helmets and shields in order to exclude the harmful light rays given off from welding. The filter lenses for electric welding are much darker and stronger than those employed for gas welding.

Firecracker welding Also known as Elinhafergut welding. Consists of laying special electrodes horizontally in the joint that is to be welded. The electrodes are longer than normal electrodes and some are made with the core wire offset, so that the side with the thinnest flux coating is placed closest to the joint. An arc is then struck between the end of the electrode and the joint, and burns along the length of the electrode. Sometimes copper blocks are employed, placed over the electrodes; the blocks have grooves in them corresponding to the electrodes. Packing is also sometimes used, consisting of paper between the copper block and the electrode. Butt and fillet joints of some length can be welded in one pass with this method, once everything has been set up. Penetration is reasonable, owing to a constant arc length, and there is usually little slag inclusion.

Fixture A mechanical device for holding components in position while work is carried out on them. *See also* **Jig**.

Flash (fin) Metal expelled from the joint made by the resistance of the flash welding process.

Flash welding (flash butt welding) A type of resistance butt welding in which the components being joined are moved together, with the current confined to localised points of contact, causing the expulsion of molten metal. When the welding temperature is reached an upset force is applied.

Fluid slag A slag that freezes slowly and flows freely during welding. *See* **Slag**.

Flush weld A weld made with minimum reinforcement or dressed level after welding.

Flux A gas or fusible material employed to dissolve and/or prevent undesirable inclusions in the weld.

Flux covering *See* **Covering**.

Forge welding (blacksmith, roll, hammer) Pressure welding processes in which the parts to be welded are brought to a suitable temperature (plastic but below melting point). The weld is then completed by pressure or hammer blows at the joint.

Formier gas A gas mixture containing 88 per cent nitrogen, 12 per cent hydrogen. It is used as a backing gas when flash welding alloy steels.

Free bend test A bending test in which the specimen is bent without the constraint of a jig.

Free flight transfer *See* **Spray transfer**.

Friable slag A slag that crumbles easily, thus aiding removal. *See* **Slag**.

Friction welding Welding in which the necessary heat is usually produced frictionally, by rotation of one component, before the parts are forced together.

Fuse 1) To melt. 2) A specially made component in an electrical circuit that melts easily if there is a fault, thus protecting the rest of the circuit from damage due to an overload, and also minimising the risk of injury to the operator.

Fusion face Place where the fusion zone joins with the parent metal.

Fusion welding Any welding process in which the weld is made between metals that are in the molten state but without the application of pressure.

Fusion zone The region where the weld metal interfuses with the parent metal.

Gas cutting A process of severing ferrous (metals which contain iron as a main constituent) metals by means of the chemical action of oxygen (oxidation) on elements in the heated base metal.

Gas pocket (blowhole) A cavity in a weld or casting which has been caused by gas inclusion.

Gas welding A fusion welding process that employs the combustion of a fuel gas or gases mixed with oxygen to provide a high-temperature flame capable of melting most metals. Acetylene burning in oxygen provides an approximate temperature of 3250°C.

Girth welding A semi-automatic form of submerged arc or flux-cored electrode CO_2 process used for welding the circumferential seams of large tanks.

Guided bend test A test made by bending the specimen(s) round a former of specified shape and size.

Hand (face) shield A piece of protective equipment used in carrying out electric arc welding. Designed to protect the face and neck, it is fitted with a suitable filter glass lens and held by hand.

Hardfacing electrode (Hardsurfacing electrode) An electrode for metal arc welding, having a core or cover-

Welding supply
Flux-coated welding electrode
Arc
Return
Deposited weld
Simplified sketch (copper block removed) of firecracker welding

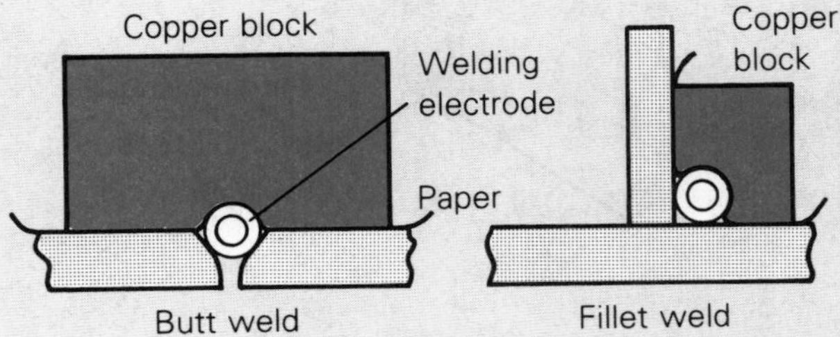

Electrodes can be $1\frac{1}{2}$ metres in length and some have offset core wires. The thinner flux coating is placed closest to the joint to be welded

Firecracker welding.

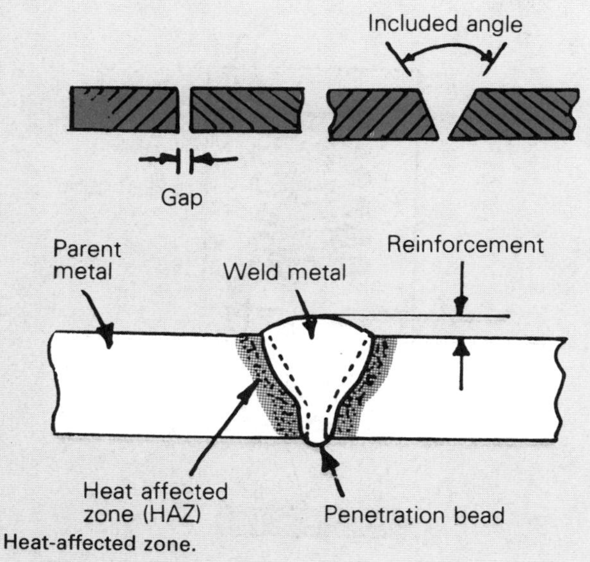

Heat-affected zone.

ing or both, that will deposit material that is harder than the parent material or can be made harder.

Hard-zone cracking *See* **Heat-affected zone**.

Head screen (helmet) Shield to protect face and neck, fitted with suitable filter lens to protect eyes from the rays of the arc, and worn on the head allowing the use of both hands.

Heat-affected zone (HAZ) The portion of the metal being welded or thermally cut that is metallurgically affected by the heat, but not melted. Hardening or cracking in this zone can indicate that the parent material is unsuitable for welding or that the preheat was insufficient.

HF ignition (spark starting) Ignition of an arc without touching the electrode to the work and risking contamination (tungsten in TAGS welding). A high-voltage, high-frequency spark is applied across the arc gap.

High-carbon steel Steel containing 0.65–1.5 per cent carbon.

High-pressure welding (system) Welding using dissolved acetylene supplied from cylinders.

Hot crack A crack or discontinuity produced by the metal tearing while at an elevated temperature.

Hot pass The weld run deposited immediately following the root or stringer bead while it is still at an elevated temperature. It is common to employ a high current to assist in 'washing' to remelt and clear any possible root defects.

Hydrogen-controlled electrode (low-hydrogen electrode or process) A covered electrode that will produce less than a specified amount of diffusible hydrogen in the deposit. Electrodes should be stored in warm dry conditions and baked in an electrode oven before use. Some other processes, such as CO_2-shielded (MAGS) welding, will give a low-hydrogen deposit.

Inconel An alloy that contains approximately 80 per cent nickel, 14 per cent chromium and 6 per cent iron.

Induction heating A heating method using current at mains or higher frequency induced in the work by means of an induction coil. Can be used for preheating, stress relieving or brazing purposes.

Inert gas arc welding A process in which the arc and molten pool are shielded from the atmosphere by a gas that is wholly or mostly inert. It is usual to use argon or helium, but nitrogen plus 5 per cent oxygen can be used for copper.

Intermittent weld A series of welds interrupted by spaces at regular specified intervals along a joint, known as an intermittently welded joint.

Iron powder electrode An electrode having a high proportion of iron in the form of powder contained in the covering, which acts as additional filler metal.

Jig A device to assist accurate and rapid assembly and production of an article or a number of identical articles. *See also* **Fixture**.

Junction (weld) A plane where the fusion zone joins with the parent metal.

Kerf The space left from which metal has been removed by a cutting process.

Lamellar tearing Cracking or tearing that can sometimes occur in rolled plate beneath a heavy fillet weld. This effect can cause a component (a lifting lug, for example) to pull away from the base metal with the welds still intact and still fused to an area of base metal, which has itself pulled away from the main section. Such tears are associated with slag inclusions or laminations in the plate material, which become pulled apart by weld contraction stresses in the plate thickness direction. Lamellar tears occur within the plate and can rarely be seen at the surface before failure. Checking plates for soundness with ultrasonic testing equipment and attention to weld procedures and joint design are methods that can help avoid this type of failure.

Lap weld A fillet weld between the edge of one plate and the surface of another plate, the plate surfaces being in contact.

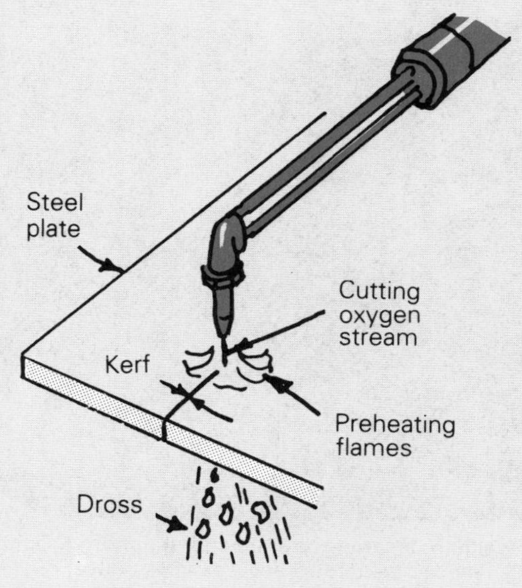

Kerf.

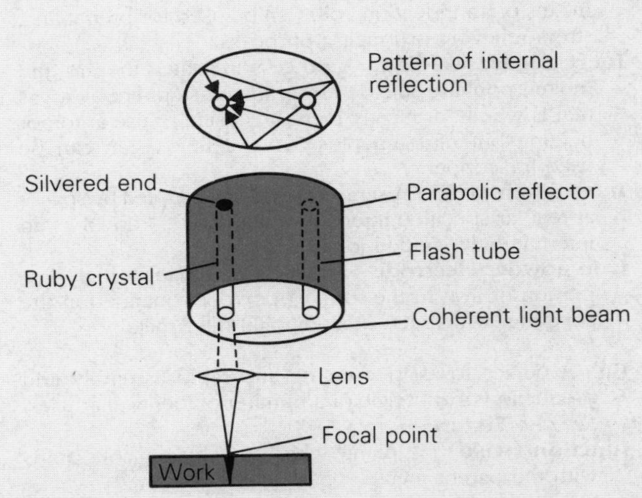

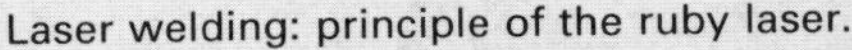
Laser welding: principle of the ruby laser.

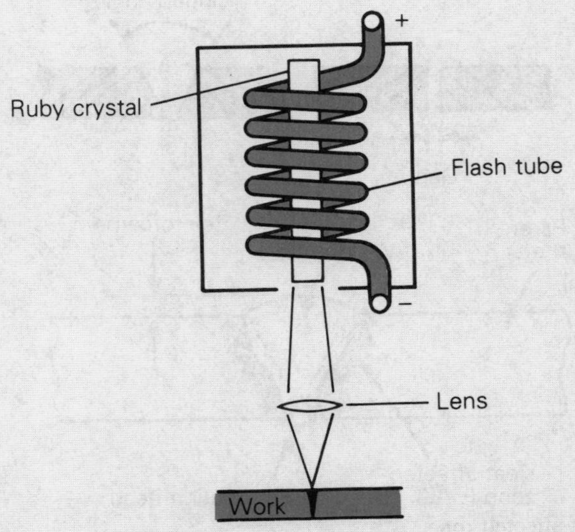

Laser welding: another type of ruby laser.

Laser welding: laser welding using light energy. One of the many advanced welding processes now in use. Picture shows a 5 kW laser. (Courtesy of TWI, UK)

Laser welding (Light Amplification by Stimulated Emission of Radiation). A fusion welding process that employs a highly concentrated beam of infrared light as the heat source. A crystal made from yttrium, aluminium and garnet (YAG) is used to convert an intense light source into the single-wavelength beam, which is highly focused. More powerful machines employ a tube filled with a mixture of carbon dioxide, nitrogen and helium gases to replace the crystal. The welding process and weld produced is somewhat similar to electron beam welding (*see* **EB welding**). Lasers can also be used for cutting. There is no need for a vacuum chamber, but the weld area must be protected with some form of gas shield, usually an inert gas such as argon or helium.

Leftward welding A gas welding technique in which the filler rod is held in front of the flame, in the direction of welding. The blowpipe follows the rod.

Leg The width of a fusion face in a fillet weld.

Leg length The distance from the intersection of the fusion faces (actual or projected) and the toe of a fillet weld, measured across the fusion face (see diagram on page 00).

Local preheating Heating the area around the joint before welding.

Low-carbon steel Steel containing up to 0.3 per cent carbon.

Low-hydrogen electrode *See* **Hydrogen-controlled electrode**.

Low-pressure welding Welding with acetylene supplied from an acetylene generator.

Macro examination The examination of a polished and etched sample (it is common to take a cross-section including weld and parent material) using only the naked eye or a magnifying glass with low magnification up to 10 ×.

MAGS welding (metal arc gas-shielded welding) *see* **MIG welding**

Manual weld A weld made by an operator rather than by a machine.

Martensite A structural constituent of hardened steels, produced by fast cooling of austenite.

Medium-carbon steel Steel containing 0.25–0.45 per cent carbon with 0.5–0.9 per cent manganese.

Melting rate or melt-off rate (burn-off rate) The weight or length of an electrode consumed in a unit of time during welding.

Metal arc cutting The process of severing metals by melting using the heat of a metal arc.

Metal arc welding Arc welding with a metal or metal-cored electrode, the melting of which provides the added metal.

Metal electrode *See* **Electrode**.

Micro examination The examination of a polished and etched specimen by the use of a microscope, magnifying more than 10 ×.

MIG welding (also known as MAGS) Metallic inert gas-shielded or metal arc gas-shielded welding uses a consumable electrode with an inert or 'semi-inert' gas shield to protect the arc, electrode and molten pool area. Argon, helium, CO_2 and various gas mixtures can be used, depending on the metal being welded. The arc is maintained from the end of a consumable electrode, fed from a spool, rather than a non-consumable tungsten as in the TIG or TAGS process.

MIG/MAGS pulsed arc welding Welding with the MIG/MAGS process in which a background d.c. arc maintains heat supply to the workpiece and electrode wire and a regular pulsed current of the same polarity (usually electrode positive), but of a higher peak value, is used to control metal transfer.

Mild steel Iron alloyed with 0.10–0.25 per cent carbon and manganese from 0.4 to 0.9 per cent, having other elements as impurities.

Mismatching A term that is used to describe a state where there is a significant difference between the tensile strength and/or hardness of the deposited weld metal compared with that of the parent metal.

Monel metal An alloy containing approximately 67 per cent nickel, 30 per cent copper.

Multirun weld A weld deposited in more than one run.

NDT Non-destructive testing: a form of testing that does not damage the component and therefore does not detract from the subsequent serviceability. Methods include radiography by X- or gamma-rays, ultrasonics, dye penetrant, magnetic crack detection and leak detection.

Neutral flame The normal oxyacetylene flame, produced when approximately equal volumes of oxygen and acetylene are burning. This is the flame used for welding low-carbon (mild) steel.

Nick break test A destructive test often used in the training of welders. A small sawcut, approximately 1.5 mm deep, is placed down the centre of a weld bead under test; the weld is then broken open, allowing examination for any internal defects.

Non-ferrous metal A metal that does not contain iron as one of the main constituents.

Normalise Refining steel by uniform heating at 850–900°C, followed by cooling in air.

Open-circuit voltage The voltage available to strike the arc, when the welding set is ready to weld but carrying no current.

Orbital friction welding A type of friction welding in which the heat is developed by moving one component (which is not rotating) in a circular orbit around the axis of a stationary component. The process allows non-circular components to be joined.

Orbital welder A machine in which a TIG/TAGS welding head is mounted in a device that travels round the outside of a pipe by automatic means.

Overlap Excess weld metal (usually unfused) protruding at the toe of a weld, beyond the limits of fusion.

Oxidising flame A flame containing excess oxygen. A slight excess is used when brazing with the oxyacetylene process.

Oxygen Colourless, odourless gas, which is chemically very active and supports and increases combustion. Made by the fractional distillation of liquid air and supplied for welding purposes in cylinders that are painted black. Medical oxygen has a white cylinder with a black neck.

Parent metal The metal(s) to be welded.

Pearlite Present in steels of the ferritic type; a constituent comprising a lamellar aggregate of iron and iron carbide. The amount of pearlite increases with the carbon content of the steel and increases hardening tendencies.

Peen (peening) To expand metal by hammering with light blows or by shot blasting. Weld metal/fabrications are sometimes peened to counteract contraction stress.

Plain Thermit A mixture of iron oxide and finely divided aluminium. *See* **Thermit welding**.

Plasma welding Plasma is the region of an ionised gas that forms the major portion of an arc column and provides a conducting path for the current. It is used as a heat source for welding and cutting by a modification of the TIG/TAGS process, where the argon (or other gas mixtures) is ionised to give a plasma jet, raising the temperature and increasing the speed of welding. A plasma weld has a characteristic 'wineglass' shape in cross-section.

Plug weld A weld made by filling a hole in one component so as to join the component to the surface of another component exposed through the hole.

Porosity A spongy condition of the metal/weld caused by entrapped gas.

Porous slag (inflated slag) A slag having a honeycombed structure. *See* **Slag**.

Post-heating Heat applied to the work after the welding or cutting operation.

Preheating Heat applied to the work before the welding or cutting operation.

Preparation *See* **Edge preparation**.

Pressure gauge A piece of equipment for recording the pressure of gases. When fitted to a cylinder, this gauge is often called the 'contents gauge' as it will indicate the approximate amount of gas remaining in a cylinder. Acetylene cylinders must be weighed to find the contents remaining, as the acetylene gas is dissolved in acetone liquid within the cylinder.

Pressure welding A welding process in which the weld is made using pressure.

Procedure (welding) A document that shows the method of welding, including preparation of joint, preheating, type and size of consumables, process, order of welding, number of runs, length and size of runs, and current settings.

Projection welding A resistance welding process in which the localising of force and current to make the weld(s) is obtained by the use of projections that have been pressed or formed into one or more of the faying surfaces before the welding operation. The projections collapse during welding.

Pulsed MIG/MAGS *See* **MIG/MAGS welding**.

Rate of deposition The weight of weld metal deposited in a unit of time.

Regulator A device for automatically regulating the oxygen or acetylene (or other gases) supply at a steady pressure, corresponding to the requirements (in gas welding, this is determined by the particular size of nozzle being used).

Reinforcement 1) A run or series of weld runs on a surface. 2) Surplus deposit on the face of a fillet weld above that which is required to make a triangle. 3) The deposit on a butt weld surplus to that required to make a flush joint.

Residual stresses Stresses that remain in a structure or member as a result of thermal or mechanical treatment, or both. *See* **Peening** and **Stress relieving**.

Resistance butt welding Resistance welding in which the components are butted together under pressure and a current is passed through them until the temperature is reached at which upset metal is produced and the weld is completed.

Resistance stud welding Stud welding using the projection resistance method; compare arc stud welding, which employs an electric arc.

Resistance welding A welding process in which, at some stage, a force is applied to the surfaces in contact and the heat for welding is obtained by the passage of an electric current through the electrical resistance at, and adjacent to, the joining surfaces.

Reverse bend test A bend test in which the face other than that specified for a face bend test is in tension. *See* **Face bend test**.

Rightward welding A gas welding process in which the blowpipe precedes the filler rod in the direction of welding, with the flame pointing towards the filler rod.

Rockwell hardness test A comparative hardness measurement obtained by measuring the increased depth of penetration of a steel ball or diamond point on applying a heavy load, after first applying a light load to take up any backlash and overcome surface irregularities.

Rod, welding (wire) A rod (wire) of metal that is melted to provide additional metal for the weld.

Root The position in a weld preparation or welded joint where the two parent plates are nearest together (the base of the weld).

Root face A surface on the parent metal to take the root of the weld, when employed with a grooved or bevelled preparation for butt welding.

Root pass (root run) The first run deposited in the root of a multirun weld.

Run-off plate A plate or plates of metal placed so as to enable the full section of weld to be maintained after the end of the joint, in order to eliminate any finishing defects, such as craters.

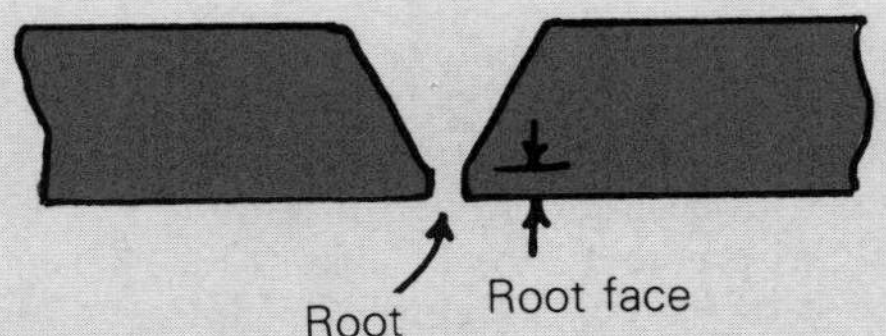

Root; root face.

Run-on plate A plate or plates of metal placed so as to enable the full section of weld to be started and run on to the test plates or work, thus eliminating any possible start defects.

Sealing run 1) A small weld to obtain tightness or fill in a gap (seal weld). 2) A small weld used to close a crevice between two pieces of parent metal to help protect against corrosion. 3) A small weld deposited on the root side of a butt weld.

Seam welding A resistance welding process in which force is applied continuously and current intermittently in order to produce a linear weld. The work, in the form of a lap joint, is fed between two wheel electrodes or between an electrode wheel and an electrode bar. The wheels apply the pressure and current and rotate during the welding process.

Semi-automatic welding Any welding process in which some of the variables are automatically controlled, but guidance is under manual control.

Set (welding) Source of welding current.

Shielded arc welding An arc welding process in which the arc and molten weld metal are protected from the atmosphere by a shielding medium.

Side bend test A bend test that puts a transverse section of the weld in tension.

Single phase (electricity supply) A.c. supply energised by a single alternating voltage. Two wires (conductors) are necessary to transmit single-phase power. (For safety an additional connection, usually to the casing, is made. *See* **Earth**.)

Skip welding (sequence) A method of welding to spread out the heat input into the work. Short lengths of weld are spaced in scattered positions in a predetermined order, eventually producing a continuous or intermittent weld, the individual welds being deposited in either longitudinal direction.

Slag A protective coating over the weld surface, formed by the melting and solidification of the electrode flux covering.

Slag inclusion Non-metallic inclusion in a weld.

Slag welding *See* **Electroslag welding**.

Spark starting The ignition of an arc by a high-voltage, high-frequency spark applied across the arc gap. *See* **HF ignition**.

Spatter Globules of metal thrown out from the arc area during welding.

Spot welding A type of resistance welding in which a weld is produced directly between electrodes as a spot in the workpiece. Force is applied to the spot through the electrodes during the flow of current and for a few

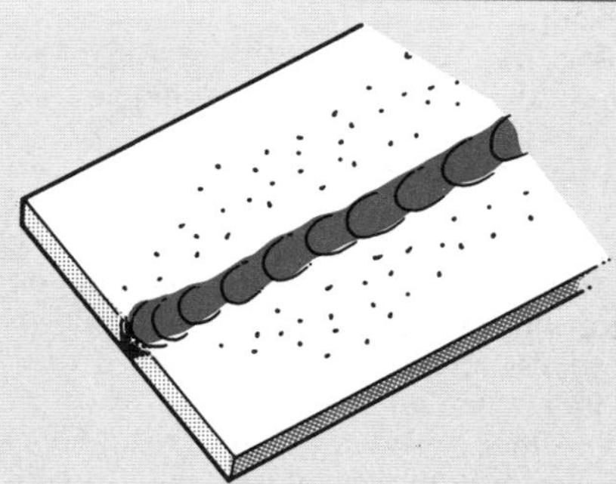

Spatter.

seconds after current ceases to flow, until the weld solidifies. Usually employed on sheet material.

Spray transfer A type of metal transfer in MIG/MAGS welding, in which a rapidly projected stream of droplets of smaller diameter than the consumable electrode travel through the arc to the molten pool. Used for welding thicker sections. Also known as free flight transfer. Compare with **Dip transfer**.

Stainless steels Nickel–chromium steels, which depend on the presence of 12–20 per cent chromium for their stainless properties.

Standing fillet A fillet weld in a corner formed by a vertical plate standing on a horizontal plate.

Stellite A mixture of tungsten and other carbides in a matrix of cobalt, giving an extremely hard alloy used for facing purposes.

Stick welding The common term for welding using normal electrodes in lengths as opposed to automatic and semi-automatic welding using coils.

Stitch welding A spot welding process in which successive welds overlap, giving a joint similar to a seam weld.

Stovepipe welding A welding technique in which the movement of the electrode is from the top of the joint to the bottom (welding downwards) using a high current density compared with the size of the electrode. The term is also applied to one system of pipeline construction, in which a new section of pipe is joined to a length already completed using this vertical-downwards method of welding.

Strain Alteration in length (per unit length) under a known stress.

Stray arcing (stray flash) 1) The damage caused to material resulting from accidental striking of an arc away from the weld. 2) The accidental striking of an arc away from the weld. Cracks may be initiated by such arc strikes, particularly on certain types of alloy steel. Stray arcing can also occur between loose connections in an electrical circuit.

Stress Load per unit area.

Stress raiser A fault in design or construction causing a concentration of stress.

Stress relief This is a post-welding heat treatment for the purpose of relieving internal stresses produced in a component by the welding operation. For mild steels (low-carbon), a temperature within the range 580–650°C is used. Below this range, longer times than one hour per inch (25 mm) are required to obtain an equivalent stress relief. The use of temperatures at the higher end can result in a loss of creep resistance (loss of resistance to elongation at elevated temperatures), particularly in aluminium-treated steels. Low-alloy steels are stress-relieved at higher temperatures: 620–700°C. For accurate details specific codes should be consulted. Austenitic stainless steels will require a temperature of 1050°C to effect a full stress relief. Composite mild steel/austenitic stainless steel fabrications cannot be fully stress-relieved owing to the difference in the coefficient of thermal expansion. The term post-weld heat treatment is also used.

Striking plate A piece of metal, kept close to the workpiece, in order to strike the arc before transferring the electrode to the work.

Strip electrode (strip welding) An electrode in the form of a strip, used for cladding purposes with the submerged-arc process.

Stripper beads Runs deposited in pipe welding between the 2–4 o'clock and 10–8 o'clock positions to bring weld metal level with other regions in the joint.

Stud welding The attachment of a stud, or other suitably shaped part, to a metal surface by the production of a weld over the whole of the end face of the stud, either by arc or resistance. (Friction welding can also be used.) *See also* **Resistance stud welding**.

Submerged-arc welding A metal arc welding process (usually automatic, although manual equipment can be obtained) in which a bare wire electrode or electrodes are used. The arc or arcs are covered in a layer of flux (the arc(s) is not extinguished), some of which fuses to form a removable covering of slag on the weld. Any unburnt flux is usually recycled, as most machines have a vacuum suction device following the welding head, which returns unused flux back to a hopper.

Surge injector A device for maintaining an a.c. arc by injecting a voltage surge into the power circuit to supply the reignition peak. When the arc is extinguished at the end of the negative half cycle the reignition peak begins to develop and triggers a capacitor discharge. (Such a device is necessary when TIG/TAGS welding aluminium and alloys, in order to overcome partial rectification of the a.c. arc.)

Tack weld A weld used for temporary assembly purposes only, to hold work in position until the complete weld run is made.

TAGS welding *See* **TIG welding**.

Tempering A heat treatment employed to remove internal stresses and reduce any brittleness caused by a hardening process.

Tempilstick A range of temperature-sensitive crayons that change colour at specific temperatures. Repeated application is required to ensure that a specific temperature is being maintained.

Temporary backing *See* **Backing bar** (backing ring on pipe).

Thermal stress The stresses produced in a structure caused by differences in temperature or coefficients of expansion/contraction.

Thermit welding A fusion welding process in which the heat is obtained from liquid steel produced by a Thermit reaction (a chemical reaction between iron oxide and aluminium oxide slag). The filler metal is supplied by the steel produced in this reaction and is fed to the weld joint, which is usually encased in a sand mould of predetermined shape. The process can be used for heavy repair work and the joining of railway lines. A modification, in which pressure is employed and the Thermit reaction is used only to heat up the ends of the work being joined, is known as pressure Thermit welding.

Three-phase (electrical supply) A.c. supply energised by three alternating voltages partially superimposed on one another. Power is transmitted by three wires: for example, A, B and C. Phase 1 is carried by wires A and B, phase 2 by wires B and C and phase 3 by wires C and A.

Throat (thickness) The shortest distance from the root to the outside of a fillet weld, or the smallest thickness of a butt weld.

Thoriated tungsten electrode Small additions of thorium (2 per cent) give what is termed an 'active' electrode for use in TIG/TAGS welding. The thorium improves electron emissivity, improving ease of striking and arc maintenance.

TIG/TAGS welding (tungsten inert gas/tungsten arc gas-shielded) An inert gas arc welding process employing a non-consumable electrode of pure or activated tungsten (*see* **Thoriated** and **Zirconiated**). A separate filler wire may be used. An inert gas (or mixture of gas) such as argon or helium protects the electrode and molten pool area from the atmosphere. Pulsed TIG/TAGS is a variation, which employs a background current (d.c.) to maintain an ionised path for the arc, and a regular pulsed current of the same polarity (usually electrode negative) is applied to control heat input to the work.

Toe Line where the surface of the weld joins the parent metal.

Touch electrode (welding) *See* **Contact welding**.

Transition temperature A temperature below which steels show a brittle fracture and above which they will show a ductile fracture, especially when subjected to a form of notched test (the Charpy impact test, in which a hammer strikes a notched test specimen held in an anvil and the energy required to fracture is recorded in joules). The transition temperature of a material will vary according to its composition, manufacturing process, physical dimensions and heat treatment. Austenitic stainless steels, aluminium alloys and copper do not indicate ductile/brittle transition and therefore often find application in low-temperature service.

Under-bead cracking Cracking that has taken place in the heat-affected zone beneath a weld deposit, particularly in fillet welds. *See* **Heat-affected zone**.

Undercut A defect in which the parent metal at the edge(s) (toe(s)) of the weld is cut away.

Upset length The total of the actual shortening of both components caused by the forging action of making the weld (with pressure processes).

Variable-voltage set A welding set in which the open-circuit voltage can be varied.

Vertical welding A technique adopted when welding in the vertical plane.

Viscous slag A slag that freezes quickly and does not flow freely during welding. *See* **Slag**.

Voltage The pressure of electricity.

Voltage (open circuit) Striking voltage. The pressure of electricity between the end of the electrode and the work before the arc is started, or struck (usually 60–100 volts). The voltage available to strike the arc.

VPN (Vickers pyramid hardness number) A comparative hardness obtained by measuring the area of a square indent made in the test piece by a 136° pyramid-shaped diamond under a given load. For soft metals VPH numbers are comparable with Brinell hardness numbers. For hard or heat-treated metals VPN tests are more accurate than Brinell.

Wandering sequence *See* **Skip welding**.

Weaving The transverse oscillation of an electrode or blowpipe nozzle during the deposition of a weld.

Weld decay A type of intercrystalline corrosion where austenitic nickel–chromium steels can form chromium carbides at the grain boundaries in the region adjacent to welded seams where the steel has been in the range of 500–900°C. The depletion of the chromium content reduces resistance to corrosion in service. Weld decay may be overcome (or liability reduced) by the addition of a stabiliser such as titanium or niobium, the use of a very low carbon content, or by quenching the component from 1050°C.

Welder qualification test A test undertaken by a welder to demonstrate competence at making welds of the type required. The welder usually follows a set procedure that has been previously qualified. The test plates (pipes) are then subjected to the non-destructive and destructive tests required by the particular code. The welder who satisfactorily completes a welding procedure qualification test is then usually automatically qualified in that procedure.

Welding leads Conductors, with insulating coatings, providing a path for the electricity between the source of welding power and the electrode(s).

Welding positions Five welding positions are recognised by definition of the weld slope and weld location. (The term 'inclined' is used to define any intermediate position not specified below.) *See* also 'G' positions in Chapter 26.

Position	Slope	Rotation	Symbol
Flat	0 – 5°	0 – 10°	F
Horizontal vertical	0 – 5°	30 – 90°	H
Vertical up	80 – 90°	0 – 180°	V
Vertical down	80 – 90°	0 – 180°	D
Overhead	0 – 15°	115 – 180°	O

Welding procedure A detail of the procedure to be followed in making a particular welded joint. Normally covers such items as: specification of parent material, welding process, joint design, type of electrode, electrical parameters, welding position, number and location of runs, pre- and post-heat requirements.

Welding procedure qualification test A welding test carried out in order to demonstrate that the welding procedure drawn up by a manufacturer or contractor is suitable and satisfactory. The completed testpiece is subjected to non-destructive and destructive testing as specified in the appropriate code. These tests and the welding operation are usually witnessed by an inspection authority. *See also* **Welder qualification test**.

Welding rod Filler metal in rod or wire, used in the gas welding process, and in arc welding processes in which the electrode does not provide the metal.

Welding screen A screen to protect the face and neck and fitted with a coloured glass filter lens to protect the eyes from the rays of the arc.

Welding set The source of welding current.

Welding wire *See* **Filler metal**.

Weld metal All the metal melted during the making of a weld and retained in the weld.

Weld zone The zone containing the weld metal and the heat-affected zone.

Worm hole An elongated or tubular type cavity that can be found in a weld, caused by entrapped gas.

Wrapped electrode A covered electrode having all or part of the covering of flux wound on to the core wire.

YAG laser *See* **Laser welding.**

Zirconiated tungsten (electrodes) Tungsten electrodes with addition of zirconium oxide to help improve arc striking and stability when TIG/TAGS welding using a.c.

Appendix 1
ISO 4063 Classification of welding processes

The table below complies with International Standard ISO 4063

No.	Process
1	**Arc welding**
11	Metal-arc welding without gas protection
111	*Metal-arc welding with covered electrode*
112	Gravity arc welding with covered electrode
113	Bare wire metal-arc welding
114	Flux cored metal-arc welding
115	Coated wire metal-arc welding
118	Firecracker welding
12	Submerged arc welding
121	Submerged arc welding with wire electrode
122	Submerged arc welding with strip electrode
13	Gas shielded metal-arc welding
131	*MIG welding*
135	MAG welding: metal-arc welding with non-inert gas shield
136	Flux cored metal-arc welding with non-inert gas shield
14	Gas-shielded welding with non-consumable electrode
141	*TIG welding*
149	*Atomic-hydrogen welding*
15	Plasma arc welding
18	Other arc welding processes
181	*Carbon arc welding*
185	Rotating arc welding
2	**Resistance welding**
21	*Spot welding*
22	*Seam welding*
221	Lap seam welding
225	Seam welding with strip
23	*Projection welding*
24	*Flash welding*
25	*Resistance butt welding*
29	Other resistance welding processes
29	HF resistance welding
3	**Gas welding**
31	Oxy-fuel gas welding
311	*Oxy-acetylene welding*
312	Oxy-propane welding
313	Oxy-hydrogen welding
32	Air fuel gas welding
321	Air-acetylene welding
322	Air-propane welding
4	**Solid phase welding; pressure welding**
41	Ultrasonic welding
42	*Friction welding*
43	Force welding
44	Welding by high mechanical energy
441	Explosive welding
45	Diffusion welding
47	Gas pressure welding
48	Cold welding
7	**Other welding processes**
71	*Thermit welding*
72	Electroslag welding
73	Electrogas welding
74	Induction welding
75	Light radiation welding
751	Laser welding
752	Arc image welding
753	Infrared welding
76	Electron beam welding
78	Stud welding
781	Arc stud welding
782	Resistance stud welding
9	**Brazing, soldering and braze welding**
91	*Brazing*
911	Infrared brazing
912	*Flame brazing*
913	Furnace brazing
914	Dip brazing
915	Salt bath brazing
916	Induction brazing
917	Ultrasonic brazing
918	Resistance brazing
919	Diffusion brazing
923	Vacuum brazing
924	Vacuum brazing
93	Other brazing processes
94	Soldering
941	Infrared soldering
942	Flame soldering
943	Furnace soldering

944 Dip soldering
945 Salt bath soldering
946 Induction soldering
947 Ultrasonic soldering
948 Resistance soldering
949 Diffusion soldering
951 Flow soldering
952 Soldering with soldering iron
953 Friction soldering
954 Vacuum soldering
96 Other soldering processes
97 Braze welding
971 Gas braze welding
972 Arc braze welding

Appendix 2
Metric and imperial units

Metric measures

Length

1 millimetre (mm)		= 0.0394 in
1 centimetre (cm)	= 10 mm	= 0.3937 in
1 metre (m)	= 100 cm	= 1.0936 yd
1 kilometre (km)	= 1000 m	= 0.6214 mile

Area

1 sq cm (cm^2)	= 100 mm^2	= 0.1550 in^2
1 sq metre (m^2)	= 10 000 cm^2	= 1.1960 yd^2
1 sq km (km^2)	= 100 hectares	= 0.3861 $mile^2$

Volume/capacity

1 cu cm (cm^3)		= 0.0610 in^3
1 cu decimetre (dm^3)	= 1000 cm^3	= 0.0353 ft^3
1 cu metre (m^3)	= 1000 dm^3	= 1.3080 yd^3
1 litre (l)	= 1 dm^3	= 1.76 pt
		= 2.113 US liq pt
1 hectolitre (hl)	= 100 l	= 21.998 gal
		= 26.418 US gal

Mass (weight)

1 milligram (mg)		= 0.0154 grain
1 gram (g)	= 1000 mg	= 0.0353 oz
1 metric carat	= 0.2 g	= 3.0865 grains
1 kilogram (kg)	= 1000 g	= 2.2046 lb
1 tonne (t)	= 1000 kg	= 0.9842 ton
		= 1.1023 short ton

Pressure, stress

1 hectobar	= 0.6475 tonf/in^2	
1 megapascal (MPa)	= 0.0647 tonf/in^2	= 145.038 lbf/in^2
1 atm	= 14.696 lbf/in^2	
1 kgf/cm^2	= 14.223 lbf/in^2	
1 bar	= 14.504 lbf/in^2	
1 kPa (kN/m^2)	= 20.885 lbf/ft^2	
1 pascal (Pa = N/m^2)	= 0.000 145 lbf/in^2	

Energy (work, heat)

1 megajoule (MJ)	= 0.2778 kWh
1 joule (J)	= 0.7376 ft lbf
1 calorie	= 0.003 97 Btu

Temperature conversion

$C = \frac{5}{9}(F - 32)$ $F = \frac{9}{5}C + 32$

Imperial and US measures

Length

1 inch (in)		= 2.54 cm
1 foot (ft)	= 12 in	= 0.3048 m
1 yard (yd)	= 3 ft	= 0.9144 m
1 mile	= 1760 yd	= 1.6093 km
1 int nautical mile	= 2025.4 yd	= 1.852 km

Area

1 acre	= 4046.86 m^2	= 0.4047 ha
1 sq yard (yd^2)	= 0.8361 m^2	
1 sq foot (ft^2)	= 0.0929 m^2	
1 sq inch (in^2)	= 645.16 mm^2	

Volume/capacity

1 cu yard (yd^3)	= 0.7645 m^3	
1 cu foot (ft^3)	= 0.0283 m^3	= 28.3168 dm^3
1 cu inch (in^3)	= 16.3871 cm^3	
1 UK gallon	= 4.5461 dm^3	
1 US gallon	= 3.7854 dm^3	
1 pint (pt)	= 0.5683 dm^3	

Mass (weight)

1 ton	= 1016.05 kg	= 1.016 t
1 pound (lb)	= 0.4536 kg	
1 ounce (oz)	= 28.3495 g	
1 grain	= 64.7989 mg	= 0.324 metric carats

Pressure, stress

1 $tonf/ft^2$	= 107.252 kPa	
1 $tonf/in^2$	= 15.4443 MPa	
1 lbf/ft^2	= 47.8803 Pa	
1 lbf/in^2	= 6.8948 kPa	= 68.9476 mbar

Energy (work, heat)

1 therm	= 105.506 MJ
1 hp h (horsepower × hour)	= 2.6845 MJ
1 kWh	= 3.6 MJ
1 British thermal unit (Btu)	= 1.0551 kJ

Power

1 horsepower (hp)	= 745.700 W	= 0.7457 kW

Appendix 3
Calculations related to welding

Fractions

A fraction is a quantity that is not a whole number. There are two kinds of fraction: **vulgar fractions**, which are usually referred to as fractions, and **decimal fractions**, which are usually just called decimals.

Vulgar fractions are shown by two numbers placed one above the other, separated by a line. The number below the line is called the **denominator** and the number above the line is called the **numerator**.

The denominator shows how many parts (of equal size) the whole is divided up into, and the numerator shows how many of these parts are taken. For example: $\frac{3}{5}$ of 20 shows that 20 is divided into five equal parts and that three of these are taken. In other form this would be $\frac{20}{5}$ (20 divided by 5 equal parts) $\times$ 3 = 4 $\times$ 3 = 12. Therefore $\frac{3}{5}$ of 20 = 12.

Proper fractions

Proper fractions are those that make up less than 1, such as: $\frac{3}{4}$, $\frac{1}{4}$, $\frac{1}{3}$, $\frac{2}{3}$, $\frac{1}{2}$, etc. – that is, when the numerator is less than the denominator.

Improper fractions

These are fractions that are greater than 1: that is, the numerator is greater than the denominator. For example:

$$\frac{7}{6} = 1\frac{1}{6},\ \frac{9}{8} = 1\frac{1}{8},\ \frac{17}{4} = 4\frac{1}{4}\ \text{etc.}$$

Decimal fractions

The decimal system enables calculations to be made more easily when using metric measurements.

Decimal fractions are shown by using a decimal point. The point is placed to the right of the unit and figures placed to the right of the point indicate tenths, hundredths, thousandths, etc., of a complete unit, depending on their place after the point. The first figure after the point represents tenths of a unit, the next hundredths, the next thousandths, and so on. Therefore

1.3 represents one and three tenths ($1 + \frac{3}{10}$)

$0.25 = \frac{2}{10} + \frac{5}{100} = \frac{25}{100}$

Decimals

This is the general term applied to the system of representing whole and fractional numbers in the base of ten. The decimal point is used to identify place values as shown in decimal fractions.

Worked examples of decimal calculations

Addition

```
 17.85
 10.20
  6.30  +
 ------
 34.35  Ans
```

Subtraction

```
 18.25
  8.41  -
 ------
  9.84  Ans
```

Multiplication

The actual multiplication is done as if there were no decimal points. Then the total number of decimal places in the two numbers being multiplied together is counted (total number of digits to the right of the decimal point in the two numbers). Count from the right towards the left this number of places in the answer, and place the decimal point in that position.

```
   6.25
   6.2   ×
 -------
   1250
   3750
 -------
 38.750  Ans
```

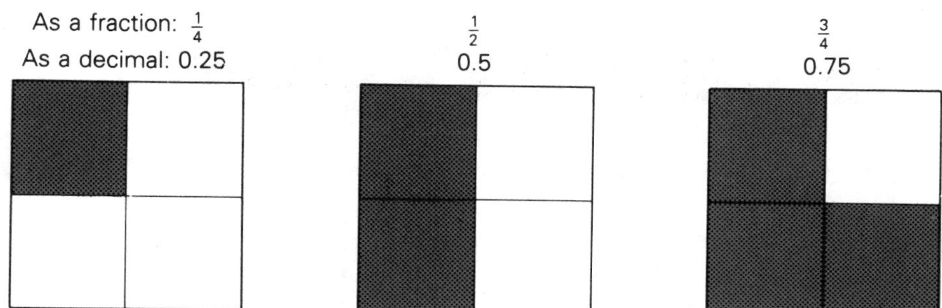

Figure A3.1 The shaded areas of the squares expressed as fractions and as decimals.

Division

Some calculations will not always finish exactly, so we can write the answer correct to a required number of decimal places. In the calculation shown below, it would go on for ever, so we have stopped it, giving the answer correct to four decimal places.

$$\begin{array}{r} 0.5266 \\ 15\,\overline{)\,7.90000} \\ 75 \\ \hline 40 \\ 30 \\ \hline 100 \\ 90 \\ \hline 100 \\ 90 \\ \hline 10 \end{array}$$

Worked examples of fraction calculations

Addition

$$4\tfrac{1}{8} + 3\tfrac{7}{12} = 7\tfrac{3+14}{24} = 7\tfrac{17}{24}$$

24 is the lowest number that both 8 and 12 will divide into equally. 8 into 24 goes 3, $3 \times 1 = 3$. 12 into 24 goes twice, $2 \times 7 = 14$.

Subtraction

$$3\tfrac{3}{8} - 1\tfrac{7}{12} = 2_{1}\tfrac{9^{24} - 14}{24} = 1\tfrac{19}{24}$$

Again, 24 is the lowest common denominator.
8 divides equally three times, $3 \times 3 = 9$.
12 divides into 24 equally twice, $2 \times 7 = 14$.
In order to subtract 14 from 9, we have to take one whole number from the $2(\tfrac{24}{24})$.

Multiplication

$$3\tfrac{3}{4} \times 1\tfrac{1}{9} = \frac{{}^{5}15}{{}^{2}4} \times \frac{{}^{5}10}{{}^{3}9} = \frac{25}{6} = 4\tfrac{1}{6}$$

The whole numbers and fractions are converted to improper fractions:

$3\tfrac{3}{4}$ becomes $(3 \times 4 = 12) + 3 = \tfrac{15}{4}$. $1\tfrac{1}{9}$ becomes $(9 \times 1 = 9) + 1 = \tfrac{10}{9}$.

On completing the calculation, the improper fraction of $\tfrac{25}{6}$ is changed to a whole number and proper fraction by dividing the denominator (6) into the numerator (25).

Division

$$3\tfrac{3}{4} \div 1\tfrac{1}{9} = \frac{15}{4} \div \frac{10}{9} = \frac{{}^{3}15}{4} \times \frac{9}{10_{2}} = \frac{27}{8} = 3\tfrac{3}{8}$$

Again, improper fractions are used and then we invert (turn upside down) and multiply after cancelling down. That is, 5 goes equally into 15 three times and into 10 twice.

Percentages

Percentage provide a method of relating a fraction of a quantity to the whole in parts per hundred. For example:

20% is the same as $\tfrac{20}{100}$ (% means 'per cent')

From this, we can also see that 20% is the same as the fraction $\tfrac{1}{5}$, as 20 will divide into 20 once, and into 100 five times.

Percentage changes in any quantity are calculated in the following way. If original value = A, and new value = B:

$$\text{per cent change} = \frac{A - B}{A} \times 100$$

Percentage equivalents of fractions are given by multiplying the fraction by 100. For example:

$$\tfrac{2}{5} = \tfrac{2}{5} \times 100\% = 40\%$$

$$\frac{2}{5_{1}} \times \frac{100^{20}}{1} = \frac{40}{1}$$

A percentage equivalent of a decimal is given by multiplying the decimal by 100. For example:

$0.25 = 0.25 \times 100\% = 25\%$

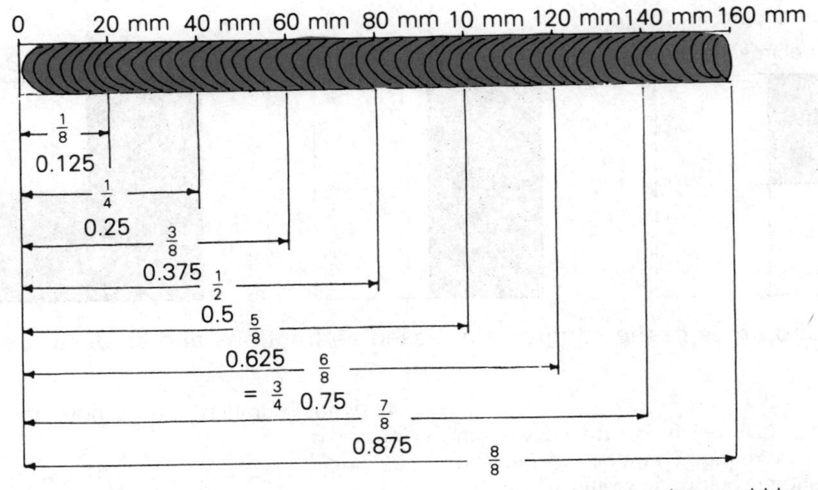

Figure A3.2 Distances represented as fractions and decimals on a given weld length of 160 mm.

A fraction may be changed into a decimal by dividing the numerator by the denominator. For example:

$$\tfrac{1}{2} = 2\overline{)\ 1\ }\ \ (0.5) = 0.5$$

$$\tfrac{3}{8} = 8\overline{)\ 3.000\ }\ \ (0.375) = 0.375$$

Electrode efficiency

When electric arc welding, the electrode efficiency is the mass of metal actually deposited compared with the mass of the core wire consumed. Electrode efficiency can be expressed as a percentage:

$$\text{Efficiency \%} = \frac{\text{Mass of deposited metal}}{\text{Mass of electrode metal consumed}} \times 100$$

With general-purpose electrodes, the efficiency can vary from about 75% up to 90%. However, with electrodes that contain iron powder in the flux, covering efficiency levels can approach 200% (Figure A3.3).

Electrode efficiency (or recovery rates) are given to the nearest 10, in the electrode coding for a particular electrode (see BS 639: 1986).

The nominal electrode efficiency percentage is given by:

$$\frac{\text{Mass of deposited metal}}{\text{Mass of core wire} - \text{mass of unused stub}} = \text{Percentage recovery}$$

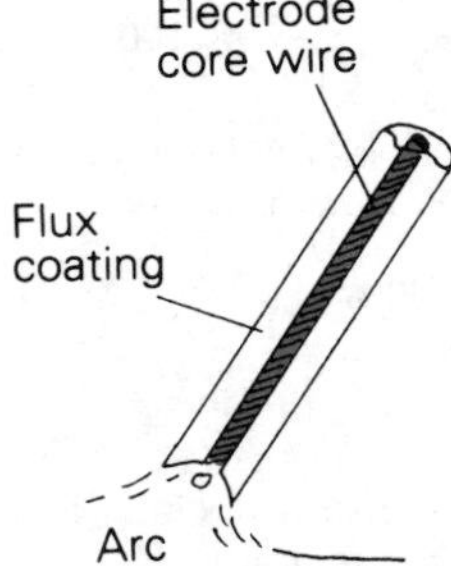

Figure A3.3 Extra-efficiency electrodes have iron powder in the flux coating.

At a welding speed of 12 metres per hour, the weld would take 60 minutes
At 24 metres per hour, it would take 30 minutes
At 6 metres per hour, it would take 120 minutes
At 8 metres per hour, it would take 90 minutes

Notice that with inverse proportion, if we double one quantity, it halves the other.

Averages

In arithmetic, the **mean** of a set of numbers is found by finding the sum of the numbers and then dividing by the number of figures in the set. This is often called the 'average'. For example, the average of 8, 9, 7, 17, 19 and 18 is found by adding the numbers together:

$$8 + 9 + 7 + 17 + 19 + 18 = 78$$

and dividing the sum of the numbers by the number of figures in the set, in this case 6:

$$\tfrac{78}{6} = 13$$

So the average is 13.

The average is not necessarily an exact number; it may include a decimal. For example, what is the average of 24, 20, 18, 21 and 15?

$$24 + 20 + 18 + 21 + 15 = 98$$

$$\tfrac{98}{5} = 19.6$$

So the average is 19.6

Here are some examples to practise:
Find the average of the following sets of numbers.

i) 9, 15, 7, 12, 8.

ii) 30, 41, 35, 36, 45, 48.

iii) (As an example to find out an average weekly wage, if the amount varies):

£84, £120, £130, £90, £165, £180, £170, £175 (over an 8 week period).

iv) (As an example to calculate the average amount of welding electrodes consumed per hour in a medium sized fabrication workshop):

100, 250, 120, 60, 300, 220, 50, 90 (over an 8 hour period)

Ratio and proportion

An an example, suppose a welder earns £5 per hour, and saves £2. Then it can be said that the **ratio** of hourly savings to earnings is 2 to 5. This is sometimes written as 2 : 5.

The ratio can be expressed in the form of a fraction, $\frac{2}{5}$. The ratio of earnings to savings is 5 to 2, 5 : 2 or $\frac{5}{2}$.

$\frac{2}{5}$ and $\frac{5}{2}$ are called **inverse ratios**.

If the welder's wages were increased to £5.50 per hour, and he saved £2.50 per hour of this, then the ratio of savings to earnings would be:

$2\frac{1}{2}$ to $5\frac{1}{2}$, which is the same as 5 to 11.

Direct proportion

If an automatic welding machine is welding heavy plate at the rate of 12 metres per hour, then the following statements could be made:

Welding 12 metres in 60 minutes:

ratio of distance to time $= \frac{12}{60} = \frac{1}{5}$

Welding 6 metres in 30 minutes:

ratio of distance to time $= \frac{6}{30} = \frac{1}{5}$

Welding 4 metres in 20 minutes

ratio of distance to time $= \frac{4}{20} = \frac{1}{5}$

Welding 1 metre in 5 minutes

ratio of distance to time $= \frac{1}{5}$

In each case, the ratio of welding distance (in metres) to time (in minutes) is equal to $\frac{1}{5}$.

When two ratios have the same value, the four quantities making up the ratios are said to be 'in proportion'. In the example shown above, the times and distances are in proportion.

In working out proportions, we assume that only the amounts being dealt with at the time vary and that everything else stays the same. An example of this would be to say that a welder's wages are proportional to the number of hours worked. Here, we are assuming that the rate of pay per hour is the constant, and ignoring the fact that some of the hours are being paid at overtime rates.

Another example would be to say that the number of welding electrodes required to make a weld is proportional to the length of the plates, width of gap (type of preparation) and thickness of the plates. When the quantities increase together, or decrease together, the proportion is called **direct proportion**.

Inverse proportion

If one quantity goes up while the other goes down, this is called **inverse proportion**. As an example, let's imagine an automatic welding machine again. Suppose a weld distance of 12 metres has to be made:

Useful formulae

Here are some useful formulae for calculating dimensions, areas and volumes. The letter symbols are as follows:

l = length		d = diameter	
b = breadth		r = radius	
h = perpendicular height		P = perimeter	
s = side		C = circumference	
sh = slant height		A = area	
V = volume		π = $\frac{22}{7}$ or 3.142	

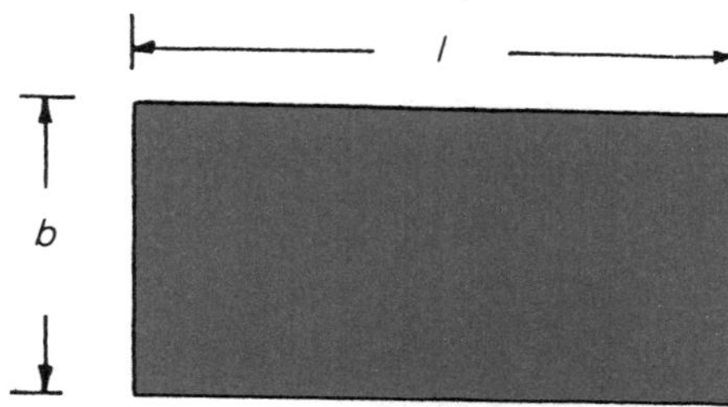

The rectangle
$P = 2\,(l + b)$
$A = l \times b$

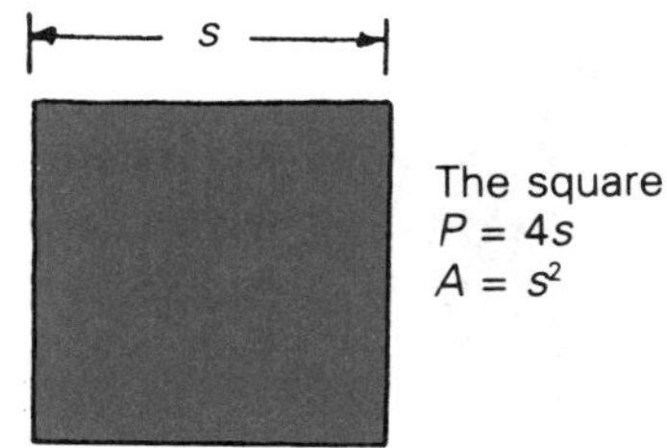

The square
$P = 4s$
$A = s^2$

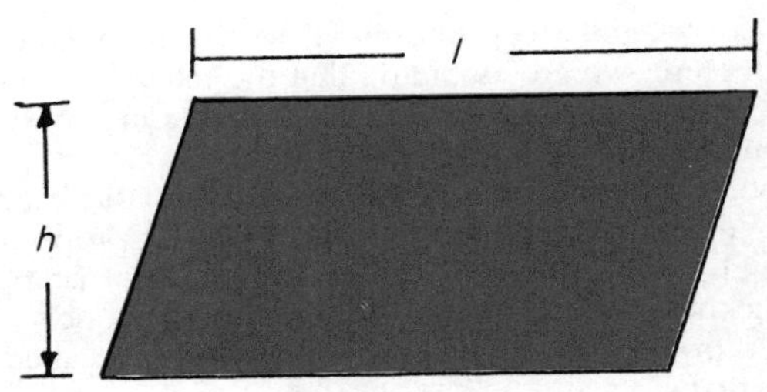

The parallelogram

P = 2(*l* + *b*)

A = *l* × perpendicular height (between measured length and one parallel to it)

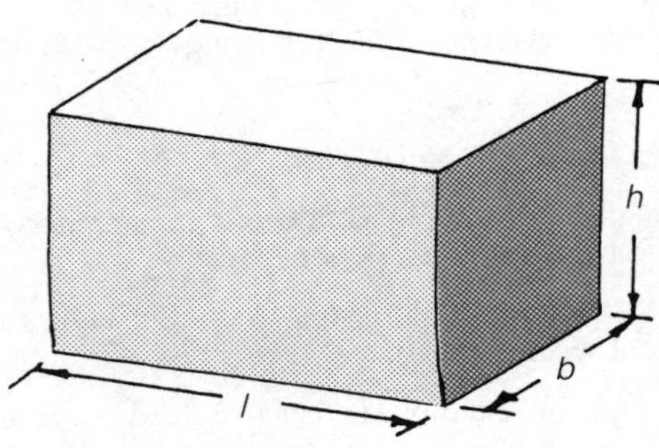

Volume of a tank

$l \times b \times h$

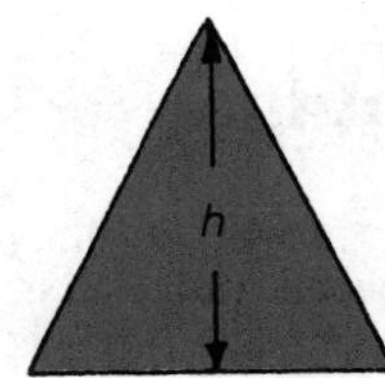

The triangle

P = sum of three sides

$A = \frac{1}{2}(\text{base} \times h)$

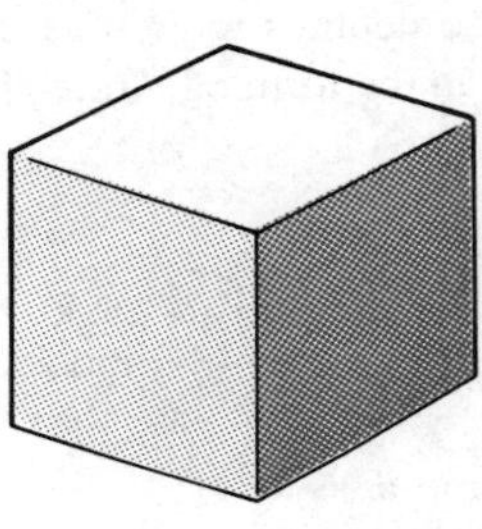

Solid

Area of four sides = $4s^2$

Total surface area

$A = 6s^2$

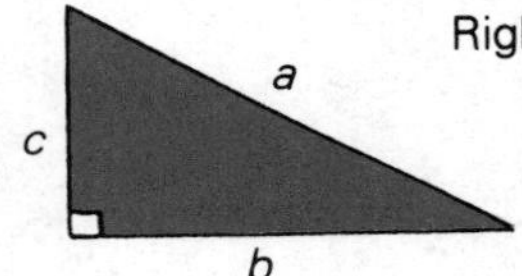

Right-angled triangle

$a^2 = b^2 + c^2$

$a = \sqrt{b^2 + c^2}$

$b = \sqrt{a^2 - c^2}$

$c = \sqrt{a^2 - b^2}$

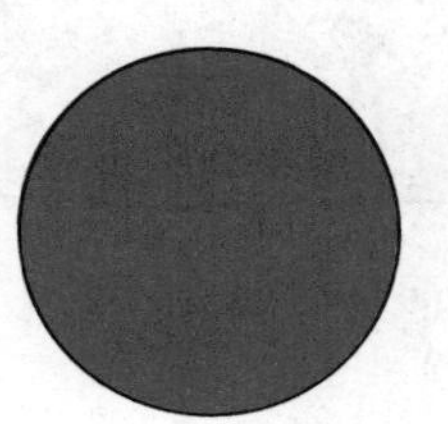

The circle

$\pi = C + d$

$C = \pi d$

$A = \pi r^2$

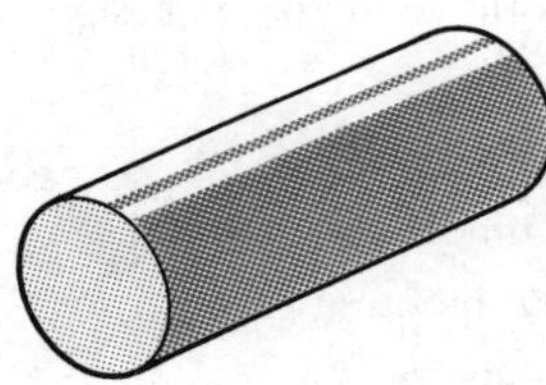

Cylinder

Area of curved surface $C \times h$

$V = \pi r^2 h$

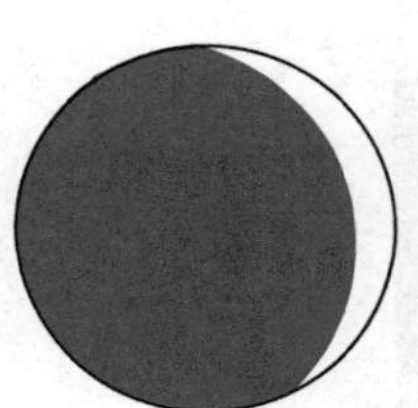

The sphere

$A = 4\pi r^2$

$V = \frac{4}{3} \times r^3$

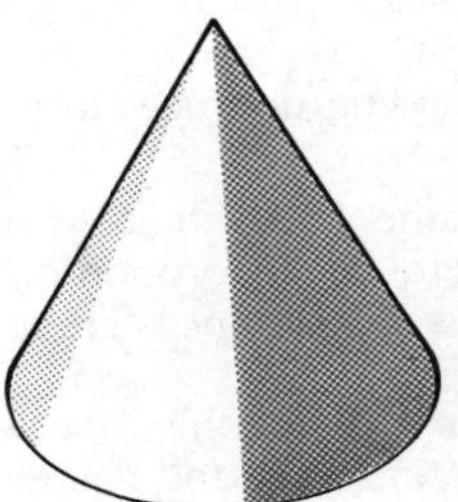

Cone

Area of curved surface

$= \frac{1}{2} C \times sh$

$V = \frac{1}{3}\pi r^2 h$

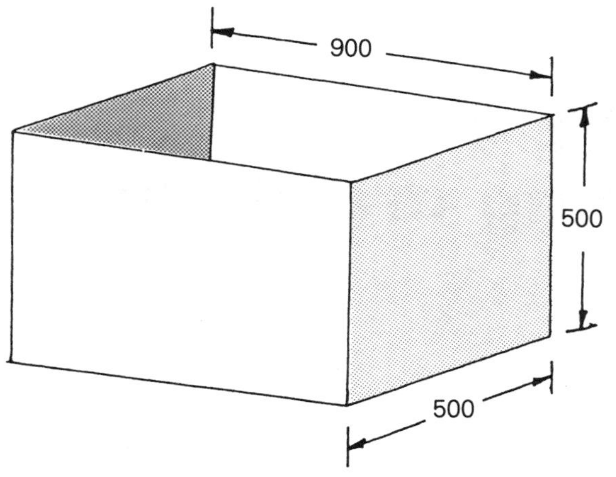

Figure A3.4 Question 1.

Summary of welding calculations for practice

Questions

1 Figure A3.4 shows an open-top water tank to be fabricated from five pieces of 6 mm low carbon steel.
  i) All welds are completed in one pass by the manual metal arc process. What will be the total length of weld per tank?
  ii) If welding is costed in this instance as 75 pence per 100 mm, what will be the cost of welding one tank?

2 A steel plate measures 1.5 m × 2.25 m. What is its area?

3 i) Draw a straight-line graph to show the number of electrodes used by a company over one year, using the monthly figures given:

Jan	Feb	Mar	Apr	May	June
10 000	15 000	8000	6000	25 000	40 000

July	Aug	Sept	Oct	Nov	Dec
60 000	50 000	20 000	10 000	9000	7000

  ii) What is the average amount of electrodes used per month?

4 A company uses electrodes 300 mm in length. If 50 mm is the average stub end loss, what percentage does this represent?

5 If a welding code requires 90% of welds on a fabrication to be radiographs and 120 welds are made, how many welds require radiographic testing?

6 What are the following percentage gas mixtures as fractions?
  i) Argon – 25% CO_2 ii) Argon – 2% O_2
  iii) Argon – 5% CO_2 iv) Argon – 2% O_2 – 5% CO_2

Answers

1 i) Total length of weld per tank would be 4800 mm.
  ii) 3600p = £36
2 3.375 m^2
3 i)

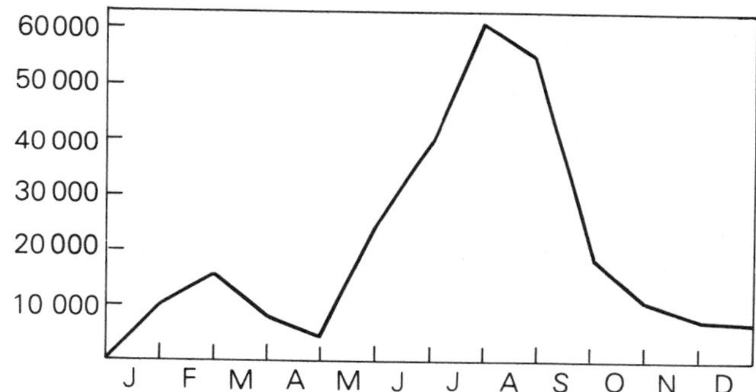

  ii) Average = 21 666.6 electrodes per month
4 16.6%
5 108 welds require radiographic testing.
6 i) Argon – $\frac{1}{4}$ CO_2 ii) Argon – $\frac{1}{50}$ O_2
  iii) Argon – $\frac{1}{20}$ CO_2 iv) Argon – $\frac{1}{50}$ O_2, $\frac{1}{20}$ CO_2

Appendix 4
Reading engineering drawings

During the course of your training and work, you will sooner or later have to read an engineering drawing. Figure A4.1 shows two isometric sketches of components. **Isometric drawings** or sketches give us an idea of what the finished product should look like. However, they are not suitable for showing all the detail for making a component, as parts are often hidden and not all the dimensions can be shown.

In an isometric drawing, the lines are laid out parallel to each other at equal distances apart, and they show equal lengths. The object's width and length are laid out to scale on lines that are usually inclined at 30° to the horizontal baseline. Because of this type of layout there is some distortion of dimensions in an isometric view. For the above reasons, the isometric view is limited and engineering drawings, although they can sometimes include an isometric view, are usually based on either **first-angle projection** or **third-angle projection**.

Let us look at these methods. In Figure A4.2 a ducting component is shown as an isometric sketch. If we turn to Figure A4.3, we can see the same component drawn in first-angle projection. Notice that we couldn't tell that there was another pipe on the other side from the isometric view. Figure A4.4 shows a third-angle projection of the same ducting component. The only difference is the way in which the views are projected. In third angle, the end views given are of the end, or side of the component closest to the view. This can be handy when reading complicated drawings, because it isn't necessary to mentally project across the drawing, as would be the case with first-angle projection. Both types of projection are easy to get used to with a bit of practice. Figures A4.5–A4.11 show different types of drawings and the use of welding drawing symbols. Figures A4.12–A4.14 give you some practice.

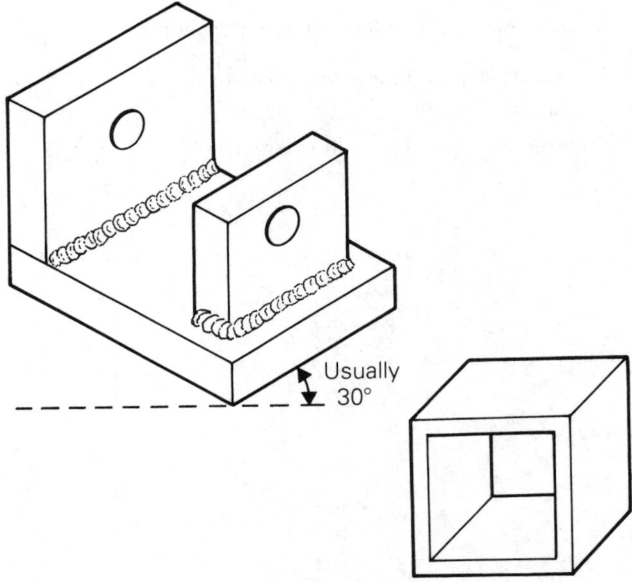

Figure A4.1 Isometric sketches of two components.

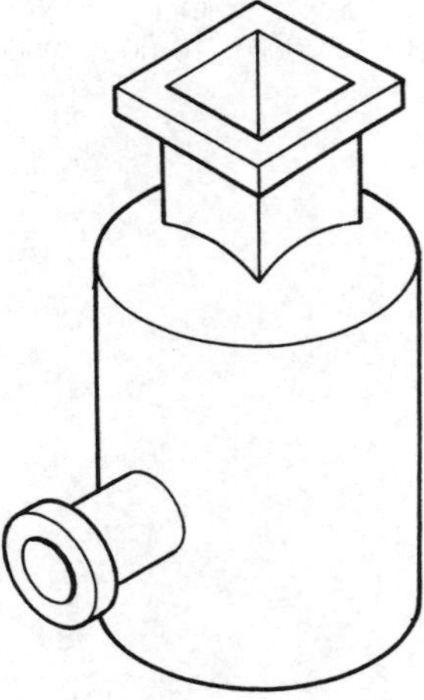

Figure A4.2 Isometric sketch of welded ducting component.

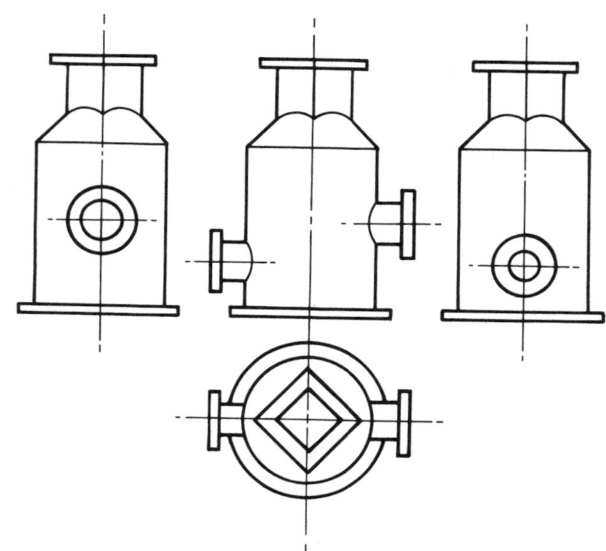

Figure A4.3 First-angle projection of ducting component.

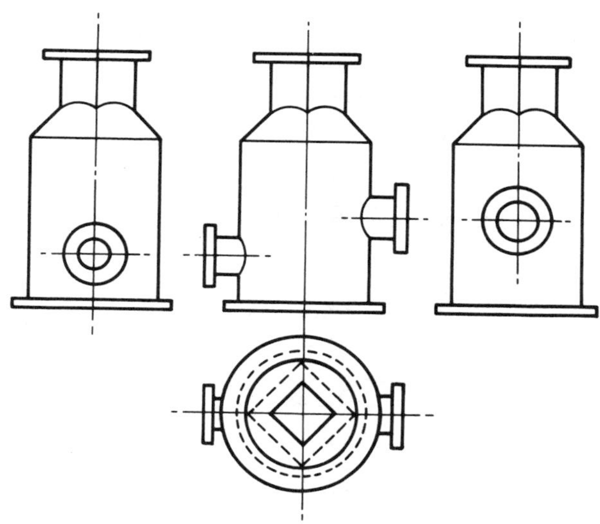

Figure A4.4 Third-angle projection of ducting component.

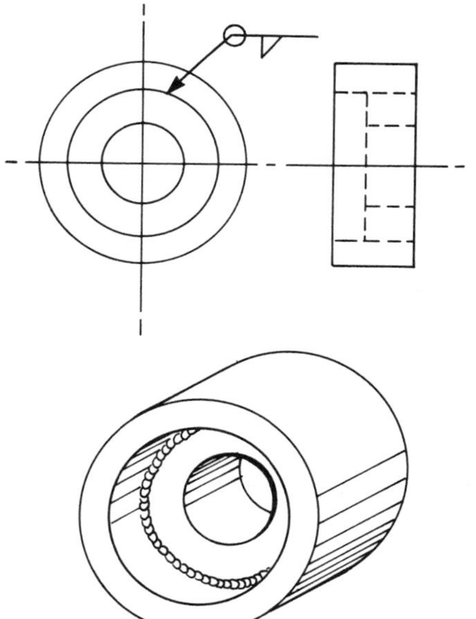

Figure A4.5 Engineering drawing and isometric sketch of a welded wheel. Symbol shows fillet weld all the way round. Dotted line indicates hidden detail.

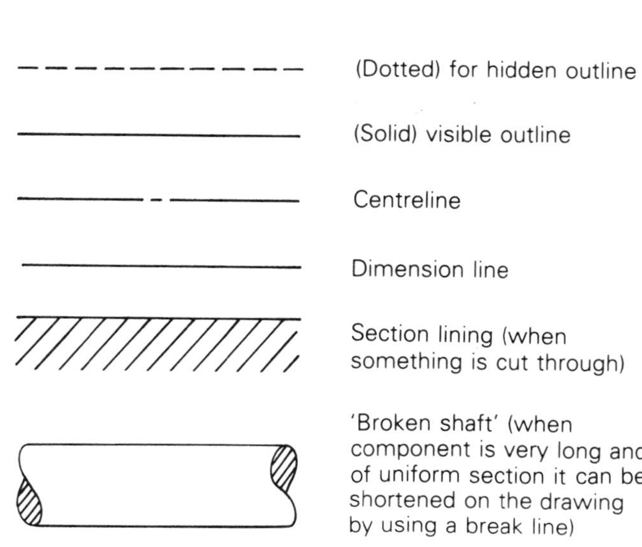

Figure A4.6 The lines used in engineering drawing.

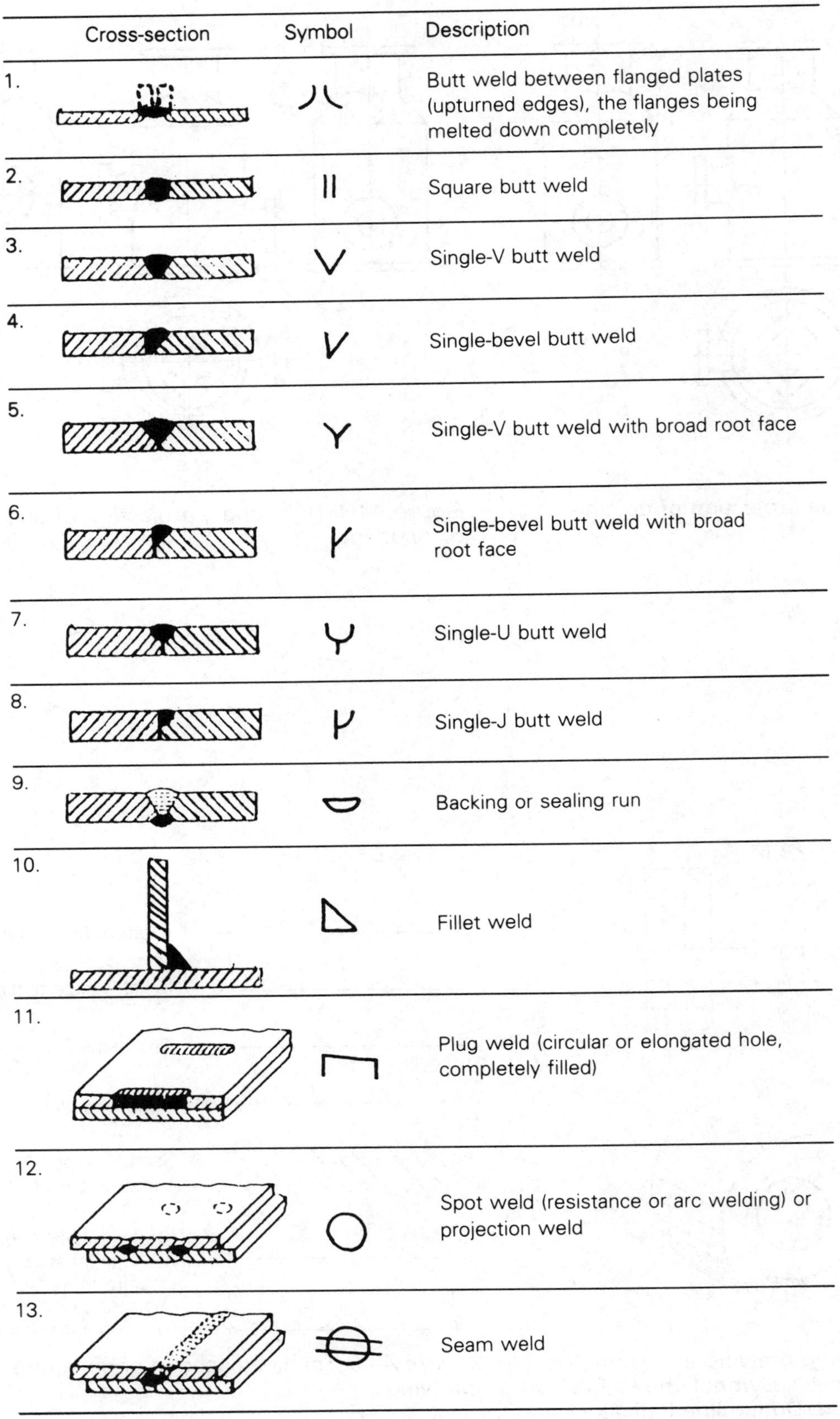

	Cross-section	Symbol	Description
1.			Butt weld between flanged plates (upturned edges), the flanges being melted down completely
2.			Square butt weld
3.			Single-V butt weld
4.			Single-bevel butt weld
5.			Single-V butt weld with broad root face
6.			Single-bevel butt weld with broad root face
7.			Single-U butt weld
8.			Single-J butt weld
9.			Backing or sealing run
10.			Fillet weld
11.			Plug weld (circular or elongated hole, completely filled)
12.			Spot weld (resistance or arc welding) or projection weld
13.			Seam weld

Figure A4.7 **Elementary welding drawing symbols (BS 499, part 2, 1980).**

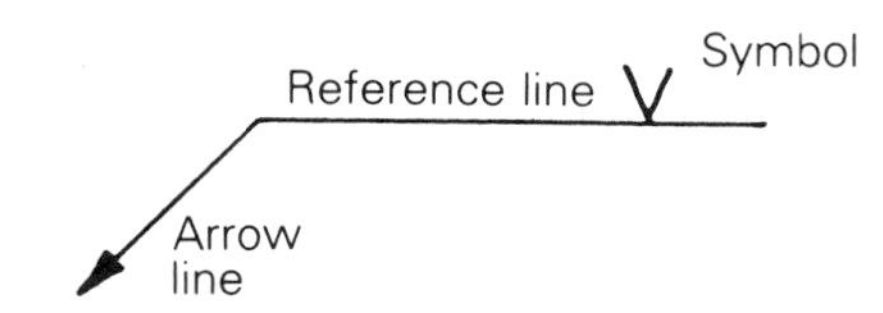

Figure A4.8 To indicate the type of weld and the position of a weld on a drawing, the symbols listed in Figure A4.7 are used in conjunction with an arrow line and reference line, as shown.

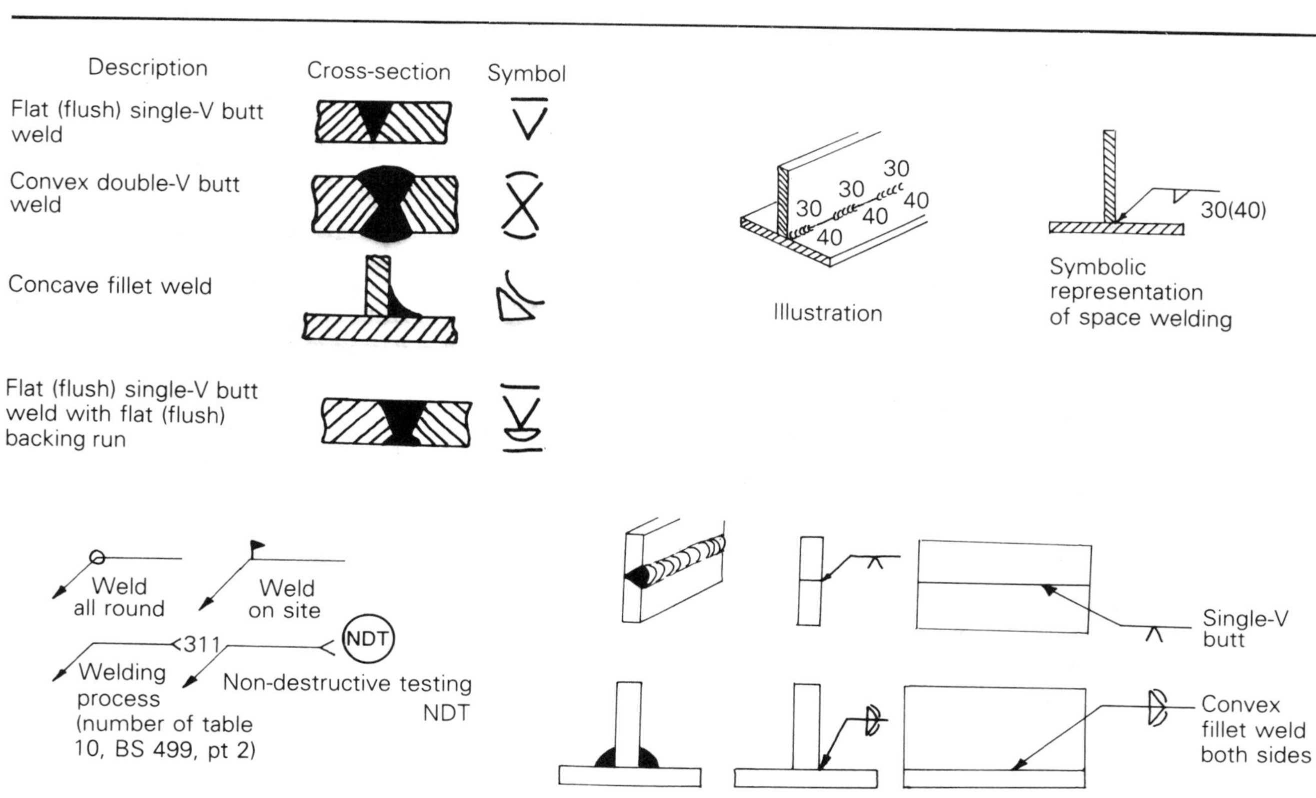

Figure A4.9 Examples of the use of symbols.

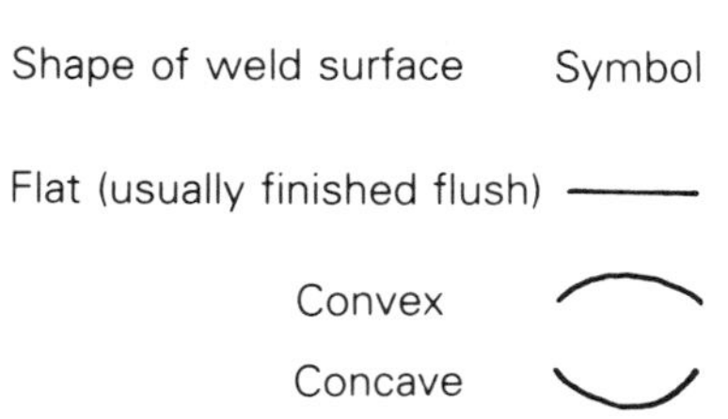

Figure A4.10 Supplementary symbols.

Indication of size of weld:

b ◺ *a* is design throat thickness

b a ◺ *b* is leg length

Figure A4.11 Examples of the use of supplementary symbols.

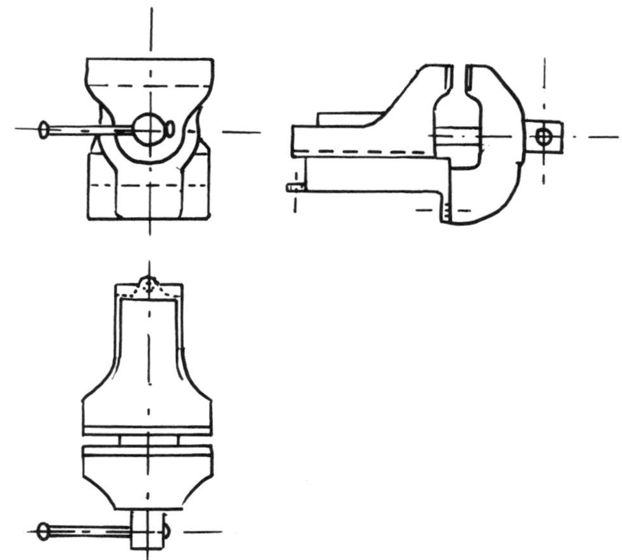

Figure A4.12 First-angle drawing of an engineer's vice. Try to sketch an isometric view. Remember: draw your lines at 30° to the horizontal.

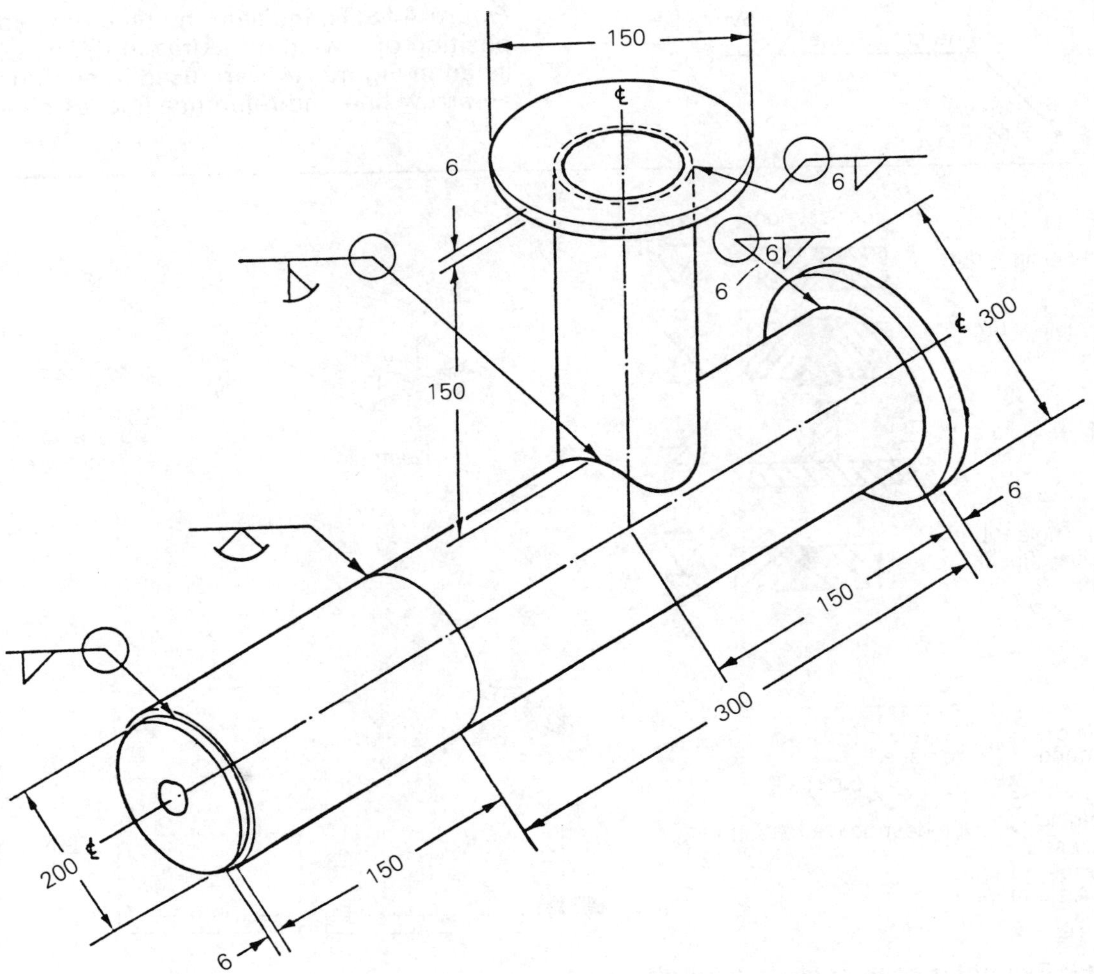

Figure A4.13 Redraw this component in an isometric view (as in this figure) sketching on all the welds.

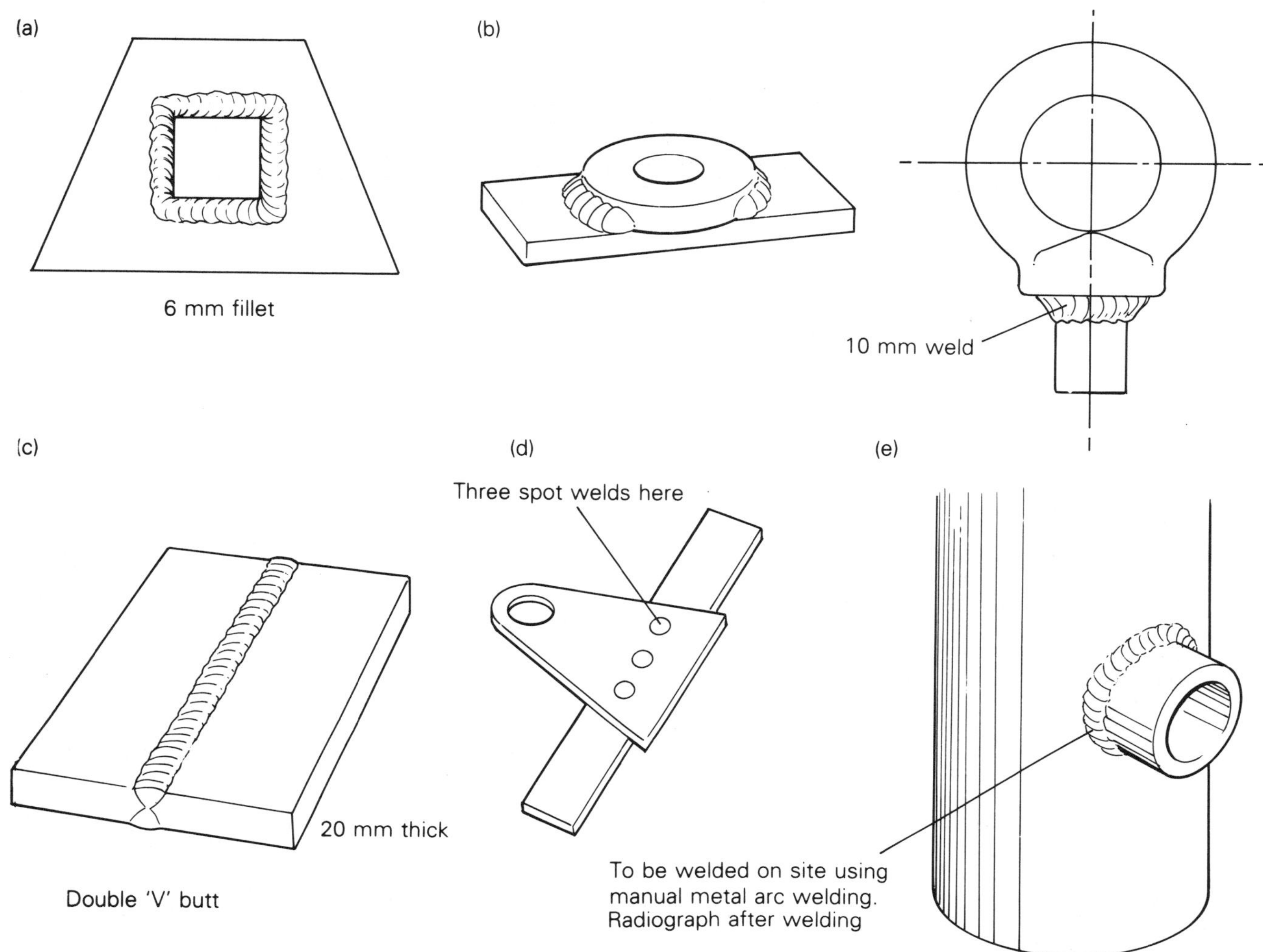

Figure A4.14 **Redraw these figures using correct welding drawing symbols to indicate welds and welding details.**

Appendix 5
Some notes on costing

Costing these days can be a very complicated affair. These few notes are intended to act as a basic guide to the subject.

Costing will vary with the different processes involved. Capital expenditure is very different: for example, on the purchase of a sophisticated electron beam welding machine, well over £100,000 or even £200,000 may be spent, while a small electric welding set can be purchased for £80 or so. Also, on overheads, a large, well-lit bay, fully heated with toilet and canteen facilities and large overhead cranes, will cost far more than a small shed, not only in rates, but also in maintenance.

Characteristics of different processes will also influence cost. For example, a MAGS operator will theoretically only have to break the arc because of fatigue or a change in the position of the work. The actual welding time should therefore be far greater than when constantly changing the electrode for manual metal arc stick electrode welding.

There should be no need to chip off slag with MAGS on ordinary work, unless of course flux-cored wire is used, and deposition speeds should be greater. However, the capital outlay for MAGS is greater than for manual metal arc. Breakdowns can be more frequent, and snarl-ups in the wire-feed systems can take time to fix. While deposition rates with MMA iron powder electrodes can match MAGS rates under certain circumstances, MAGS welding is not accepted for certain codes of work.

Costing of production and repair work must be done on a scientific basis, to ensure that fair prices are charged to customers, and to meet competition from other firms, while paying fair wages, cost of materials, overhead charges, and allowing a fair margin of profit.

The operations involved in welding production and repair work may be divided into:

1. preparation – includes dismantling, cleaning, machining, setting up in jigs or fixtures, preheating;
2. welding – the actual welding operation and the deslagging or descaling while welding;
3. finishing – includes post-heat treatment, stress relieving, cleaning, machining to final dimensions, erection, painting and packing.

In production work it is important to provide a weld of the required strength in the most economical way. For example the U preparation costs more to machine than the V, but takes less weld metal and can be welded more quickly. For arc welding, the cost of each type of weld is arrived at from the following data:

1. cost of preparation and setting up;
2. number of weld beads required;
3. current used (giving the cost of energy used);
4. speed of welding in metres per minute, allowing for change of electrodes and operator fatigue;
5. weight of electrodes used per metre of weld.

The cost of these five items is added up and the total cost per metre of weld is calculated for the particular joint and thickness being welded. In production work, ready-made tables are employed that can give this information very quickly, and therefore the most economical method can be worked out. Job cards (Figure A5.1) are used quite a lot, particularly in repair work, so that complete figures are available for costing. The cost card (Figure A5.2) is made out from the job card. The welder's time is charged at the correct rate of pay and this gives the labour charge for the job. The costs of:

1. electrodes or filler rods and flux,
2. electricity or gas,
3. incidentals

are calculated from the items on the card, and this gives the total cost to work on the job. To this must be added a definite percentage (which will vary with the amount of machinery installed) for overhead charges such as office staff, wear and tear of plant, and depreciation. A certain percentage of this is now added as clear profit. Any packing, carriage and freight charges are then added to this unless previously arranged.

JOB CARD

Job no: ____________ Date: ________

Workman's Name: ______________________ Time in hours: ________

Instructions:
Electrodes/welding rods used:
Size of welding/cutting tip:
Time burning:
Cleaning materials:
Pre/post-heating materials.
Fluxes:
Extra:
Additional materials and sundries:

Date completed: ____________ Remarks:

Figure A5.1 Job card.

COST CARD

Customer's Name: ______________ Address:
____

Job no: __________ Job description: ______________

Date commenced: ______________ Date completed: ______________

Time:
Gas/electricity:
Welding rods:
Electrodes:
Cleaning materials:
Pre/post-heating materials:
Fluxes:
Additional expenses:
Extras:

TOTAL ________

Plus
overhead charges: ________

TOTAL ________

Profit: ________

TOTAL ________

Packing, freight or postage: ________

TOTAL ________

Figure A5.2 Cost card.

Appendix 6
Extract from the table of elements

Element	Symbol	Atomic weight	Melting point in °C
Aluminium	Al	26.97	658.7
Antimony	Sb	121.77	630
Argon	Ar	39.94	–188
Arsenic	As	74.96	850
Beryllium	Be	9.02	1280
Bismuth	Bi	208.98	271
Boron	B	10.82	2200–2500
Cadmium	Cd	112.41	320.9
Calcium	Ca	40.07	810
Carbon	C	12.01	3600
Chlorine	Cl	35.45	–101.5
Chromium	Cr	52.01	1615
Cobalt	Co	58.94	1480
Copper	Cu	63.57	1083
Fluorine	F	19.0	–223
Gold	Au	197.2	1063
Helium	He	4.0	–272
Hydrogen	H	1.0078	–259
Iron	Fe	55.84	1530
Lead	Pb	207.22	327.4
Magnesium	Mg	24.32	651
Manganese	Mn	54.93	1230
Mercury	Hg	200.61	–38.87
Molybdenum	Mo	95.97	2620
Neon	Ne	20.18	–253
Nickel	Ni	8.69	452
Niobium (Columbium)	Nb (Cb)	92.9	1950
Nitrogen	N	14.008	–210
Oxygen	O	16.00	–218
Phosphorus	P	30.98	44
Platinum	Pt	195.23	1755
Potassium	K	39.1	62.3
Silicon	Si	28.06	1420
Silver	Ag	107.88	960.5
Sodium	Na	22.99	97.5
Sulphur	S	32.06	112.8
Thorium	Th	232.12	1700
Tin	Sn	118.70	231.9
Titanium	Ti	47.9	1800
Tungsten	W	184.0	3400
Uranium	U	238.14	1850
Vanadium	V	50.96	1720
Xenon	Xe	131.3	–140
Zinc	Zn	65.38	419.4
Zirconium	Zr	91.22	1700

Appendix 7
Useful addresses of some welding organisations

American Welding Society
550 NW Le Jeune Road
PO Box 351040
Miami
Florida 33135
USA

Central Metallurgical Research and Development Institute
PO Box 87
Helwan
Cairo
Egypt

Hussein Nagui and Co
13 Abdul Salam Aref Street
PO Box 2737
Cairo
Egypt

Tel: (00202) 3930022
Fax: (00202) 3920562
Telex: 93047 TSUN

Jos Hansen and Sohne Ltd
Jimma Road
PO Box 1501
Addis Ababa
Ethiopia

Tel: 447270/447273
Fax: Not available
Telex: 21033 DAHANJED ADDIS

UTC Engineering
Knutsford Avenue/Kwame Nkrumah Avenue
PO Box 543
Accra
Ghana

Tel: 664661
Fax: 663050
Telex: 2079 UTRACO GH

Sciencescope Ltd
Kimathi Street
PO Box 72963
Nairobi
Kenya

Tel: (002542) 2229241
Fax: (002542) 2229241
Telex: Not available

UTC Engineering
23–27 Wharf Road
PMB 1005, Apapa
Lagos
Nigeria

Tel: 803720
Fax: 873159
Telex: 21232 UNITRANG

Schmidt Scientific (Pte) Ltd
460 Alexandra Road No 19–21
PSA Building
PO Box 380
Singapore

Tel: 2727233
Fax: 2734750
Telex: RS 23736 SCHMSS

Leica RSA (Pty) Ltd
Lowliebenhof Building
Smit and Simmond Street
PO Box 3954
Johannesburg 2000
South Africa

Tel: (0027) 11 4036434
Fax: (0027) 11 3393444
Telex: 422427

South African Institute of Welding
PO Box 527
Crown Mines
2025 Johannesburg
South Africa

Tel: 27 11 836 4121/4131
Fax: 27 11 836 4132

Emso Ltd
Hyde Park Corner
PO Box 312
Colombo 2
Sri Lanka

Tel: (0094)1–547385/548003
Fax: Not available
Telex: 21739 EMSO CE

International Trading Company
Khartoum Industrial Area
PO Box 659
Khartoum
Sudan

Tel: 45612/40304/44668
Fax: Not available
Telex: 24092 ITCO SD

Freser Ltd
Nkrwmah Street 430/158
PO Box 5326
Dar es Salaam
Tanzania

Tel: 30837
Fax: Not available
Telex: 0989 41516 FESERTZ

Berli Jucker Co Ltd
542/1 Ploenchit Road
PO Box 173
Bangkok
Thailand

Tel: (00662) 252 4071
Fax: (00662) 2535159
Telex: 84331 BEJUCO TH

Jas Hansen and Sohne
Cairo Road
Hamburg House
PO Box 1104
Lusaka
Zambia

Tel: 211063/211058/212896
Fax: Not available
Telex: 41521 JHSLUS 2A

Business Equipment Corporation
CBH House
1 Victoria Street
PO Box 1611
Harare
Zimbabwe

Tel: 702031
Fax: 00263–0731901
Telex: 0907 26018 CONHD ZW

Appendix 8
Duplex stainless steels

These types of steel are increasingly being used in the oil, natural gas and chemical industries. They are alloys of chromium and nickel with iron. They can have twice the yield strength of stainless steels containing 18 per cent chromium and 8 per cent nickel. They also have excellent low-temperature strength and high corrosion resistance.

Duplex steels give the best compromise between corrosion resistance and strength/toughness, with a ferrite/austenite ratio close to 50/50. They are known as 'duplex' because the metallurgical structure consists of this mixture of both ferrite and austenite.

There are many different types of duplex steel to suit specific environments, but the chemical composition generally falls within the following range:

1. carbon, less than 0.3 per cent;
2. chromium, 18.0–27 per cent (principal contributor to corrosion resistance);
3. nickel, 5–10 per cent (improves toughness and assists austenitic formation);
4. molybdenum, 0–3.5 per cent (improves corrosion resistance);
5. nitrogen, 0.1–0.35 per cent (helps to maintain a balanced austenite/ferrite ratio);
6. copper, 0–1.5 per cent.

Duplex stainless steels can be readily welded by tungsten arc gas-shielded (TAGS) welding, metal arc gas-shielded (MAGS) welding, manual metal arc welding with flux-coated electrodes, submerged arc welding, and plasma arc welding (PAW).

The amount of ferrite in the weld should be controlled, because high ferrite levels – over around 80 per cent – will reduce the material's toughness, and also increase the possibility of hydrogen embrittlement.

Filler metals can be obtained to provide a structure around the 50 per cent ferrite, 50 per cent austenite levels by increasing the nickel content, and semi-automatic or automatic welding processes can quite accurately control the amount of filler metal that is added, and therefore the amount of dilution.

With manual processes, however, the filler metal must be carefully controlled; insufficient filler could significantly increase the ferrite content, which might cause brittleness. To overcome this, 'V' preparations with a root gap can be employed, to ensure that the root run contains the correct amount of filler metal, with minimum dilution. If the gas-shielded processes are being used, gas backing with argon is generally recommended.

The physical properties of duplex steel usually require special welding procedures. For example, when welding heavy sections, the slower cooling rates of the base metal and HAZ (heat-affected zone) can prolong the time spent within the temperature range at which embrittlement can occur. The weld metal and localised base metal can also retain heat longer during welding, making it more difficult to control the weld pool. Differences in the electrical conductivity may necessitate a reduced welding current, to avoid overheating of the electrode.

Appendix 9
WRC DeLong and WRC 1988 diagrams

The Schaeffler diagram is now considered to be outdated in some circumstances. One reason for this is the fact that it does not consider the effects of nitrogen.

An improvement, which includes nitrogen (N) and can be used to estimate the level of ferrite, is the WRC (Welding Research Council) DeLong Diagram (Figure A9.1).

However, the most accurate predictions are thought to be provided by the WRC 1988 diagram (Figure A9.2). On this diagram the Ni equivalent and Cr equivalent are different from those on the Schaeffler and WRC DeLong diagrams.

The ferrite number can be estimated by drawing a line horizontally across the diagram from the nickel equivalent number and a vertical line upwards from the chromium equivalent number. The ferrite number will then be indicated by the diagonal line that passes through the intersection of the horizontal and vertical lines.

Predictions for common grades are similar with WRC 1988 and WRC DeLong, but the WRC 1988 diagram is generally the most accurate for the less common grades such as manganese austenitic or duplex austenitic-ferritic stainless steels.

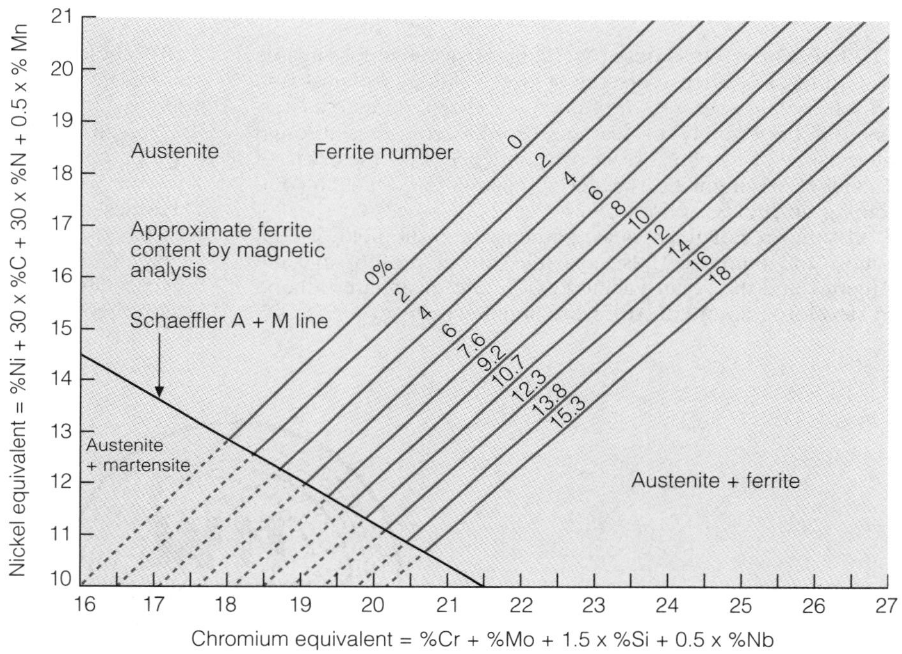

Figure A9.1 The Welding Research Council DeLong diagram for austenitic stainless steel weld metal.

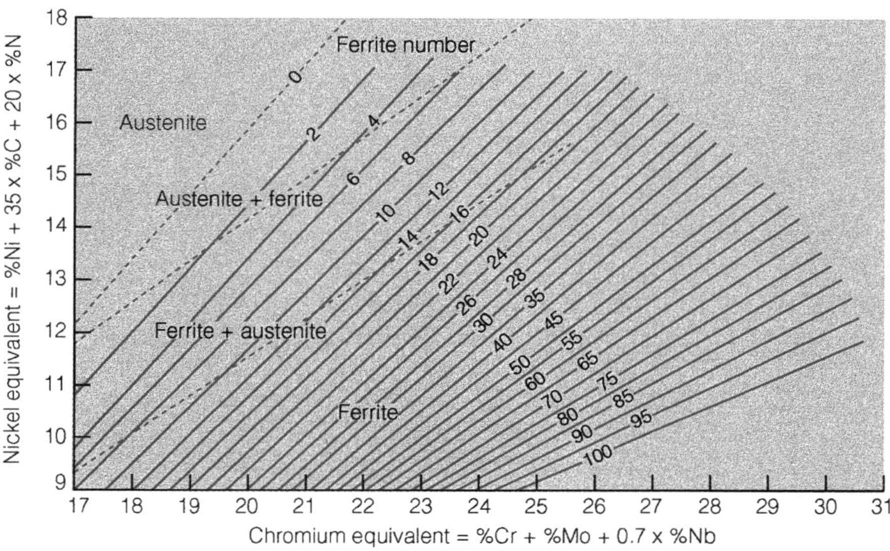

Figure A9.2 The WRC 1988 diagram, including solidification mode boundaries. (adapted from T.A. Stewart, C.N. McCowan and D.L. Olsen, *AWS Welding Journal*, December 1988)

The International Institute of Welding

The International Institute of Welding (Institut International de la Soudure) is an association of the welding institutes and societies of 40 countries. It offers researchers and manufacturers the opportunity of learning from each other through attendance at meetings or correspondence with members of 15 technical commissions covering materials and welding and joining, including non-metallics.

IIW has regional activities, particularly in the field of education and training. These activities are at present in Latin America and the Asian Pacific Region, and plans are in hand to develop a Southern African regional activity.

IIW holds consultative status with UNIDO, the United Nations Industrial Development Organisation, and is recognised by the International Organisation for Standardisation (ISO) as an international standardising body with the authority to prepare ISO standards. This gives members of the commissions the opportunity of drafting international standards.

Further information may be obtained from: IIW General Secretariat, Institut de Soudure, Paris Nord II, BP 50362, 95942 Roissy CDG CEDEX, France. UK representation: IIW Representative, Welding and Joining Society, c/o the Welding Institute, Abington Hall, Abington, Cambridge CB1 6AL, UK.

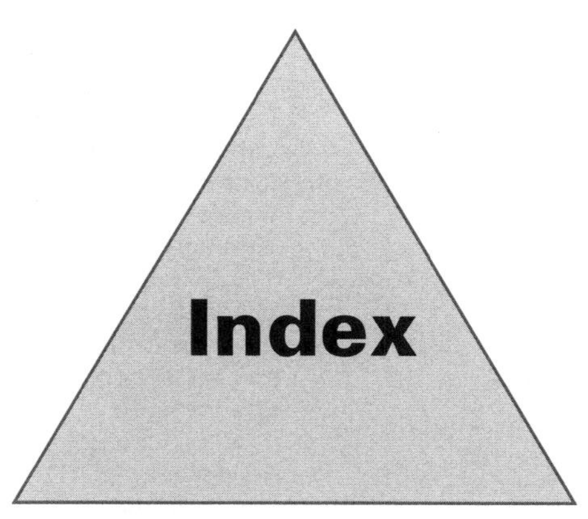

Index